# CREATION BASICS & BEYOND

An In-Depth Look at Science, Origins, and Evolution

## SECOND EDITION

# CREATION
# BASICS &
# BEYOND

An In-Depth Look at Science, Origins, and Evolution

## SECOND EDITION

Henry M. Morris III, D.Min. • John D. Morris, Ph.D.
Randy J. Guliuzza, P.E., M.D. • Jeffrey P. Tomkins, Ph.D.
Vernon R. Cupps, Ph.D. • Brian Thomas, Ph.D.
Timothy Clarey, Ph.D. • Jake Hebert, Ph.D.
Frank Sherwin, M.A. • James J. S. Johnson, J.D., Th.D.

### INSTITUTE FOR CREATION RESEARCH

Dallas, Texas
ICR.org

# CREATION BASICS & BEYOND
## An In-Depth Look at Science, Origins, and Evolution

First edition: July 2013
Second edition: August 2020

Unless otherwise specified, all Scripture quotations are from the New King James Version.

ISBN: 978-1-946246-51-6
Library of Congress Catalog Number: 2020941241

Please visit our website for other books and resources: ICR.org

*Printed in the United States of America.*

# TABLE OF CONTENTS

# INTRODUCTION

Today's younger generations include more atheists than ever before in America. Barna poll results show that the number two reason they give is that science disproves God and the Bible. Every mainstream media outlet that influences youth—and movies in particular—assumes evolution and its billions of years.

If nature made humans over eons instead of God creating them in a mere moment, then of course Genesis got it wrong. And so did the Lord Jesus Christ, who quoted Genesis in passages such as Mark 10:6. Who's right—people who were not there, or the God of the Bible who was? What really happened in the beginning?

We at the Institute for Creation Research are pleased to reveal in the pages of this book solid scientific and historical evidence that supports the Genesis creation.

Much lies at stake. If we came from apes through natural processes instead of coming from dust through supernatural processes like Genesis teaches, then why not live our lives solely for ourselves? If we play no part in a grand and divine historical narrative and instead are just random splotches across an unimaginably long and uncaring canvas, then why not live for the moment instead of living for our great Creator and Savior?

We were made for God. Genesis begins to tell us how and why. And *Creation Basics & Beyond* provides solid, observable science—not the stories secular thinkers use in place of science—that supports the Bible's foundational events recorded in Genesis.

Our goal as a research team of Bible-believing, credentialed scientists is for this book to reveal the insights that point us back to this book of beginnings. We include answers to some of the most-asked and most-relevant origins questions. Each chapter tackles a would-be stumbling block to creation. We grouped the chapters under general topics so readers can use this as a reference book. Just jump right to the question that bothers you the most. Or read the whole book through to get equipped with answers. 1 Peter 3:14-16 says:

> "And do not be afraid of their threats, nor be troubled." But sanctify the Lord God in your hearts, and always be ready to give a defense to everyone who asks you a reason for the hope that is in you, with meekness and fear; having a good conscience, that when they defame you as evildoers, those who revile your good conduct in Christ may be ashamed.

Believers are to be ready. This book will help you prepare a solid defense.

Let it no longer be said that science disproves the Bible! On the contrary, good science supports Scripture. This evolution-soaked generation now has ready answers to so many science-sounding objections to the Bible.

*Creation Basics & Beyond* will equip God's people to read the Bible with confidence that it means what it says and says what is true.

Brian Thomas, Ph.D.

# WORLDVIEW

## GOD DETERMINES TRUTH
## OR MAN DETERMINES TRUTH?

# 1

# GENESIS AND THE CHARACTER OF GOD

Henry M. Morris III, D.Min.

**Summary:** The God of the Bible is absolutely holy, and we must view His actions in the light of His perfect being. In the beginning, the world He created was good and perfect in all aspects. There was no death, as would be required if the world developed through purely natural processes.

How can we resolve a good creation with the evil and death around us? God created people with free will, and the first humans freely chose to go against God's commands. Their sin brought death and evil into our once-perfect world. God sent His Son to conquer sin and death on the cross.

The nature of our holy, omniscient, good God demands that He could never be the source of death, evil, and suffering. The message of Genesis is true.

The message of Genesis is not confusing. The repetitive information throughout the rest of Scripture is consistent. The universe was created by an omnipotent, omniscient, and transcendent Being. The words of Scripture insist that God's work was recent, complete, and "good." Our struggle with that message is that everything we observe is tainted by evil and death.

Secular history presupposes that the "normal" of today has been the dominant operational force behind everything that exists. Geological processes, fossil evidence, sociological development, all are interpreted with no God in the story. Some theologians attempt to explain the differences between the biblical message and secular naturalism by suggesting that dying processes were a normal part of God's creation. Some religions embrace the idea that good and evil are nothing more than two sides of the same reality—that our perception of such contrasts are merely a product of our experience and culture.

How can we resolve the conflicting message of a good creation with the evil that surrounds us? For those of us who believe that an omnipotent and omniscient God has existed from eternity past, we must correlate what *that* God has revealed to us and our growing understanding of science, with God's divine nature as the controlling factor. What does the revealed nature of God demand of the original creation? How does natural revelation (what we can observe in today's universe) shape the written words of Scripture?

Some have suggested that the processes of nature in that original creation could not have included a deathless universe since all natural processes function around deterioration and death. Living things would have worn out and died—even if the environment then was much better than the environment we know today. Animals would have died normally, and Adam and Eve would have died eventually unless they ate of the Tree of Life that God planted in the garden "eastward in Eden" (Genesis 2:8).

But the Bible tells us that death is the result of Adam's sin, and as a result of God's judgment "death spread to all men" (Romans 5:12). When God tells us death is the "last enemy" to be conquered by the Lord Jesus (1 Corinthians 15:26) and death will not exist in the new heavens and the new earth (Revelation 21:4), are we to expect the new bodies promised upon our resurrection to be still mortal in eternity?

Before we approach these issues, it is absolutely necessary to acknowledge what has been recorded about the origin of the universe.

## God's Own Commentary

"Everything…was very good" (Genesis 1:31). The repetition of God's comment is worth noting. Five of the six working days of the creation week are pronounced "good" by the Creator. It is the same Hebrew word each time and means just what would be expected: good, pleasant, agreeable, excellent, of benefit, etc. That word is used well over 500 times in Scripture. There is nothing very unusual about God's use of the word except that it is repeated often and that it is God who uses the term.

Given that the Creator is using the term, we should consider the character of the Evaluator. We should gain some understanding of His attributes before we render an opinion of the meaning of the term "good"—especially as it applies to the original creation.

## God Is Holy

Holiness is the preeminent attribute of God. Everything God does is subject to the unchangeable rock of God's holy nature. Even the love that drove Him to become man and die a substitutionary death for our sins is driven by the holiness that demands justice for the horrible rebellion against that very holiness.

> Who is like You, O LORD, among the gods? Who is like You, glorious in holiness, fearful in praises, doing wonders? (Exodus 15:11)

> No one is holy like the LORD, for there is none besides You, nor is there any rock like our God. (1 Samuel 2:2)

> For I proclaim the name of the LORD….He is the Rock, His work is perfect; for all His ways are justice, a God of truth and without injustice; righteous and upright is He. (Deuteronomy 32:3-4)

> God…cannot lie. (Titus 1:2)

> The judgments of the LORD are true and righteous altogether. (Psalm 19:9)

## God Is Omniscient

Everywhere we look—into the deepest recesses of space or the minutia of the microscope—the intricacy, precision, and complexity of all things stagger us with the enormity of details and vastness of information.

> O LORD, how manifold are Your works! In wisdom You have made them all. The earth is full of Your possessions. (Psalm 104:24)

> I am God, and there is no other; I am God, and there is none like Me, declaring the end from the beginning, and from ancient times things that are not yet done, saying, "My counsel shall stand, and I will do all My pleasure." (Isaiah 46:9-10)

> Known to God from eternity are all His works. (Acts 15:18)

This is the consistent message of Scripture. God cannot be progressively aware. God's knowledge is immediate. God is free from imperfection. God knows all there is to know. God's purpose and order flow from His omniscience. His decisions are unchangeable and without confusion. God's specific will and pleasure are always implemented.

## God's Flawless Good

Whatever God said was good would have to be in harmony with His divine nature. Since God is holy, He could not deceive us about the order of the creation week. Since God is omniscient, He could not guess or use trial and error methodology. God would not experiment. God would not produce inferior things. He can do only holy acts. He cannot create, make, or shape nonfunctional processes. All of this clear evidence requires that we who read Genesis 1 understand "good" to mean "flawless function."

- **God's "good" functions properly.**

God's own account of His work specifies His organization and purpose. Because God is omniscient, everything in the universe works as designed. Because God is omnipotent, everything has all it needs to operate, live, reproduce, and populate under the orders of and in agreement with the Creator's design. Each component was designed to function without flaw. Every part works as ordered, and all living things function under the limits and in the places for their lives. Nothing was misplaced. Nothing was left to chance.

- **God's "good" could not include sin.**

For the holy, omniscient, omnipotent, loving Creator to conclude that everything that He had created was "very good," there could be nothing in that completed creation that did not function as designed. Nothing existed in conscious rebellion against the immutable nature of the Creator—there was no sin.

Sin became a part of human nature through Adam. Death was introduced into the creation because of the Creator's sentence upon Adam.

- **God's "good" could not include death.**

God is life. Everything that is revealed about God centers on His eternal Being. The most personal name that God reveals is "I AM"—the One who exists by the right and nature of who He is. Jesus insists that He is "the way, the truth, and the life" (John 14:6). The awesome *Apokalypse* of Jesus Christ opens with the loud voice "as of a trumpet, saying, 'I am the Alpha and the Omega, the First and the Last" (Revelation 1:10-11).

There is absolutely no indication anywhere in the Scriptures that the living God—the God of life—created death. Nothing in the Bible suggests that death was a part of the good that God designed into His creation. Death in Scripture is separation from God. Death stops life. Death intrudes into and destroys everything. Death is *not* normal.

When God completed His work, *He* pronounced "it was very good" (Genesis 1:31). If words mean anything at all, "good" must include the flawless functioning of every molecule and all systems and all life. "Good" demands that nothing be out of order or in rebellion to His nature. No sin or death existed in all of creation—until the third chapter of Genesis.

## Rebellion in the Garden

Most of us have wondered how much time elapsed between the end of Day 7 and the world-changing events that took place at the Tree of the Knowledge of Good and Evil. No specific time period is stated, but it does not appear that it was very long. Eve did not conceive the first human child until after the pronouncement of the judgments and after they were cast out of the garden (Genesis 4:1). Given the basic command to "be fruitful and multiply" (Genesis 1:28), it is unlikely that either Adam or Eve delayed attempting to fulfill this mandate.

However one interprets the information, it could *not* have been "ages." More than likely it was less than a year—and probably only a few days after they both were created.

## A Mixed Message

If physical death is part of the design of God in the original creation, that makes God the author of death. Since the creation is part of the revelation of the nature of God (according to Romans 1:20), such a design would require that death is part of the holiness of God. How could this be? The Bible calls death the "last enemy" and insists that the Lord Jesus will destroy it. If God Himself created death, then why would He destroy it later? Did God deliberately confuse us?

If death is *not* the judgment for sin as the Bible insists, then the whole of the gospel message is foolishness. What would salvation rescue us from? If death is not the judgment for sin, then the death of the Lord Jesus on the cross at Calvary is nothing more than a foolish end to an idealist—a martyrdom for an illusionary cause.

The Bible demands that an innocent sacrifice be substituted for the awful sin of humanity. Christ's death is required for salvation. We are sanctified through the offering of the body of Jesus Christ on Calvary (Hebrews 10:10), done once, with and for eternal consequences (Hebrews 10:12-14).

Twisting the words of Scripture so that Christ's physical death had no meaning is a terrible heresy. If eons of pain, suffering, and death existed before Adam's awful rebellion, then a whole sweep of biblical teaching is thrown into the black hole of allegory.

## The Demands of God's Nature

God is omnipresent Spirit (John 4:24). God is not nature. God is not the universe. God is not a cosmic consciousness or a force of mystery. God is *not* man—He is greater than man (Job 33:12) and does not change His mind (Numbers 23:19).

Since God is holy, God does *not* author confusion. He is light (1 John 1:5). He is the truth (John 3:33; 14:6); therefore, God cannot deceive us.

Because of who God is, we can be assured of an original creation that functioned as it was designed—a creation that fits the Creator. The "groaning" of the creation now (Romans 8:22) is a constant reminder that rebellion against the holiness of the Creator required His judgment. God Himself reconciles His creation to Himself through the death of His sinless Son in substitution for our well-deserved guilt.

## The Good News

The gospel message insists on the "birth from above" (John 3:3) that brings about a transfer from death to life (John 5:24). It involves a "new creation" (2 Corinthians 5:17) made possible by the death of the Creator Himself (Hebrews 2:9).

The earthy condition of flesh and blood cannot inherit the kingdom of God. Physical changes are required. Resurrection is the absolute opposite of physical death. Corruption must become incorruption. Dishonor must become glory. Weakness must become power. The natural must become spiritual (1 Corinthians 15:50-54). Physical death is an intrusion into the eternal order of things, and it takes a resurrection to correct it.

The "new man" must be created in God's righteousness and true holiness (Ephesians 4:24). We await the fulfillment of that promise when the Creator "will transform our lowly body that it may be conformed to His glorious body, according to the working by which He is able even to subdue all things to Himself" (Philippians 3:21).

# 2
# WHY DOES GENESIS MATTER SO MUCH?

Brian Thomas, Ph.D.

**Summary:** Genesis accurately describes our world and reality. It reveals the identity of God, the beginning of the universe, and the origins of humanity and sin.

Belief in Genesis has a tremendous impact on society and human behavior. Governments in the 20th century that ignored its teachings destroyed millions of people. Genesis also established marriage, which is the foundation of the family. Disdain for Genesis has led to broken homes.

God's plan to redeem our fallen world also began in Genesis. Humanity's sin brought the curse of death, but Christ Jesus paid our sin penalty and rose from the grave to redeem us and offer us eternal life with Him.

Christians who embrace Genesis like Jesus and the apostles did do exactly what they are supposed to do.

The world in general treats Genesis as a book that relays anything but actual history. It may have parables, poetry, or platitudes, but not real historical events. This approach yields devastating consequences in at least three broad realms of human life. On the other hand, a high view of Genesis—one that treats its words as God-written, accurate, and as meaning what they most plainly say—can make all the difference for time and eternity.

Genesis teaches the most fundamental truths about reality. For example, God exists and created the universe using no pre-existing material. This Creator can obviously do anything. Genesis 1 explains why planets and creatures are so well designed, whereas Genesis 3 explains why that originally perfected world now suffers decay.

God is good, for He noted at the end of the sixth and final creation day, "Indeed it was very good" (Genesis 1:31). God made humans originally good, but something went drastically wrong. From Genesis we know He sets the standards since He gave Adam and Eve the first law. It shows that God justly judges sin.

That's why He later flooded the world to judge humanity's wickedness. Such a flood helps explain rock layers with fossils, as well as the eroded landscapes throughout our world. Genesis teaches that God pursues us even when we run from Him and try to hide our sins. It even indicates that individuals can have their broken relationships with God restored by His grace, for "Noah found grace in the eyes of the LORD" (Genesis 6:8). In short, Genesis reveals the identity of God, the beginning of the universe, and the origins of humanity and our sin. What happens when we reject all this?

## Genesis in Society

If the 20th century teaches nothing else, it should showcase the wickedness of the human heart. The years 1900 to 2000 brought two world wars, hundreds of smaller wars, bloody revolutions, the holocaust, and continent-wide genocides. Some have said, and it may be accurate, that more people died in 20th-century conflicts than in all of human history before that. What has this to do with Genesis?

Societies that ignore Genesis can more easily justify their violence. Consider Nazism, around which World War II was fought. Nazi leader Adolf Hitler took his radical ideas from Charles Darwin's evolutionary survival of the fittest theme. Nazis believed that blond-haired, blue-eyed people are the fittest, and it was their evolutionary duty to exterminate the unfit. Nazi Germany and others treated like a plague of rats people that Genesis says bear the image of God (Genesis 1:27).

When communism toppled Russia to form the USSR in 1922, new leader Joseph Stalin ran death camps and genocide campaigns that wasted millions of lives. Atheistic (there is no God) humanism (humanity is the center of all things) took the form of communist governments. Communism kicks Genesis to the curb. Historians haggle over how many tens of millions of lives were lost under communist regimes like those of Stalin in Russia, Pol Pot in Cambodia, and Mao in China.

These leaders took naturalists' words over those of the Creator as revealed in Genesis. They assumed that humans emerged from apes—a view that today's textbooks still teach as scientific. They thus denied the Genesis origin of humans by miracle and in God's image. The 20th century proved that this one difference meant life or death for untold numbers of men, women, boys, and girls.

Now consider those countries that hold a higher view of Genesis. For example, the United States began with these words in its Declaration of Independence: "We hold these truths to be self-evident, that all men are created equal." It is hard to deny the general prosperity and peace so far enjoyed by this and other nations that make and enforce Genesis-friendly, people-protecting laws.

Overall, history shows that societies rise when they happen to respect Genesis. But a high regard for Genesis brings benefits much closer to home.

## Genesis and the Family

The book of Genesis opens with the world's first family. A solemn commitment that each spouse strives to "become one" (Genesis 2:24) with the other forms the foundation for marriage. In turn, marriages make up the core of every ideal family. Animals have no such thing as solemn commitments. They just have instincts. Therefore, couples who consider themselves merely evolved animals sometimes start to act like animals. They reject Genesis and the holy Creator that it introduces. That makes it easier to justify following fleshly lusts when they conflict with wedding vows. Marriages crumble across the land. Clearly, a firm grasp of our origins in Genesis strengthens marriages and families.

Genesis even tells us why God invented marriage. "And the LORD God said, 'It is not good that man should be alone; I will make him a helper comparable to him'" (Genesis 2:18). He made husbands and wives to complement one another, similar to the ways the different Persons of God interact. Genesis even teaches that although God is one Creator, He is made of more than one person, saying, "Let Us make..." (Genesis 1:26). He also equipped marriages to fulfil His command in Genesis 1:28:

> Then God blessed them, and God said to them, "Be fruitful and
> multiply; fill the earth and subdue it; have dominion over the fish
> of the sea, over the birds of the air, and over every living thing that

moves on the earth."

Adam recognized this purpose for family when he "called his wife's name Eve, because she was the mother of all living" (Genesis 3:20). When Jesus' detractors asked Him about divorce, He answered:

> "But from the beginning of the creation, God 'made them male and female.' 'For this reason a man shall leave his father and mother and be joined to his wife, and the two shall become one flesh'; so then they are no longer two, but one flesh." (Mark 10:6-8)

This small selection illuminates the value of Genesis. First, the Lord Jesus, who "made the worlds" (Hebrews 1:2), quoted directly from Genesis 1:27 and 2:24. Also, Jesus allowed no space for evolutionary time. Instead, God "made them male and female" right from the beginning of the world, during the creation week, not billions of years after some Big Bang beginning.

In both these ways Jesus treated these words as actual history, not some myth. Of course, Jesus also based His doctrine of marriage on the historical events that Genesis describes. Like the prophets who wrote the Old Testament and the apostles who wrote or approved the New Testament, Jesus treated Genesis like real history even when defining broad realms of human life such as marriage and family.

Broken homes litter our cultures. It should come as no surprise that a disdain for Genesis derails marriages. How desperately families need to return to their Creator, to take Him at His Word, and to see individuals, marriages, families, and societies restored to right relationships with Him, beginning at the beginning.

## Genesis and Eternity

Societies and families only occupy this life briefly. What about our existence beyond this world? Our attitudes toward Genesis impact life beyond the grave, when each person will remain either with God or without Him forever.

Genesis sets up the central problem of every life. Like Adam and Eve became, we are born rebels. We know the right action or word, but we refuse to do or say it. Not only did we inherit wicked hearts from those two who first rebelled in the Garden of Eden, but we also fan the flames of that wickedness! So what? Well, Genesis reveals that sin brings the consequence of death. Death means separation. Everlasting separation from God is deadly serious.

What is required to enforce a well-deserved death penalty? A just judge. Genesis introduces God as the ultimate Lawgiver. By jettisoning Genesis and the Judge it reveals, we pretend we can sin behind His back. Some try to outmaneuver God's rightly enforced curse on us and the world by rejecting Genesis.

And what about inserting billions of years' of fossils sometime before Adam and Eve? This man-made version of history puts death long before sin. It erases the basis for the gospel. If sin did not cause death as Genesis 3 and the rest of the Bible teaches, then why did the Lord Jesus come to defeat death?

Those who take Genesis as history can restore the logic of the gospel. Genesis sets up the problem that Jesus began to solve at His first appearance as the suffering Servant and will finally solve when He returns to rule: "So when this corruptible has put on incorruption, and this mortal has put on immortality, then shall be brought to pass the saying that is written: 'Death is swallowed up in victory'" (1 Corinthians 15:54).

Creation was corrupted in the Garden where Adam and Eve became mortals, all according to Genesis. But a new garden throne will arrive with its tree of life, and the Lord Jesus Himself will live with us forever. He rose from the dead, having paid our sin penalty. The great and holy Judge of all mankind will acquit our death sentence if we repent of sins and trust Him. Now that's good news, and it makes the most sense against the backdrop of Genesis as history.

## The Heart of the Matter

Why does Genesis matter so much? Well, God wrote it. Whoever takes His Words at face value, who treasures "the words of His mouth more than my necessary food" (Job 23:12), engages in a lifelong journey of trusting Him. "Says the Lord. 'But on this one will I look: on him who is poor and of a contrite spirit, and who trembles at My word'" (Isaiah 66:2).

Christians who embrace Genesis like Jesus and the apostles did, even if that means getting laughed at by a world deluded into disdaining God's Word, do exactly what they are supposed to, "teaching them to observe all things that I have commanded you" (Matthew 28:20)—beginning in Genesis.

# 3

# NO DEATH BEFORE ADAM SINNED

James J. S. Johnson, J.D., Th.D.

**Summary:** The "no death before sin" issue is an important theme in the Bible. According to Genesis, God's original creation was good and perfect—death was completely unknown. Despite the clear and dire warning from God, Adam sinned, and the whole world was subsequently cursed.

Theistic evolutionists believe death existed before Adam sinned. If this is true, then the Bible's creation account is false. And the gospel itself is unreliable since it clearly relates the penalty of Adam's sin to the need for Jesus to come to Earth and provide the payment for sin. What we believe about death as the consequence of Adam's sin is a test of our own faith in God.

Death was alien to God's "very good" creation, until Adam sinned.

The trustworthiness of the Holy Bible hangs upon the accuracy of this fact: There was no death before Adam sinned. To err about when and why death came to Earth is to err about the theological and historical foundation of the gospel. The death of Christ, and therefore the gospel of Christ, won't make sense if death came to Earth any other way than by Adam's sin in Eden. If death came first, the New Testament would be worse than unreliable—it would be irreparably wrong about salvation.

Although more could (and should) be said about how and why Adam's sin triggered death,[1] two major points will be reviewed here: (1) The gospel of Christ depends on the truth of Adam's sin triggering death on Earth; and (2) the reliability of the Bible depends upon the truth of Adam's sin triggering death on Earth.

Put bluntly, if death somehow came to earth apart from Adam's sin, we cannot be confident that hell is escapable. Those reasons guarantee that this topic is anything but trivial. The stakes are as high as can be.

## "Very Good" Creations Don't "Groan"

The original condition of God's creation at the end of Day 6 was "very good" (Genesis 1:31), displaying the perfection of providence. However, the earth is now fallen—the current condition of God's creation is good (Acts 14:17) yet "groaning" (Romans 8:20-22).

That groaning now includes the reign of sin and death over humans and animals, a terrible situation that will one day be overcome (1 Corinthians 15:26, 54-56; Revelation 21:4; 22:3).

What caused this change? God did not leave us to guess the answer: Genesis 3 provides the history of that change; the New Testament (especially in Romans 5 and 8) provides the theology of that change.[2]

If we ignore God's authoritative explanation in Genesis and Romans by relying on theistic evolutionist mythologies—in which death was supposedly a necessary part of God's "creative" activities—we err.[3-5] Why? Because only the Bible's teaching of the history and theology of human sin reveals the true etiology of death (Romans 5:12).

## The Bible's First Mention of Death

Death had a beginning; death is not eternal. In order to have the possibility of death, there must first be mortal life. Accordingly, death could never occur unless and until God created living creatures that were capable of dying. Genesis 1 and 2 describe and report how God created such creatures.

To understand how "life" can be lost to "death," it is important to note that God worked in different ways during the creation week. Some of God's deeds were acts of absolute creation (i.e., God making something from nothing), while other deeds God did were acts of creative development (i.e., God modifying something that already exists into something else).

Various Hebrew verbs help us to distinguish when God was "creating" versus when God was "developing" His creation into the diverse products that He wanted to exist. As we shall see, the creation week involved three kinds of creating: (1) God creating physical stuff on Day 1; (2) God creating animal life on Day 5; and (3) God creating human life on Day 6.

The Hebrew word that means "to make something from nothing" is *bara'*—in English, this verb is almost always translated as some form of the verb "to create."[6] However, various other construction/development-related verbs appear in the Genesis creation report, such as "made," "divided," "gathered together," "brought forth," etc.[7]

Genesis 1:1 is the first verse to use the Hebrew verb *bara'* ("created"). This verse reports that God created (i.e., made from nothing) something new: physical stuff. There was no physical stuff before then. Period. It was decreed into existence, by God, on Day 1.

Physical stuff is not "alive," so it cannot "die." Nothing made on Day 1 was mortal (i.e., capable of dying) because there was no created life yet. Between Genesis 1:1 and 1:21, through Day 4, God worked with the physical stuff He made on Day 1. God continued this work on Day 5, yet added something new.

Genesis 1:21 is the second verse to use *bara'*. This verse reports that God created the first kinds of animal life—"every living thing that moves"—life with a *nephesh* (often translated as "soul"). These marine and flying creatures—such as birds, bats, barnacles, bass, butterflies, barracudas, and brittle stars—had something qualitatively new that had never been created before: *life!*[8]

Animals are much more than reprogrammed heaven-and-earth physical "stuff." Something that has never had life cannot die. Life "that moves" on Earth, however, can die.

The first blessing in the creation week was pronounced when God blessed the animals of the air and waters in Genesis 1:22 as He commanded these living creatures to "be fruitful and multiply, and fill" the earth's aquatic and terrestrial habitats. Animals are blessed!

Genesis 1:27 is the third and last verse in Genesis 1 to use *bara'*. This verse reports that God "created" mankind (i.e., male and female) in God's own image, a unique kind of life that is infinitely different in quality from that of animal life. (In time, God would eventually provide redemption for human life, proving that God prizes human life moreso than any other kind of life that He created.) The creation of mankind was so important that the verb *bara'* is used thrice in this one verse.

Like Day 5, God's blessing was tied to His decree to "be fruitful and multiply, and fill" the earth (1:22, 28), with an extra responsibility to humans:

subdue and dominate.

This extra dominion responsibility that God imposed upon Adam would make a difference in the destiny of all life forms on Earth, because Adam's jurisdictional authority over the world (including all of its animals) would eventually mean that Adam's subsequent fall would include all that belonged to him (as Romans 8 explains).

At the end of Day 6, all was "very good" (Genesis 1:31)—which means that there could not be any death on Earth at that time because death is not good (Romans 8:20-22; 1 Corinthians 15). The Bible reports no animals dying before Adam sinned. (Note that no animals were to be eaten by humans until after the Flood, according to Genesis 1:29-30 and 9:1-4.) Likewise, theistic evolutionists' imaginations notwithstanding, the Bible reports no pre-Adamite subhuman primates of any kind, much less any dying before Adam sinned. Furthermore, the Bible reports no humans dying before Adam sinned.[3]

Rather, the Bible clearly reports that it was Adam's sin that triggered the curse of death, in fulfillment of God's warning:

> Therefore, just as through one man [i.e., *Adam*] sin entered into the world, and death through sin, and thus death spread to all men, because all sinned—(For until the law sin was in the world, but sin is not imputed when there is no law. Nevertheless death reigned from *Adam* to Moses, even over those who had not sinned according to the likeness of the *transgression of Adam*, who is a type of Him who was to come....For if by the one man's offense death reigned through the one, much more those who receive abundance of grace and of the gift of righteousness will reign in life through the One, *Jesus Christ*.) Therefore, as through one man's offense judgment came to all men, resulting in condemnation, even so through one Man's righteous act the free gift came to all men, resulting in justification of life. For as by one man's disobedience many were made sinners, so by one Man's obedience many will be made righteous. Moreover the law entered that the offense might abound. But where sin abounded, grace abounded much more, so that as sin hath reigned in death, even so grace might reign through righteousness to eternal life through Jesus Christ our Lord. (Romans 5:12-14, 17-21, emphasis added)

Death was unknown to Adam and Eve before Adam sinned. Adam had never seen death before. Just as people on Earth today do not personally see "heaven" and "hell," God teaches us via Scripture vital truths about the conditions of eternity. When we are taught what we should believe about such things, our own faith in God's Word is tested: Either we believe what God reveals to us about the unseen (e.g., heaven and hell), or we don't. God is pleased to test our faith about such unseen things, just as God was pleased (6,000+ years ago) to use information about unseen realities to test Adam's faith and loyalty. That kind of testing is the essence of faith (Hebrews 11:1-3).

Note that, like Adam's testing by God, God's testing of our faith and our loyalty to Him (as our Creator) is always coupled with *consequences*—good consequences for good choices, bad consequences for bad choices.

> Then the LORD God took the man and put him in the garden of Eden to tend and keep it. And the LORD God commanded the man, saying, "Of every tree of the garden you may freely eat; but of the tree of the knowledge of good and evil you shall not eat, for in the day that you eat of it you shall surely die." (Genesis 2:15-17)

Adam, the first human to sin, quickly learned a lot about consequences—the consequences of his sin included a new thing, death (Romans 5:12; 6:23).

## The Bible Teaches That the Wages of Sin Is Death

Consider how God chose to test Adam's faith and loyalty. The test was simple: Don't eat from one specific tree in the Garden of Eden. God designed Adam's test to have built-in consequences. Adam could make the choice, but Adam could not control the consequences that would flow from that choice. Why not? Because the consequences were built in to the alternative choice options: The good choice would produce a good result (life eternal); the bad choice would produce a bad result (death).

In effect, God designed the gun, including the trigger—but it was Adam who aimed the gun and pulled the trigger, thus starting the dying process ("you shall surely die" could be rendered "dying, you will die") that leads ultimately to death itself.

The test was all part of God's glorious plan for human history, and God foreknew what would happen.[2] However, Adam's choice was nonetheless a true test of Adam's faith and loyalty, because Adam did not *experientially* know the outcome in advance.

Adam could have believed God to avoid the "death" that God warned of, but he chose otherwise. Only then did Adam *experience* the "dying" condition that God had warned him about. Dying began, as did thorns, pain in childbirth, and, in time, death itself.

But the dying was not limited to Adam!

Because God had placed all of the life forms of the world under Adam's authority (Genesis 1:26-31; Psalm 8), the world fell with Adam and was "cursed" with death (Genesis 3:17-19).

> For the creation was subjected to futility, not willingly, but because of Him who subjected it in hope; because the creation itself also will be delivered from the bondage of corruption into the glorious liberty of the children of God. For we know that the whole creation groans and labors with birth pangs together until now. (Romans 8:20-22).

Consequently, all of the world's living creatures—both humans and animals—have been "groaning" under the curse of sin and death ever since, although eventually the time will come when Christ's redemption will be applied to the earth itself to overcome the Edenic curse of death (Revelation 20:11; 21:1-5; 22:3).

## Faith and Unbelief Are Tested in Time and Space

The Bible never says that Adam was punished before he sinned. Any such advance punishment (based on God's foreknowledge) would not truly test Adam's faith and loyalty. God never punishes a human sinner before he or she sins, because to do so would be unjust. Also, to punish a bad choice in advance would negate the decision as a true test of faith and loyalty.

Accordingly, even though God foreknows all human choices,[2] He does not disqualify the testing of our spiritual character by showing us (in the sense of visible experience, since a decision's real test is whether we will "walk by faith," not by sight) the future in advance, so there cannot be retroactive consequences for a human sinning against God.

Consider how people are tested by choices in real time. If you see the consequences of a choice in advance, how much of a real test is it?

Joseph tested his brothers in space and time (Genesis 42–44), not revealing himself to them until after they made character-revealing choices.

Daniel's three friends Shadrach, Meshach, and Abednego were tested in time and space (Daniel 3). They did not know in advance whether their godly choices would be rewarded with a miraculous deliverance or by an agonizing (and very painful) martyrdom.

What kind of testing of faith in and loyalty to God would there be if the consequences were provided before the choices were made?

Consider the amazing testing of Job's faith in and loyalty to God. Satan accused Job of worshiping God only if, as, and when God blessed Job—as if God was not worthy of being worshiped just because He is who He is. Satan was wrong, of course; Job praised God throughout his undeserved suffering (James 5:11; 1 Peter 4:19). But what if Job had been allowed to read the last chapter of the Bible book that bears his name—what kind of faith/loyalty test would all of that suffering have been?

Adam was tested in time and space. Eden was a real test in real time, and Adam failed the test. The test had real consequences, *dying* (i.e., the cursed process of mortality that inexorably leads to death) being the most immediate consequence for Adam's immoral and tragic choice.

Thankfully, God had a redemptive provision tied to the Curse's punitive outcome—a redemptive solution God did not reveal until the Messianic promise of Genesis 3:15 (which foreshadowed the truth of Romans 6:23).

In fact, God foreknew the need for human redemption; He planned for it before He created space, time, matter-energy, and bio-information (Revelation 13:8; 17:8).

But, because God wanted to truly test Adam's character (as He later would test Job), God did not reveal the consequence of Adam's sin, visibly, until Adam actually made his historic choice. Only then did this horrible cursed reality called death arrive on Earth, in real time.

## What's Wrong with Backdating Adam's Punishment for His Sin?

In order for theistic evolutionary theories to work, death had to have existed before Adam arrived and rebelled against God. Some have argued that backdating the punishment of his sin (i.e., applying the penalty of death "retroactively") by imposing death on creation before Adam sinned is juristically acceptable (i.e., acceptable as a matter of justice), because the sins of modern Christians were punished retroactively at Christ's crucifixion.

But this lopsided analogy is illogical and misfitted. It is not a mere comparison of apples and oranges, it is more like the contrast between apples and aardvarks!

Christ's advance choice to voluntarily accept *undeserved* punishment as the innocent substitute for Adam's race is not at all like Adam's involuntary experience of receiving *deserved* punishment for his sin in Eden.

Christ foreknowingly agreed to His Messianic role—including His redemptive death and resurrection—before the vicarious punishment was imposed upon (and accepted by) Him at Calvary. As a matter of God's holy justice, this voluntary consent on Christ's part made all the difference in how God's justice fit the situation.

In other words, before Christ ever created the heavens and the earth, He consented to the Trinity's plan for His incarnation so that He would, as the Lord Jesus Christ, be sacrificed (in future Earth time) as the Lamb of God, fulfilling the Messianic Kinsman-Redeemer role necessary to provide a just redemption for Adam's race. God foreknew prior to the creation week that the human race would fail and thus would need a rescue (see Revelation 13:8).

The punishment of Christ as the innocent substitute for human sinners would occur chronologically after some people sinned (those who lived during Old Testament times), as well as before others sinned (those who lived during New Testament times and afterwards). Yet, all of that sin was foreknown to Christ before He committed to accepting punishment for it, as the Just suffering for the unjust in order to justify many. There was no punishment imposed, historically, prior to Christ's consent.

There is therefore no "retroactive injustice" problem, because Christ's voluntary decision to pay for all of the foreknown human sin before any of it occurred was a fate that Christ willingly volunteered for before He created the heavens and the earth (John 1:3, 10-13). It was *not unjust* for Christ to accept that role in advance of performing it.

In other words, Christ was not being "cheated," as a matter of justice, by being punished before He failed a test of moral accountability, because He never failed at anything! Rather, Christ's punishment was volunteered for, and that punishment occurred after He voluntarily accepted the role of the Lamb of God who would take away the sin of the world.

Even in our profane human experience, we do not regard it as unjust when someone pays in advance for anticipated debts of an intended beneficiary. For example, although it is not a common practice in this selfish world, there is nothing shocking about the idea of one unselfish man depositing a sum of money to pay for the expected expenses of someone else. The good Samaritan provided an advance payment for the foreseeable expenses of the robbery victim he had rescued (Luke 10:35).

As a matter of justice, the Samaritan was not "cheated," because his money was not involuntarily taken from him before a debt was incurred. Rather, he anticipated a foreseeable debt that would soon be owed, and he chose voluntarily to provide for its payment, as a matter of grace, before it was incurred. (Of course, in the case of Christ's substitutionary sacrifice for our sins, there will *never* be a supplemental payment, because the death of Christ is a once-for-all and more-than-sufficient payment for all of the sins of the human race, no matter how many sins that may ultimately add up to.[9])

However, in Adam's case, the punishment, which included the curse of sin and death chronicled in Genesis 3 and explained in Romans 5, was *involuntarily* imposed on Adam. Because Adam did not volunteer for his punishment, it would be unjust to impose that punishment on him (even though God foreknew that Adam would sin) unless and until he actually sinned, in space and time. When Adam actually sinned, it was then a just time for him to receive the "wages of sin"—death.

In other words, Adam was not "cheated," as a matter of justice, by being punished before he sinned (as theistic evolution would require), because (1) God warned Adam of the consequence of sinning *before* he sinned, and (2) God did not impose the curse of sin and death until *after* Adam actually sinned.

There was no miscarriage of justice in Eden! Rather, God's justice was manifested in Adam's lifetime (as it is reported to us in Genesis), for those who have the eyes to see it. Also, there was no *ex post facto* punishment (i.e., defining an action as wrong only after it was committed). Adam had advance notice of what God prohibited, but knowingly committed the sin anyway; only then was the just penalty to Adam imposed by God.

There was no "backdated" involuntary punishment in Eden (or anywhere else). Adam never received a penalty from God until the time when he deserved it.

God is just. Because He is just, any theological compromise of the Genesis 3 narrative, or its New Testament commentaries (e.g., in Romans 5 and in 1 Corinthians 15), is an insult to God's perfect justice.

## Appreciating the Bible's Authoritative Relevance

All of this is plainly taught in the history of Genesis 1–5 and is clarified theologically in Romans 5 and 8. So why do some people, especially theistic evolutionists, have a problem understanding that there was no death until Adam sinned? The simple answer is that theistic evolutionists are ignoring the authoritative truth in Genesis and Romans—due to negligent or willful ignorance of those biblical texts.

In sum, theistic evolutionists prefer to accommodate secular evolutionary teachings, so they ignore or distort the plain teaching of Genesis and Romans.[3, 4, 5]

But such unbiblical accommodation is not Christ-like. The Lord Jesus Christ did not "accommodate" unbiblical teachings when He physically walked this earth—rather, He healed the blind on the Sabbath (e.g., see John 9) just to prove that the Pharisees were false teachers espousing bad theology.

## Why Does It Matter?

The New Testament directly links the gospel of salvation to the sin of Adam (Romans 5; 1 Corinthians 15). Note that Paul's definition of the gospel of Christ in 1 Corinthians 15:3-4 twice contextualizes the gospel as being "according to the [Old Testament] Scriptures"—the gospel is dependent upon the Old Testament being true!

Indeed, the Old Testament is authoritatively relevant and true and perfect—every "jot and tittle" of it—from Genesis forward. So much so that Christ Himself said that Moses would judge people according to whether they believed the words of Moses (John 5:45-47).

In other words, if the Bible's five books of Moses (which include Genesis) were authoritatively good enough for the Lord Jesus (Matthew 24:35; John 17:17), they are authoritatively good enough for us.

What we really believe about death being the consequence of Adam's sin in Eden is a test of our own faith in and loyalty to God.[10] And that test is an open-Book exam.

## Notes

1. Chaffey, T. and J. Lisle. 2008. *Old-Earth Creationism on Trial: The Verdict Is In.* Green Forest, AR: Master Books, 23-30, especially 27-29. God's moral character is another hugely important truth, tied directly to Genesis 3 and Romans 8. This theological issue is addressed elsewhere in this book by Dr. Henry M. Morris III. Theologically speaking, this chapter also relies upon the analytical critiques of the gap theory and day age theory, as well as interpreting Genesis exegetically (as the Lord Jesus Himself role-modeled, e.g., in Matthew 19:4 and Mark 10:6), as well as the clarification that the book of Genesis is *not* Hebrew poetry (see the earlier chapters on these topics).

2. Regarding the balance of God's sovereignty and human choice, accountability, and suffering, see Johnson, J. J. S. 2011. Human Suffering: Why This Isn't the "Best of All Possible Worlds." *Acts & Facts.* 40 (11): 8-10.

3. Theistic evolutionists (whether they endorse gap theory, day age, or Intelligent Design Movement cosmogonies) routinely posit millions or billions of years of cosmic time before Adam, as well as eons of animal death before Adam, and pre-Adamite races of subhuman primates—all of which imaginary concepts accommodate secularists' evolutionary dogmas. See, e.g., Dembski, W. 2009. *The End of Christianity: Finding a Good God in an Evil World.* Nashville, TN: Broadman and Holman Academic, 77, 154-155; and William Dembski's "Christian Theodicy in Light of Genesis and Modern Science" paper (n.d.). Both are quoted and cited in Ham, K. and G. Hall. 2011. *Already Compromised.* Green Forest, AR: Master Books, 173-174, and endnotes 3, 4, and 6 on page 202.

4. Johnson, J. J. S. 2011. Just Say No to Trojan Horses. *Acts & Facts.* 40 (2): 17-18, citing Whitcomb, J.C., and H. M. Morris. 1961. *The Genesis Flood: The Biblical Record and Its Scientific Implications.* Phillipsburg, NJ: Presbyterian & Reformed Publishing, 91-99. See also Morris, J. D. 2007. *The Young Earth: The Real History of the Earth—Past, Present, and Future.* Green Forest, AR: Master Books, 128-129, cited in Johnson, J. J. S. 2011. Biblical Devastation in the Wake of a "Tranquil Flood." *Acts & Facts.* 40 (9): 8-10.

5. Johnson, J. J. S. 2011. Culpable Passivity: The Failure of Going with the Flow. *Acts & Facts.* 40 (7): 8-10.

6. Wigram, G. V. 2001. *The Englishman's Concordance of the Old Testament.* Peabody, MA: Hendrickson, 270 (reprint of 3rd edition of 1874).

7. Hebrew verbs used to describe God's creative work in Genesis 1 besides *bara'* ("created") include *hayah* ("let there be," vv. 3, 6, 14, 15); *badal* ("divided," vv. 4, 6, 7, 18); `*asah* ("made," "yielding," vv. 7, 11, 12, 16, 25, 26); *qavah* ("be gathered together," v. 9); *ra'ah* ("appear," v. 9); *rasha'* ("bring forth," v. 11); *zara*` ("yielding seed," i.e., "seeding," vv. 11, 12); *yatsa'* ("bring forth," vv. 12, 24); *nathan* ("set," vv. 17, 18); *sharats* ("bring forth," vv. 20, 21).

8. Wigram, 829-833. Plants were created on Day 3, but, biblically speaking, they don't have what the Bible calls "life," so "life" did not exist until Day 5. Life was something completely new to God's creation, so the Hebrew verb *bara'* ("created") is used in Genesis 1:21 to described it being commanded into being. Regarding the animated life of animals ("that moves") in contrast to plants, see Morris III, H. M. 2012. It's Alive! *Acts & Facts.* 41 (8): 4-5.

9. Regardless of how much sin is ultimately committed by humans, the aggregate (although huge beyond human comprehension) is still a finite amount of sins, committed by a finite number of fallen humans. By contrast, the worth of the human life of Christ, however, is infinite, because Christ is both God and man simultaneously. Christ's perfection and infinite value as the incarnate Creator God immeasurably outweighs all of the possible wrongs that could ever be committed by any possible number of fallen humans. Accordingly, the vicarious death of Christ when He shed His blood at Calvary more than pays for all of the possible sins of humans, for all time. See Romans 5, especially verses 9, 10, 15, 17, and 20.

10. This controversy is best understood when it is recognized that it is one major battlefront in a larger war over Genesis' perfect authenticity, accuracy, authority, understandability, and authoritative relevance. See especially pages 22-27 of Cooper, W. R. 2011. *The Authenticity of the Book of Genesis,* Portsmouth, UK: Creation Science Movement, as well as pages 7-21, 33-99, 109-130, 162-359, and 369-405. See also Johnson, J. J. S. 2012. Tonsils, Forensic Science, and the Recent Fabrication Rule. *Acts & Facts.* 41 (6): 8-9; and Morris, H. M. 1976. *The Genesis Record.* San Diego, CA: Creation-Life Publishers, 17-25.

# 4
# THREE GENESIS COMPROMISES

John D. Morris, Ph.D., and James J. S. Johnson, J.D., Th.D.

**Summary:** Genesis clearly describes a creation that took place in six 24-hour days, but Christians who hold an old-earth view try various ways to squeeze billions of years into the creation account to make it align with secular origins stories.

The language used in Genesis 1 indicates that the days of the creation week can only be normal days and not periods or eons. The day age/progressive creation theory attempts to force the six days of creation into vast ages of time, but this twists the text and negates humanity's sin as the means by which death entered our world.

The gap theory inserts billions of years into the supposed time period between the first two verses of Genesis—but no such gap exists. Attempts to tweak Genesis to match human expectation not only don't work, they compromise the clear Word of God.

Bible readers have tried various ways to squeeze billions of years into the Genesis creation account. In testing how these ways might work, we have found that each such attempt violates the plain words of Genesis and undermines important theology, including the character of God and the origin of sin—the very foundation of the gospel. Let us examine three Genesis compromises.

## Genesis "Day" Means a Real Day

Christians who hold to an extremely old earth acknowledge that both Scripture and history teach Abraham lived just a few thousand years ago. Furthermore, chronologies in Scripture identify the time between Abraham and Noah, and the time between Noah and Adam as a total of only a few thousand years. Even using the maximum timespans given in various manuscripts yields a total of only a few thousand years between Adam and the present. But maybe the creation took billions of years, they say.

The Bible specifies that God's work of creation took "six days," at the end of which He created Adam and Eve. He provides a record of His activities on Day 1, Day 2, etc. He even brackets each day by the terms "evening and morning." Adding six days to the time since Adam still equals only a few thousand years, or so it seems. Those who advocate an earth of billions of years in age do so by asserting that the days of creation were really of vast duration. Is there any biblical and linguistic evidence that a "day" can be of great length?

As a matter of fact, the Hebrew word *yom*, here translated "day," can have a variety of meanings, just like in English.

In both languages, the term most often refers to a solar day, defined by one revolution of the earth on its axis. If I say "today," you know what I mean. Or when I say "the day of your birth," it's clear. Perhaps I could modify the word by a numerical adjective, like "first day" or "three days," and you would know what I meant. But I could say "in the day of George Washington" and you would know I was referring to a period of time around the Revolutionary War. It all depends on context. How the word is used specifies its meaning in any particular usage.

In Genesis 1, God apparently went out of His way to make sure we didn't misunderstand, for He defined *yom* the first time He used it. On Day 1, after creating the heavens and the earth, God created light (v. 3), and "God divided the light from the darkness" (v. 4). This light/dark cycle was further identified when "God called the light Day [*yom*], and the darkness He called Night" (v. 5). Throughout the rest of the passage, He uses the term for the first day through the seventh day.

The door to misinterpretation is closed in Exodus 20:11, where God wrote in stone some things He really didn't want us to misinterpret. The fourth of the Ten Commandments concerns our workweek, where we are commanded to work six days and rest on the seventh: "For in six days the LORD made the heavens and the earth, the sea, and all that is in them, and rested the seventh day." Same word, *yom*, same context, same modifiers, same tablet of stone, same Author, same finger that wrote it. If words have meaning, then God created in six days just like our days. His work of creation becomes the pattern for our workweek.

"Day" can mean a period of time when the context demands, but in the creation account "day" means a real day. Christians need to allow the unchangeable Scripture to define its own terms and not rely on the temporal musings of men.

## Day Age Theory and Progressive Creation

The history of the church has featured many individual battles, all of which were eventually won by those who stood firm on the Word of God. For instance, the early church fathers were victorious over legalism and Gnosticism. During the Reformation, the doctrine of salvation by grace through faith was the battleground. In each case, insistence on Scripture in its purity and simplicity carried the day. Creation doctrine has also seen controversy. Beginning with the gap theory in the early 1800s and theistic evolution in the late 1800s, Bible believers have been able to defeat these compromises with truth.

The compromise of choice today is known as progressive creation, a modern revision of the day age theory that God didn't create in six days but over six "eons." Advocating that the days of creation can be equated with billions of years of geology and astronomy, it proposes that God's creative acts occurred on widely separate occasions over the ages. To adherents, the world before Adam was identical to that of the secular view, with extinction of the majority of life forms, with disease, bloodshed, and carnivorous activity predating Adam's rebellion and the resultant curse of death as the penalty of sin. By necessity, progressive creation minimizes the extent of Christ's work on the cross, limiting it to the redemption of man's spirit only, not his body or the rest of creation.

Some have labeled this issue as the seminal issue facing the church today. Most Christians are unaware of the problem. Many Christian leaders are fighting on the wrong side of the battle. Both are often intimidated into compromising Scripture by authoritative-sounding scientists. We feel God has raised up ICR, as a group of uncompromising Bible-believing scientists, to lead the church back from the precipice of compromise.

To do so, ICR called together a group of recognized creation spokesmen equipped to address the errors of progressive creation and the scientific truth of biblical creation. The team found, among may other problems, that progressive creation views force the word "day" in Genesis 1 to mean an indeterminate timespan. When does it ever mean that anywhere in Scripture, and why should it ever mean that when the text clearly defines "day" as a period between morning and evening? This view also inadvertently undermines the gospel by placing death long before—and thus not caused by—Adam's sin.

## Gap Theory

Like a high-speed, head-on collision, the Bible's creation account directly smashes into the modern majority opinion on origins, especially on the topic of how old the earth is.

Because of this conflict, many have tried to produce a third option—a lop-sided compromise that attempts to harmonize the evolution myth's old-universe concept with the "six days during the creation week" narrative content of Genesis. Perhaps the cleverest example of this kind of compromise is the gap theory, the most popular version of which is called the "ruin and reconstruction theory."

There isn't any legitimate exegetical reason to believe that the days reported in Genesis 1 were anything but ordinary, 24-hour days, yet some Christians insist we must somehow accommodate the idea that the universe is billions of years old. They may think that this age has been established by science, but nothing could be further from the truth. (See the chapters in this book on the age of the earth and the universe.)

Whatever the reason, since it is clear within the scriptural context that the days of creation were ordinary days, some people have suggested that there was an enormous span of time between Genesis 1:1 and 1:2. They redefine the creation week as more of a "re-creation" (i.e., restoration) week. Some in this camp believe that God originally made the world billions of years ago and then it was ruined, perhaps by Satan, so that the creation week of Genesis 1 recounts how God (re)made the world in six ordinary days.

This view is called the gap theory because its advocates aver that an enormous gap of time (billions of years) lies between the first two verses of Genesis.

## Imagine "Gap," Insert Evolutionary "Time"

Some Christians mistakenly believe that the billions of years (originally it was just millions) featured in the gap theory are an accommodation of Charles Darwin's natural selection theory. Not so! The gap theory was championed by Thomas Chalmers in 1814, 45 years before Darwin's *Origin of Species*![1] So those who think the eons-of-time gap was inserted in response to Darwin have misdiagnosed the real explanation for why Christians decided to implant eons of time into the space between the Bible's first two verses.

Unfortunately, Thomas Chalmers invented the time gap in order to accommodate deists (like Charles Lyell and James Hutton) who taught old earth theories that disagreed with Moses' writings. Perhaps Chalmers thought that he was helping to make the Bible more credible to the educated people of his generation. This so-called solution to what would in time be called the creation-vs.-evolution problem demonstrates a failure, during the early 1800s, of due diligence to recognize who is right and who is wrong.

Called a synthesis (or hybrid) solution, this syncretistic theory attempts to hybridize Bible history with secular mythology.

> *The widest rift between science, so-called, and traditional Christianity is the controversy over the age of the earth.* Is it not possible that the Christians have been as badly mistaken as the scientists?... [The world] may have been revolving quite a while before Adam ever caught sight of it. *There is room for all the geologic ages between the first two verses of the Bible.*[2]

Why has the idea of a gap of "deep time" between Genesis 1:1 and 1:2 been so carelessly and quickly endorsed by so many Christians? Why the big rush to endorse billions of years that are not actually mentioned in the Bible?

Many people try oh-so-hard to please both sides of the fence, but all such amalgamations are logically inconsistent. Biblical creation and Bible-rejecting evolution[3] are, in reality, mutually exclusive explanations for Earth's origins, so there cannot be any true mixture of the two (see Amos 3:3; Luke 16:13). The yoking of Genesis 1 with imagined eons of time presents a challenge in trying to force-fit these disparate epistemologies. How can someone believe in the six literal days of the creation week, followed by a Sabbath day of rest, while simultaneously allowing the so-called geologic ages of millions or billions of evolutionary years?

The proposed harmonization is this: The creation week is recognized as a true week of six 24-hour days of God's work, followed by one literal day of God's rest—yet eons of time elapsed before any of the creation week days.

In short, the gap theory teaches that Day 1 was not really Day 1.

But how can this idea measure up to the text of Scripture? The gap theory uses these assumptions:

1. It is okay to have a literal creation week after the action described in Genesis 1:1;

2. So, the creation week does not include Genesis 1:1; and

3. Therefore, God's actions described in Genesis 1:1 may be read as taking countless eons of (pre-creation week) time.

But this question logically follows: What Scriptures, including Genesis 1, do gap theory proponents argue from as they advocate their gap of "deep time" lodged between Genesis 1:1 and 1:2?

First, they contend that the Hebrew verb *hayah* is evidence that Earth qualitatively changed between the Bible's first and second verses. Carey Daniel illustrates how the gap theory argues that the original orderly creation changed catastrophically, somehow, into a formless waste:

> But if the word "created" [in Genesis 1:1] refers more correctly to an instantaneous action, and if it means that our world, together with all others, was called suddenly into being (Hebrews 11:3), the question remains as to why Moses said it was a formless waste and Isaiah pronounced it an orderly creation [in Isaiah 45:18]. In this case the only answer is that there must have been a lapse of time between the first and second verses of the first chapter of Genesis, during which there took place some great upheaval that overthrew the primitive creation. That such a catastrophe did occur as the result of God's judgment on the early inhabitants seems to have [happened]....Just who these inhabitants were we dare not venture to say. [Ironically, the author promptly ventures a guess anyway.] They could scarcely have been human beings, for of such Eve is called the "mother of all living" (Genesis 3:20). Some hold that they were the angels who like Lucifer, lost their first estate (Jude 6; 2 Peter 2:4; Isaiah 14:9-14). This supposition is probably as credible as any other.[2]

Note the conjecture, imagining a pre-Adamite world.[4] But what does the Scripture say (and not say) about pre-Adamite "ruin" and "reconstruction"? Likewise, is there any legitimate basis for a gap of time between Genesis 1:1 and 1:2?

## Genesis 1

Gap theorists believe that the phrase "in the beginning" used in Genesis 1:1 refers to the original creation, which occurred sometime in the very distant past billions of years ago. The next verse becomes the key to their theory: "The earth was without form, and void" (Genesis 1:2).

Gap theorists would prefer to translate this as "the earth *became* without form, and void," and suggest that a "formless" creation means some kind of ruin, some change from "very good" to "wasted."[5]

But should 1:2 say "became" (which denotes a change of condition) instead of "was" (which denotes a condition that continues the same as before)? In fact, there is no philological need to replace the English translation verb "was" with "became." The Hebrew word *hayah* used here is the normal Hebrew verb that means "to be." This same verb is the etymological root of God's special name *YHWH* (Yahweh = "He is" or "He who is," emphasizing God's unchanging being), as is confirmed by Exodus 3:14 ("I AM WHO I AM" twice uses the verb *hayah*). God never changed; God can't change. So why would He pick a form of *hayah* to be His own name if *hayah* must mean "change"?

The Hebrew verb *hayah* likewise appears in Genesis 2:18, when God stated that it was "not good that man [Adam] should be alone." The English phrase "should be" translates the verb (specifically, a simple active infinitive construct form of *hayah*), yet Genesis reports nothing to suggest that Adam's singleness at the time was a "changed" condition, as if he was then alone after a previous marriage.

In some cases, a sentence using *hayah* can make sense whether it is translated as a form of "to be" or a form of "to become," but it also appears that a form of "to be" makes better theological or historical sense in those contexts (e.g., Genesis 13:8; Judges 18:19; 2 Samuel 7:24).

## Does Isaiah Support a Billions-of-Years-Old Earth?

As noted above, gap theory advocates claim that the description of Earth in Isaiah 45:18 clashes with the creation history reported in Genesis 1:2.

> In Isaiah 45:18 we are told that God created the world to *not be formless* (*lô' tohû*), yet in Genesis 1:2 we are told that the world *was formless* (*tohû*). Likewise, we read in Genesis 1:2 that earth was

41

"void" (*bohû* = "empty," i.e., empty of inhabitants), yet in Isaiah 45:18 it says God created the earth "to be inhabited" (a form of *yashab* = "to inhabit"). How can both verses be true unless they are describing different times in Earth history?[6]

The Hebrew word *tohû* does appear in both Genesis 1:2 and Isaiah 45:18. Isaiah 45:18 says that God, the Creator, "established" (an intensive perfect form of the verb *kûn*) the earth so it would not be a formless mass. And it's not! Before Day 1, God had a plan in mind. At the beginning of the creation week, God already knew what His goal was for planet Earth—a world that was orderly, completely formed, and populated with inhabitants. And by the end of Day 6, sure enough, that goal was accomplished and the result was "very good."

But notice that God's complete goal for forming the earth and populating it was not yet accomplished on Day 1, so Genesis 1:2 correctly reports that on Day 1 the world was "formless," waiting for God to further develop it geologically and geographically.

Likewise, it was always God's planned intention to "establish" Earth as a home for both human and animal inhabitants. That plan of God is noted in Isaiah 45:18, using an infinitive construct form of the common Hebrew verb *yashab* ("to dwell"), emphasizing that God's action was pointed toward that teleological target. As of Day 1, that divine plan was not fully implemented, because none of the animals would appear until Day 5. And it would be Day 6 before Earth's first human inhabitants arrived, along with land-dwelling animals.

Genesis is a chronological narrative reporting *how* and *when* God created the universe and its inhabitants, and what He did sequentially to implement His intended purposes for creation. Isaiah, however, emphasizes *why* God created stuff and later developed it because He wanted an inhabited, orderly world.

A careful analysis of Genesis 1:1-2 and Isaiah 45:18 does not justify inventing a gap of evolutionary "geologic time." There is no need for pre-Adamite races, either! The Bible makes perfect sense as it is.

**Notes**

1. See Johnson, J. J. S. 2011. Just Say No to Trojan Horses: Worldview Corruption Is Lying in Wait. *Acts & Facts.* 40 (2): 17-18. See Whitcomb, J. C. and H. M. Morris. 1961. *The Genesis Flood.* Phillipsburg, NJ: Pres-

byterian & Reformed Publishing Company, 91-99. Regarding the fact that the phrase "in the beginning" in Genesis 1:1 really means "in *the* beginning" (not "in *a* beginning"), see Johnson, J. J. S. 2013. Does *Bereshith* Mean "in a beginning"? *Creation Matters.* 18 (3): 6-7.

2. Daniel, C. L. 1941. *The Bible's Seeming Contradictions: 101 Paradoxes Harmonized.* Grand Rapids, MI: Zondervan, 83-84. Emphasis added.

3. In the phrase "Bible-rejecting evolution," we are using the broader meaning of the word evolution; i.e., the common notion that all of creation was generated from a materialistic Big Bang that somehow, over eons of time and accidents, converted itself into stars, planets, Golgi bodies and bacteria, gecko lizards and bugs, girls and boys. The more narrow use of the word evolution would pertain only to the imagined processes beginning with abiogenesis (i.e., life spontaneously generating from non-life), followed by all life forms somehow morphing into other kinds of life.

4. The notion of pre-Adamite creatures populating the earth, with death on Earth before Adam sinned (notwithstanding Romans 5:12 and Romans 8:20-22), has spread. For example, note that theistic evolutionist William Dembski promotes old earth, pre-Adamite subhuman primates, death before sin, and a miraculous amnesia supposedly provided by God that caused Adam and Eve to forget "their former animal life." See Johnson, J. J. S. 2011. Culpable Passivity: The Failure of Going with the Flow. *Acts & Facts.* 40 (7): 8-10, quoting William Dembski's "Christian Theodicy in Light of Genesis and Modern Science" paper (n.d.), as quoted in Ham, K. and G. Hall. 2011. *Already Compromised.* Green Forest, AR: Master Books, 174 and 202, especially endnotes 3 and 7.

5. Gap theorists say Genesis 1:2 reports events that occurred billions of years *after* "the beginning" mentioned in Genesis 1:1; i.e., after an unrecorded history dominated by pre-Adamite death and suffering.

6. This hypothetical quote paraphrases correspondence received by ICR personnel from gap theory advocates.

# 5

# GENESIS IS NARRATIVE HISTORY, NOT HEBREW POETRY

James J. S. Johnson, J.D., Th.D.

**Summary:** Some people try to dismiss a literal reading of Genesis 1–3 by claiming that it's poetry, not history. But an examination of the text reveals this can't be true. While English poetry relies heavily on rhyme and sound, Hebrew poetry uses parallelisms that compare or contrast the meaning of ideas.

The opening chapters of Genesis are written in historical narrative language—not some form of Hebrew poetry. The only poetry is a two-verse section in chapter 4, Lamech's song. The rest of the book is set down as clear sequential history.

There is no need to distort the reading of Genesis in order to accommodate evolutionary mythology. Genesis 1–11 is easy-to-understand narrative prose, not poetry.

"Why are you guys so literalistic about Genesis? Don't you know that it's just Hebrew poetry? There's no need to treat it like real history!" This was the comment of a young English literature teacher at a Christian educators' conference that featured Institute for Creation Research speakers. What followed was an energetic discussion that exposed hidden assumptions and misinformation about what Hebrew poetry is and is not.

The bottom line is that Genesis is not Hebrew poetry. Genesis is Hebrew narrative prose. In other words, Genesis is a record of accurate, true history. Not mysticism or mystery or myth. There is no need for anyone to guess about what Genesis is. Anyone who can read an English Bible can prove that Genesis is not Hebrew poetry.

Why is this important? Because the New Testament's theology of our salvation in Christ Jesus hangs upon the historicity of the Genesis record (Romans 5:12-21).

## What Hebrew Poetry Is and Is Not

To see why the young English teacher was wrong, we must first recognize that English poetry and Hebrew poetry are different—hugely different. The difference is not like comparing apples and oranges; the difference is more like contrasting apples and aardvarks.

English poetry is defined by its verbal "hardware," with its pronounced sounds qualifying the text as poetry. Hebrew poetry, however, is defined by its "software," its verbal information and meaning, presented with parallelism of thought (not sound).

In short, Hebrew poetry is defined by parallelism in meaning, whereas English poetry is defined by the format of verse and sound (rhyme, alliteration, assonance, and/or meter). This is easier to illustrate than to explain. Consider the examples below of both kinds of poetry.

## Example of English Poetry, Using a Limerick Rhyme and Meter Format

### Some Get a "Bang" Out of Fables

The Bible, to read, some are able,
Yet prefer to read a false fable;
   Though God's Word says "six days,"
   A Big Bang gets their praise,
Their doctrine, therefore, is unstable.[1]

Verses of English poetry routinely rely on rhyme. In limerick poems, the rhyme pattern is AA, BB, A (because able, fable, and unstable all rhyme, as do days and praise). Other poems use other patterns, but almost without exception some kind of rhyme is used to identify English verse-based literature as poetry.

English poetry, being dominated by sound, also relies on meter, the poem's rhythmic "beat." The number of stressed syllables in all A lines should match, as should those in the B lines. One English tradition uses iambic pentameter, employed by poets John Donne, William Shakespeare, and John Milton.[2] Note that rhyme and rhythm neither provide nor depend upon a poem's meaning.

Unlike the sound-dominated rhyme and rhythm of English poetry, Hebrew poetry is defined by informational parallelism—i.e., parallelism of meaning.[3] The paralleled thoughts may emphasize good and bad, wise and unwise, reverent and blasphemous. They may or may not recount historical events, although time and place, if mentioned at all, are less emphasized than in narrative prose. This informational parallelism—using comparative lines and phrases—portrays similarities (synonymous parallelism) and/or contrasts (antithetical parallelism), or comparisons of whole and part, or some other kind of logical associations of meaning.

Knowing this linguistic trait helps us to correctly read biblical Hebrew poetry. Since such poetry requires complementation of meaning (not sound), both halves of a verbal parallelism must be reviewed together as a complementary unit in order to understand fully what either half means, as well as to understand how they complement each other in meaning.

In Hebrew poetry, almost always the paralleled lines come in pairs,[4] but sometimes a triplet is used.[5] Major examples of Hebrew poetry in the Old Testament are Psalms, Proverbs, Lamentations, and Song of Solomon—but not Genesis.

## Example of Hebrew Poetry, Illustrating Parallelisms of Similarity and Contrast

Psalm 104:29
> You hide Your face, they are troubled:
> You take away their breath, they die and return to their dust.

Psalm 104:30
> You send forth Your Spirit, they are created:
> And You renew the face of the earth.

Note how both lines in verse 29 show parallel similarity of meaning, as do both lines in verse 30. Yet verse 29 informationally contrasts with verse 30; verse 29 tells how God controls the *death* of certain creatures (like leviathan, mentioned in verse 26), but verse 30 tells how God controls the *life* of His creatures. In order to get the full meaning of either verse 29 or verse 30, the total parallelism must be appreciated. This is the hallmark of Hebrew poetry.

For another example, read any chapter in Proverbs. They are dominated by parallelism of meaning, verse after verse. Sometimes the parallelism spreads over consecutive verses, as in Proverbs 28:15-16 ("wicked ruler" in verse 15, "a ruler" who is a "great oppressor" in verse 16). Sometimes the parallelism is condensed within one verse, as in Proverbs 28:28 ("when the wicked arise, men hide themselves: but when they perish, the righteous increase").

Parallelism dominates the informational structure of Hebrew poetry. Careful reading cannot miss it.

## Example of Genesis History, Exhibiting the Format of Narrative Prose

> Now Cain talked with Abel his brother; and it came to pass, when they were in the field, that Cain rose up against Abel his brother and killed him. And the LORD said to Cain, "Where is Abel your brother?" He said, "I do not know. Am I my brother's keeper?" And He said, "What have you done? The voice of your brother's blood cries out to Me from the ground. So now you are cursed from the earth, which has opened its mouth to receive your brother's blood from your hand." (Genesis 4:8-11)

There is no informational parallelism in this passage. What we read is history. Genesis 4:8-11 provides the reader with a narrative account of the first hate crime—an unbeliever tragically persecuting a believer, a terrible precedent that preceded millions of later copycat martyrdom murders. It's a terribly sad report of real history (except that for Abel it was not sad for long because as a redeemed believer he went to heaven).

There is no poetic parallelism anywhere in Genesis 4, with the only apparent exception being the wicked "song" of Lamech the polygamist recorded in Genesis 4:23-24.

> And Lamech said unto his wives,
>
> > Adah and Zillah, hear my voice;
> > > Wives of Lamech, listen to my speech!
> > For I have killed a man for wounding me,
> > > Even a young man for hurting me.
> > If Cain shall be avenged sevenfold,
> > > Then Lamech seventy and sevenfold.

Note the synonymous parallelism format of meaning in the first two-thirds of the poetic boasting of Lamech.

> Adah and Zillah = wives of Lamech
> Hear my voice = listen to my speech

A man (I killed) for wounding me = a young man for hurting me

The last part of Lamech's boasting exhibits comparative parallelism, where Cain is compared in a somewhat contrasting way with Lamech. Cain was to be avenged sevenfold if he was killed (Genesis 4:15), yet Cain's murder of Abel was unprovoked. Lamech, however, felt himself morally superior to Cain because Lamech was provoked by a man who "wounded" him (i.e., the young man who hurt him), so surely—Lamech self-righteously rationalized— Lamech would be avenged much moreso than Cain, perhaps 11 times more.

The fact that the book of Genesis records Lamech's "song" does not mean that Lamech was theologically correct. However, its inclusion—in its Hebrew poetry parallelism format—proves that Hebrew poetry as a literary genre was known to the divinely inspired author of Genesis (i.e., Moses[6]), but it was not used to report any of the historical events of Genesis other than in Lamech's song.

Except for this song, Genesis 4 is not unusual in its narrative prose presentation of early Earth history. There is no poetic parallelism in Genesis 1, 2, 3, or any other chapter in Genesis. Note that the restrictive features of Hebrew poetry, as Lamech's song illustrates, contrast with Genesis 1, 2, and 3, which narratively chronicle the sequential events of Earth's first week and Adam's first sin.

Genesis is narrative history; it introduces God the Creator, and then introduces the family history of Adam's race. Virtually all of Genesis illustrates what we expect from historical narrative—careful attention to sequenced events (this occurred, then this occurred, then this occurred, etc.), as well as inclusion of time-and-space context information (when such is relevant to the narrative) and a noticeable absence of Hebrew parallelism.[7]

## Conclusion: No Meaning-Based Parallelism Structures the Sentences in Genesis

The sentences in Genesis read like narrative history (i.e., prose) *not* informational parallelism (poetry). But the "elephant in the room" question is: Why would anyone even pretend that Genesis 1–11, or any part of Genesis, is Hebrew poetry?

For those who know better, it is intellectual dishonesty to avoid the obvious truth that Genesis is real history. Their most likely motive is a desire to accommodate evolutionary mythology by discounting the real history of our origins, stealing credit from Christ so that a fable called "natural selection" can be credited with "selecting" (and creating) Earth's creatures.

Some think Genesis is Hebrew poetry because they have been misled by an "expert." Hopefully, this quick summary can clear up any such confusion. But an even simpler test is this: How did Jesus treat Genesis? As *real history*, just like Paul.[8]

Genesis 1–11 is easy-to-understand narrative prose. Don't naïvely fall for the misinformation of a so-called scholar who, because he wants to rationalize his own evolutionary mythology, tries to dissuade you from believing that Genesis is an inerrantly inspired historical narrative—because that's exactly what it is.

### Notes

1. Johnson, J. J. S. The Religion-and-Science Connection Between *Pseudônumos* and *Pseudomarturia*: How Special Revelation Describes the Limitations of General Revelation, technical paper presented at the Southwest regional meeting of the Evangelical Theological Society at The Criswell College, Dallas, Texas, March 27, 2009.

2. Another traditional poetic meter is trochaic tetrameter, used in the German translation of the Finnish national epic *Kalevala* and later mimicked by American poet Henry Wadsworth Longfellow in his fictional epic *Hiawatha*. Both *Kalevala* and *Hiawatha* also use parallelism, though parallelism is not required to be recognized as poetry in German or English. Johnson, J. J. S. Finnish Literature, Language, and Lore. *Baltic Heritage Review*. April 2006: 5-7, citing Lönnrot, E. 1963. *The Kalevala, or Poems of the Kaleva District*, F. P. Magoun, Jr., transl. Cambridge: Harvard University Press, 162-163.

3. Robert Lowth is often recognized as clarifying this trait of Hebrew poetry in his *Lectures on the Sacred Poetry of the Hebrews*, published in 1753.

4. For example, Psalm 2:1 compares the raging of "the heathen" with "the people" imagining a vain thing. Likewise, Psalm 2:2 compares the "kings of the earth" setting themselves against the Lord with the "rulers" taking counsel together against the Lord.

5. For example, Psalm 1 compares a triplet of "walking" in the counsel of the ungodly with "standing" in the way of sinners and "sitting" in the seat of the scornful.

6. John 5:39-47. See also Morris, H. 2005. *The Long War Against God*. Green Forest, AR: Master Books, 132-133. For a thorough confirmation of Genesis' Mosaic authorship, see Cooper, B. 2011. *The Authenticity of Genesis*. Portsmouth, UK: Creation Science Movement.

7. Genesis 1–11, as well as 12–50, also routinely uses the *vayyaqtil* forms (i.e., conjunction-modified verbs that older Hebrew grammars call *waw* consecutives or *waw* conversives), an awkward Hebrew language feature that pervades Hebrew narrative prose but *not* Hebrew poetry. See, e.g., Practico, G. D. and M. V. Van Pelt. 2001. *Basics of Biblical Hebrew Workbook*. Grand Rapids, MI: Zondervan, 192-205. See also the discussion of consecutive preterite verb forms in Hackett, J. A. 2010. *A Basis Introduction to Biblical Hebrew*. Peabody, MA: Hendrickson, 89-94.

8. Compare Mark 10:6 with Matthew 15:1-9, John 5:44-47, and Romans 5:12-21.

# 6

# GENESIS DATA ADD UP TO A YOUNG EARTH

James J. S. Johnson, J.D., Th.D.

**Summary:** The age of the earth is theologically important because (1) God records important time data in the Bible, so that information must be true and relevant; and (2) the Bible's history of Earth time rejects the "deep time" notions of evolutionary history.

Genesis provides timespans that are counted by the time between specific events—most often the "begetting" of key people. This event-to-event documentation allows calculations of the maximum and minimum number of years included in Genesis history. Earth's possible age falls between 6,100 and 6,200 years old.

For anyone who trusts the Bible as divinely inspired, understandable, and accurate, evolutionary deep time is out of the question. The data add up to a young earth.

Time matters. Likewise, measuring time matters—especially where origins are concerned. Every Christian should recognize that the age of the earth is theologically important for two reasons: First, because God records important time data in the Bible (so that its chronological information must be authoritatively true and relevant); and second, the Bible teaches a history of Earth time that wholly rejects the "deep time" of millions or billions of years imagined and advocated by evolutionists (so evolution's deep-time notions must be false).

As we shall see, the Bible presents a relatively young earth—between 6.1 and 6.2 thousand years old—and that range of time is certain because the Bible teaches that time frame through a combination of verses. Consequently, for anyone who trusts the Bible as divinely inspired, understandable, and accurate, the deep time required by evolutionary theories is out of the question.

Likewise, the young age of the earth is highly relevant for showing that a Christian cannot logically rationalize being a theistic evolutionist—i.e., someone who believes God used evolution to make His creation. Because the historical information recorded in Genesis is authoritatively relevant to understanding Earth history, theistic evolutionary thinking should be recognized as the Trojan horse[1] that it really is.

Also, proof that the earth is young is a major problem for anyone who tries to persuade Christians that evolution is compatible with the Bible. In short, evolutionists cannot bluff anyone with their theory apart from eons of deep time, so the importance of disproving the possibility of such deep time—using biblical data alone—should be obvious to anyone who regards the Holy Bible as divinely inspired and therefore inerrant, infallible, and authoritative about Earth history.

## Some Argue That Genesis "Gaps" Permit Old-Earth Creation Interpretations

Some Christians promote a form of theistic evolution that features an old earth that somehow originated from a primordial Big Bang, even though those notions are foreign to the text of Genesis.

Question: If old-earth Christians claim to believe the Holy Bible is inerrant, infallible, and authoritative—and some say as much—how do they reconcile the chronological data in Genesis with their old-earth theories?

Answer: By a "straw man" analysis of what Genesis says about time. Some Big Bang proponents argue against the Genesis record's young-earth data by dodging behind the assumption that the Genesis genealogies contain gaps.

> A common argument against young-earth creationism is that gaps exist in the genealogies listed in the fifth and tenth chapters of Genesis. The old-earth proponent assumes that if gaps exist, then one cannot claim to know an approximate age of the earth based on biblical data. As a result, they say we must rely on extra-biblical sources to discover the age of the earth.[2]

This argument proposes that the chronological data in Genesis are open to interpretation because we cannot be certain whether the genealogical lists in Genesis 1–11 are complete ("closed") or whether they skip generations and have gaps (and are thus "open"). In effect, the "open genealogy" theory claims that the genealogies contain gaps that are stretchable into huge numbers of years, enough to accommodate human evolution and "geologic time" theory timescales.

An example of this kind of Big Bang-promoting old-earth cosmogony is illustrated by evangelical philosopher Norman Geisler, who confidently dismissed the chronological data in Genesis by endorsing the open genealogy theory and then immediately assuming that if the Genesis genealogies are open, there are no biblical data that provide proof of the actual time frame from Adam to Abraham.

> Bishop James Ussher (1581–1656), whose chronology was used in the old Scofield Bible, argued that Adam was created 4004 B.C. However, his calculations are based on the assumption that there are no gaps in the genealogical tables of Genesis 5 and 11. But we know this is false.[3]

Geisler quoted no Scripture to support his confidence that "we know this is false." And as Dr. Jonathan Sarfati has shown, there is no good reason to impute any gaps to the Genesis genealogies.[4] However, the open-versus-closed controversy is itself a red herring distraction because it employs a straw man counterfeit in lieu of the Genesis record's actual data—as the Institute for Creation Research has demonstrated previously.[5]

## Even If Genesis Had Genealogy Gaps, They Would Be Irrelevant to Earth's Age

When Abraham was born, how old (or young) was the earth? Can we know the answer with confidence? Yes, because God has given us the information we need in Genesis. But to recognize it requires reading, writing, and 'rithmetic—and one more critical ingredient: avoiding the irrelevant issue of whether Genesis genealogies are open or closed. Read that last sentence again; it is the key to avoiding confusion.

As indicated above, some people assume that the historical events related in the early chapters of Genesis cannot be precisely dated because we cannot be certain whether the genealogical lists are complete ("closed") or whether they skip generations and have gaps (and are thus "open"). The issue is irrelevant, however, because the time frames given in Genesis are measured by the number of years between one event and another event, regardless of how many generations occurred between those "bookend" events.

For example, Genesis 5:3 states that Adam was 130 years old when Seth was "begotten" (which likely refers to Seth's conception). How old was Adam when he begot Seth? Adam was 130. Does it matter whether Seth was Adam's son, grandson, great-grandson, or an even later descendant? No, the answer is the same: 130. Seth's exact filial relationship to Adam is irrelevant to the chronology because the time frame reported in Genesis 5:3 is measured by the number of years that separated one historical event (God creating Adam) from a later historical event (Seth being begotten)—regardless of how many generations may have occurred between Adam's creation and Seth's begetting.

One obvious "wrinkle" in measuring the above time frame involves the probable presence of a partial year, since Seth was not likely begotten on Adam's birthday. For a precise range to use in our calculations, we must consider that Adam was at least 130 but not yet 131. To allow for this extra time, we need to include a partial number in our calculation of not more than one year. That is why this study counts time with precision ranges…yet the ranges themselves are absolute!

The begetting of Seth begins the next time frame "link" in the unbroken chain of events from Adam to Abraham. At this point, another range adjustment is needed to include the normal duration of a human gestation (i.e., "womb time") to take Seth from conception to birth. No gestation will take longer than one year, so an extra year of precisional tolerance is added to each time frame that is bordered by a "begetting."

A couple of our time frames are not linked by a begetting but by a geological event. In Genesis 7:6, Noah's age at the time of the Flood is given as 600 years. Since the preceding bookend event was the begetting of Noah, the length of the time frame connected to Genesis 7:6 will need to include a "womb time" of not more than one year (since Noah's birth started the count to 600 years), and will also need to include a partial amount of not more than one year since it is unknown how much past 600 years old Noah was when the Flood arrived.

One more range adjustment is needed for the begetting of Arphaxad, Noah's grandson. Genesis 11:10 states that Shem beget Arphaxad two years after the Flood. It is logical to assume that this refers to two years after the Flood first began rather than when it ended, since the start of that cataclysmic event is when the earth changed forever. When the Flood hit Earth, the "clock" of humanity was dichotomized as "pre-Flood" and "post-Flood." (A weightier event, the first advent of Christ, would later divide Earth time as BC and AD) So, the time frame defined as the time between the Flood's outbreak and the begetting of Arphaxad includes two years, plus another partial amount of not more than one year since Scripture does not indicate how many days past the two-year mark Arphaxad was begotten.[6]

Otherwise, it is straight event-to-event math, with the number of generations that are included between the bookend events being irrelevant. The 19 sequential links in this unbroken chain are given in the chart below.

| The time frame in years from Adam's creation to Abraham's birth, based on event-to-event time frame links as recorded in Genesis | | | | | |
|---|---|---|---|---|---|
| Time Frame Links | Bookend Events | Womb Time | Stated Years | Partial Year | Total Years |
| 1. Genesis 5:3 | Adam is created / Adam begets Seth | n/a | 130 | ≤ 1 | ≤ 131 |
| 2. Genesis 5:6 | Seth is begotten / Seth begets Enosh | ≤ 1 | 105 | ≤ 1 | ≤ 107 |
| 3. Genesis 5:9 | Enosh is begotten / Enosh begets Cainan | ≤ 1 | 90 | ≤ 1 | ≤ 92 |
| 4. Genesis 5:12 | Cainan is begotten / C. begets Mahalalel | ≤ 1 | 70 | ≤ 1 | ≤ 72 |
| 5. Genesis 5:15 | Mahalalel is begotten / M. begets Jared | ≤ 1 | 65 | ≤ 1 | ≤ 67 |
| 6. Genesis 5:18 | Jared is begotten / Jared begets Enoch | ≤ 1 | 162 | ≤ 1 | ≤ 164 |
| 7. Genesis 5:21 | Enoch is begotten / E. begets Methuselah | ≤ 1 | 65 | ≤ 1 | ≤ 67 |
| 8. Genesis 5:25 | Methuselah is begotten M. begets Lamech | ≤ 1 | 187 | ≤ 1 | ≤ 189 |
| 9. Genesis 5:28-29 | Lamech is begotten / Lamech begets Noah | ≤ 1 | 182 | ≤ 1 | ≤ 184 |
| 10. Genesis 7:6 | Noah is begotten / Flood hits | ≤ 1 | 600 | ≤ 1 | ≤ 602 |
| 11. Genesis 11:10 | Flood hits / Arphaxad is begotten | n/a | 2 | ≤ 1 | ≤ 3 |
| 12. Genesis 11:12 | Arphaxad is begotten / A. begets Salah | ≤ 1 | 35 | ≤ 1 | ≤ 37 |
| 13. Genesis 11:14 | Salah is begotten / Salah begets Eber | ≤ 1 | 30 | ≤ 1 | ≤ 32 |
| 14. Genesis 11:16 | Eber is begotten / Eber begets Peleg | ≤ 1 | 34 | ≤ 1 | ≤ 36 |

| | | | | | |
|---|---|---|---|---|---|
| 15. Genesis 11:18 | Peleg is begotten / Peleg begets Reu | ≤ 1 | 30 | ≤ 1 | ≤ 32 |
| 16. Genesis 11:20 | Reu is begotten / Reu begets Serug | ≤ 1 | 32 | ≤ 1 | ≤ 34 |
| 17. Genesis 11:22 | Serug is begotten / Serug begets Nahor | ≤ 1 | 30 | ≤ 1 | ≤ 32 |
| 18. Genesis 11:24 | Nahor is begotten / Nahor begets Terah | ≤ 1 | 29 | ≤ 1 | ≤ 31 |
| 19. Genesis 11:26 | Terah is begotten / Abraham is born | ≤1=≤1 | 70 | ≤ 1 | ≤ 73 |
| | | Total: ≥1,948 | | | Total: ≤1,985 |

The chart above assumes that Abraham was born during the 22nd century BC, which is not a controversial assumption among serious biblical history students, whether they be liberals or conservatives.[7]

Accordingly, using generous qualifications for gestation periods and for birthday-qualified partial years, the qualified time frame links become:

Least time: 130 + 105 + 90 + 70 + 65 + 162 + 65 + 187 + 182 + 600 + 2 + 35 + 30 + 34 + 30 + 32 + 30 + 29 + 70 = not *less* than 1,948 years

Most time: 131 + 107 + 92 + 72 + 67 + 164 + 67 + 189 + 184 + 602 + 3 + 37 + 32 + 36 + 32 + 34 + 32 + 31 + 73 = not *more* than 1,985 years (roughly 1/3 of all time!)[8]

The bottom line is that the Genesis record from Adam to Abraham provides event-to-event time frames, each measured in literal years, and those time frames connect sequentially together like adjoining links in a gapless chain. God provided inerrant biblical chronological information in Genesis, one of the Mosaic books that Christ Himself regarded as perfect,[9] so whether the genealogies are open or closed is *irrelevant* to the question of the age of the earth (as applied to the Adam-to-Abraham years).

Accordingly, the open-or-closed genealogy question is a needless distraction. There is no good excuse for doubting this biblical chronological data, especially since these event-to-event time frame links all connect in sequence, so open-versus-closed genealogy arguments are beside the point.[10]

Therefore, the total Earth-time in years from God's creation of Adam to the birth of Abraham *cannot be more than 1,985 years*, although it is likely somewhat less than that,[11] yet it *cannot be less than 1,948 years*.

Add five days[12] and you have the age of the earth when Abraham arrived here. The same Genesis time data detailed above, assuming Abraham was born in the 22nd century BC, prove that the earth must be between 6.1 and 6.2 thousand years old.[13]

Yes, it was a young earth into which Abraham was born—*absolutely!*

### Notes

1. Johnson, J. J. S. 2011. Just Say No to Trojan Horses: Worldview Corruption Is Lying in Wait. *Acts & Facts.* 40 (2): 17-18, especially endnotes 4 and 5.

2. Chaffey, T. and J. Lisle. 2008. *Old-Earth Creationism on Trial: The Verdict Is In.* Green Forest, AR: Master Books, 179.

3. Geisler, N. L. 1999. *Baker Encyclopedia of Christian Apologetics.* Grand Rapids, MI: Baker Books, 272, quoted in Chaffey and Lisle, 180. Not only does Geisler provide no scriptural or other evidence to support these purported genealogical gaps, his non-literalist approach to Genesis history also leads him to bypass Genesis' Flood data (especially the catastrophically violent character of that divine judgment) for the so-called "tranquil flood" theory, thus placing human-based, fallible "science" (with its ever-changing explanations of Earth history) over the authority of Scripture. See Johnson, J. J. S. 2011. Biblical Devastation in the Wake of a "Tranquil Flood." *Acts & Facts.* 40 (9): 8-10, quoting from Morris, J. D. 2009. *The Young Earth: The Real History of the Earth—Past, Present, and Future.* Green Forest, AR: Master Books, 128-129.

4. Sarfati, J. 2009. *Refuting Compromise.* Green Forest, AR: Master Books, 296, cited in Chaffey and Lisle, 181.

5. Johnson, J. J. S. 2008. How Young Is the Earth? Applying Simple Math to Data in Genesis. *Acts & Facts.* 37 (10): 4-5. See also Johnson, J. J. S. 2012. Staying on Track Despite Deceptive Distractions. *Acts & Facts.* 41 (5): 9-11.

6. It should be noted that since time frames 10 and 11 are linked to the "bookend" event of the Flood, the consideration of Noah's age at Shem's begetting and Shem's age at the begetting of Arphaxad is irrelevant.

7. See, e.g., page 478 of *The Genesis Flood* by John C. Whitcomb and Henry M. Morris (Philadelphia: Presbyterian and Reformed Publishing Co., 1961), which suggests 2167 BC as Abraham's probable birth year. The authenticity of Genesis history is well-established in the New Testament and is corroborated in many extrabiblical sources. See Cooper, W. R. 2011. *The Authenticity of the Book of Genesis.* Portsmouth, UK: Creation Science Movement, 1–423.

8. Gestation time is included for both Terah and Abraham, since the time frame being measured is from Adam's creation to Abraham's birth. In particular, see time frame 19 in the chart above.

9. Compare Mark 10:6 with Matthew 15:1-9 and John 5:44-47. See also Romans 5:12-21.

10. This analysis is an adaptation of a more detailed analysis by Thomas D. Ice and James J. S. Johnson (with preparation help from Dr. Bill Cooper) titled "Using Scriptural Data to Calculate a Range-Qualified Chronology from Adam to Abraham, with Comments on Why the 'Open'-or-'Closed' Genealogy Question Is Irrelevant," originally presented to the Evangelical Theological Society, Southwest Regional Meeting, March 1, 2002. A copy of this paper is available on ICR.org.

11. The range-qualified high is extra high since adding a "buffer" of one extra year for every period of human gestation is overly generous—no mother would want a 12-month pregnancy!

12. Adam and Eve were created on Day 6 (Genesis 1:23-31).

13. The time calculation, which assumes that Abraham was born in 2167 BC and which recognizes that there is no year "0," provides these minimum and maximum time frames, as of 2013—at least: 1,948 + 2,167 + 2,013 – 1 = 6,127 years (minimum); at most: 1,985 + 2,167 + 2,013 – 1 = 6,164 years (maximum). To the extent that Abraham was *not* born in 2167 BC, these numbers would need to be shifted accordingly, but

the result would still be very close to the same. (Thus, Archbishop Ussher hit very close to the bull's-eye!) Therefore, assuming Abraham was born in a year close to 2167 BC, the absolute age of the earth must be between 6.1 and 6.2 thousand years old—no millions or billions! This is an absolute age range for planet Earth.

# 7

# REAL TRUTH IS ABSOLUTE, EVEN IF IT'S INCONVENIENT

James J. S. Johnson, J.D., Th.D.

**Summary:** The postmodern world holds that there is no objective truth. But there's a real truth out there, and that's what we are here for—to try to find it.

Postmodern thought embraces relativism, the view that assumes nothing can be known for an absolute certainty. This mindset at its core is humanistic, asserting that all truth originates from human experience, which leads to a great deal of nonsense that passes as knowledge.

But objective truth is part of reality even if some people don't want to accept it. Christ Jesus is the truth incarnate, and He alone can set us free.

Imagine a courtroom where a litigating party tells the judge that different people have different truths. This situation actually occurred when a hostile witness accused a government contractor of wrongdoing during testimony. Notice how the contractor demonstrated his flimsy view of truth after the trial judge informed him of his right to cross-examine his adversary:

> JUDGE: It's now your turn to ask any cross-examination question of [the hostile witness] that you want to ask of him at this time.
>
> CONTRACTOR: I don't really have a question directed towards him, because...he has his own truth. I have my own truth.
>
> JUDGE: Well, there's a real truth out there, and that's what I'm here for, is to try to find that.[1]

Did the contractor really think a judge would attempt to adjudicate a courtroom trial based upon the assumption that everyone has his or her own truth? Is real truth subjective? No, the judge was right: There's a real truth out there, and that's what we are here for—to try to find that truth.

The attitude that there is no objective truth—"you have your truth and I have my truth"—appears in many places today, and sometimes even surfaces in learned journal articles authored by respectable scientists. The fancy name for this subjective attitude about truth is *postmodernism*. However, the attitude is not all that modern because even Pontius Pilate swept aside the notion of objective truth when he asked his infamously rhetorical question "What is truth?"[2]

Something similar to Pilate's truth-ignoring dismissiveness has mushroomed among postmodern thinkers. They deny confidence in absolute truth because their mindset at its core is humanistic, asserting that all truth originates from human experience. Postmoderns argue that human finiteness and fallibility prevent us from knowing anything with certainty. This is just another way of denying that God is powerful and intelligent enough to effectively communicate His truths to fallen humans. Like the Sadducees whom Christ rebuked, postmodern thinkers and teachers are blamably ignorant of both the Scriptures and the power of God.

> Jesus answered and said to them, "Are you not therefore mistaken, because you do not know the Scriptures nor the power of God? (Mark 12:24)

Postmodern thinking has corrupted the promotion of truth about origins, including the teaching of basic truths about God's creation. How does this controversy—this choice between objective truth and subjective preferences—apply to the arena of biblical creation apologetics?

Postmoderns eagerly jettison objective truth for a counterfeit truth-substitute that "liberates" and allows them to escape accountability to God's absolute truth and authoritative morals. Consider this quotation from an article by New York University physicist Dr. Alan Sokal, which he later admitted was a nonsense-riddled parody that he submitted for publication just to prove the fallibility of peer review "quality control" journal practices:

> Madsen and Madsen have recently given a very clear summary of the characteristics of modernist versus postmodernist science....."A simple criterion for science to qualify as postmodern is that it be

free from any dependence on the concept of objective truth."... However, these criteria, admirable as they are, are insufficient for a liberatory postmodern science: they liberate human beings from the tyranny of "absolute truth" and "objective reality", but not necessarily from the tyranny of other human beings. In Andrew Ross' words, we need a science "that will be publicly answerable and of some service to progressive interests" [i.e., promoting po-litically humanistic "progress" such as achieving so-called "libera-tion theology" agenda goals].[3]

Notice that "absolute truth" and "objective reality" are labeled as a form of tyranny. The article proposes that real truth is a terrible ruler, a dictator who deprives us of liberty and the pursuit of happiness! But Sokal's article also advocates a specific postmodern version of truth, a relativistic approach that favors a particular political agenda.

The point here is not that Sokal is a postmodern. Sokal's hoax article proves a scarier point: Postmodern bias is so prevalent that a reputable journal promoted his nonsense as if it was serious science-based truth analysis. Even though Sokal's article was a hoax, he cited real sources, and the fact that a so-cial science journal published it shows that denying the fact of objective reality is often considered to be scholarly.

But does Sokal's readily accepted idea of "liberatory postmodern science" really answer our greatest need for genuine knowledge about life and the world in which we live, more so than objectively true science? Absolutely not. Post-moderns would likely disagree, hypocritically arguing that they know with absolute certainty that we cannot know anything with absolute certainty.

Now contrast the truth-rejecting disposition of the postmoderns with the authoritative teaching of the Lord Jesus Christ, who taught that real liberty comes from accepting real truth.

> Then Jesus said to those Jews who believed Him, "If you abide in My word, you are My disciples indeed. And you shall know the truth, and the truth shall make you free." (John 8:31-32)

Why do postmoderns close their Bibles and refuse to acknowledge author-itative, certain, objective truth? Because God's truth imposes accountability. When truth is absolute, it cannot be your puppet; you cannot manipulate it to be what you want it to be. Attempting to control what is truth—rather than accepting God's objective truth—is really just another form of human-glori-fying idolatry, manufacturing a substitute for the real God. This is the origi-nal temptation the serpent offered Earth's first human couple in Eden: "You will be like God" (Genesis 3:5). When postmoderns invent counterfeit truths, such as theistic or atheistic evolution mythologies, they are guilty of the same ludicrous idolatry that Jeremiah decried more than 2,000 years ago when peo-ple ascribed their origins to sticks and stones.[4]

The problem of questioning objective reality is not new. It was illustrated in a historic conversation almost 500 years ago when the Spanish conquista-dor Hernando Cortez confronted the Aztec emperor Montezuma about who really rules the heavens and the earth. In effect, Montezuma was satisfied with the Aztec religion and told Cortez to keep his own religion to himself. Monte-zuma was acting like the government contractor who told the judge, "He's got his truth, I've got my truth"—as if there is no objective truth.[5]

But real truth is not a tyranny we should run from, because real truth liberates (John 8:31-32). It is Jesus Christ, Truth incarnate, who alone gives us an abundant life of true liberty, for it is His Word that truly sets us free.[6]

*Notes*

1. *Athens I.S.D. v. Johnson*, TEA Dkt. # 033-LH-11-2012.

2. John 18:38.

3. Sokal, A. 1996. Transgressing the Boundaries: Toward a Transformative Hermeneutics of Quantum Gravity. *Social Text.* 46/47 (spring/summer), 217-252. After publishing his postmodernism-promoting "epistemolo-gy" article in *Social Text*, Sokal exposed his journalistic experiment in "A Physicist Experiments with Cultural Studies," *Lingua Franca*, May/June 1996, pages 62-64, describing his successful experiment as publishing "an article liberally salted with nonsense…[that] sounded good and…flattered the editors' ideological pre-conceptions." Embracing a hoax in order to embrace evolutionary assumptions is known to happen in pale-ontology as well. Dr. Timothy L. Clarey debunked the *Archaeoraptor* hoax (also known as the Piltdown bird) that *National Geographic* fell for; Clarey, T. 2006. Dinosaurs vs. Birds: The Fossils Don't Lie. *Acts & Facts.* 35 (9). See also Austin, S. A. 2000. *Archaeoraptor*: Feathered Dinosaur from *National Geographic* Doesn't Fly. *Acts & Facts.* 29 (3).

4. Jeremiah 2:27-28. This epistemological controversy, at its most fundamental level, is a dispute about who God is and how He has communicated in words to mankind. In other words, is the real God accurately described in and by Genesis? Is Genesis a reliable record of who God is and what He has done? See Cooper, B. 2012. *The Authenticity of the Book of Genesis*. Portsmouth, UK: Creation Science Movement, 129-130, 328-333, 403-405.

5. Eidsmoe, J. A. 1992. *Columbus and Cortez, Conquerors for Christ*. Green Forest, AR: New Leaf Press, 202-203.

6. John 14:6, in light of John 10:10 and Galatians 5:13.

# 8

# EVOLUTIONISTS FLUNK BASIC FORENSIC SCIENCE

James J. S. Johnson, J.D., Th.D.

**Summary:** Empirical science examines presently existing circumstances, while forensic science analyzes evidence from past events. Evolutionists often fail to adequately apply forensic science principles because of their uniformitarian assumptions.

Methods for understanding present processes don't work equally well for understanding past events. A forensic scientist is a detective of sorts, exploring past causes that produced what we see today. When it comes to origins, the beginnings are the key to the present, not the other way around.

The beginnings of our cosmos and the human race are unrepeatable, unique historical events. Uniformitarian "the present is the key to the past" thinking will never be adequate as a substitute for reliable eyewitness testimony for learning about our origins. But God wanted us to know about origins, so He revealed them in the Bible.

Those who criticize the factual history recorded in Genesis are like the foolish Pharisees whom the Lord Jesus condemned as inconsistent hypocrites. Christ gave them credit for filtering out "gnats"—yet He condemned them, simultaneously, for irrationally swallowing down whole "camels."

> Woe to you, scribes and Pharisees, hypocrites! For you pay tithe of mint and anise and cumin, and have neglected the weightier matters of the law: justice and mercy and faith. These you ought to have done, without leaving the others undone. Blind guides, who strain out a gnat and swallow a camel! (Matthew 23:23-24)[1]

This word picture actually fits evolutionists of today.

In essence, Genesis critics flunk the basics of forensic science. In fact, although they try to act like experts when discussing and teaching forensic science principles, most evolutionists are completely clueless about what such science even is. To appreciate how this occurs, we first must differentiate between *empirical* science and *forensic* science, because they are not the same thing.

Note that the Pharisees were correct in their careful attention to tithing mint, anise, and cumin. However, they completely missed the boat when they "neglected the weightier matters" (the obligations of justice, compassion, and personal belief in God's Word). Likewise, evolutionists today (both atheistic and theistic evolutionists) get some "lightweight" science right, but not the "heavier matters"—as we shall see below.

## Straining Out Bugs from Beverages

To appreciate this metaphor, which applies to modern-day evolutionists, consider the following account by Alaskan explorers.

> How in the world could there be this many bugs?…We tried once to have hot chocolate and coffee, but heating water without making mosquito tea first was impossible. The mosquitos are attracted to heat, and one could always count on a dozen or so [mosquitos] ending up in the drink before it was boiling.[2]

In biblical times, before serving or drinking a beverage, it was not unusual to use filters to strain out bugs and other impurities.[3] The hygienic practice of straining out gnats would have been quite common and understandable to the Lord's immediate audience. But the idea of swallowing whole an *entire camel* while drinking would have been a jarring thought to imagine! Christ criticized the cleanliness-obsessed Pharisees for practicing outrageous irrationality that resulted in truly unclean results.[4]

This picturesque metaphor describes the nonsensical illogic of the Pharisees, who filtered out small impurities from their daily living while ignoring gargantuan intrusions. That same failure of logic infects the uniformitarian approach routinely used by evolutionists to learn about our beginnings.

## Beginnings Are the Key to the Present, Not Vice Versa

If humans really want to understand themselves, their world, their destinies, and their Maker, they need to understand their *origins*. Origins are the key to understanding cause and effect relationships. Present effects are often not representative of what their temporal causes physically looked like. It is the past that provides the key to understanding the present, not vice versa—because past causes produced present effects.[5]

For an extreme example, look at a city devastated by an earthquake or by an atomic bomb. Just by looking at the physical results, how would one guess at the physical causes?

For a less extreme (yet miraculously more complex) example, consider the amazing processes and details that accompany the conception, gestation, and birth of a human baby. The way a baby "breathes" inside the womb has virtually no resemblance to how it acquires oxygen after it is born. Placentas serve as super-organs during gestation, yet after birth they are superfluous. Baby lungs don't breathe inside the womb, yet afterward they begin to breathe. Life inside the womb is starkly different from life after birth.[6]

Consider also the amazing processes and details that accompany the formation of an acorn—its fall to the ground, its burial and germination, and its early sprouting above its burial site. The beginning of an oak tree's botanical life as an acorn is not much like its growth and development after it sprouts above the soil level.

This is not surprising because *beginnings* are qualitatively different from what follows a beginning. This is seemingly so basic that any well-educated scientist could not miss it; yet missing the distinctiveness of earth's beginning is exactly what uniformitarian evolutionists routinely do. This does not negate the fact that evolutionary scientists sometimes do good *empirical* science work, but it does mean that the *forensic* aspect of origins science is frequently botched by their uniformitarian thinking habits.

## Straining Out Cosmological Bugs, Swallowing Cosmogonical Camels

A gigantic stumble in scientific thinking occurs when cosmology is confused with cosmogony.[7] Cosmology is the empirical (i.e., present observations-based) study of the cosmos as it exists today.

> Cosmology: The science of the world or universe; or a treatise relating to the structure and parts of the system of creation, the elements of bodies, the modifications of material things, the laws of motion, and the order and course of nature.[8]

Cosmogony, however, is the non-empirical study of how that cosmos began in the unobservable past.

> Cosmogony: The generation, origin or creation of the world or universe. In physics, the science of the origin or formation of the universe.[9]

Cosmology involves using observation tools (such as radio telescopes and spectrophotometry equipment) to learn about presently existing matter in the universe. Cosmogony, however, is an origins science, a type of forensic science that focuses on learning the past, not examining the present.

Some methods that work well for understanding present processes do not work equally well for understanding past events. For example, at what temperature does water boil at sea level today? To learn the answer, use a repeatable experiment: Boil water at sea level and read the thermometer. This is empirical science, analyzing a present process.

But what if the question concerns the causality of a past event? For example, what physical cause produced a patient's fever last Saturday night? A thermometer reading today tells nothing about the cause of a previous thermometer reading.

Or, for another example, what physical cause produced a patient's drop in blood pressure yesterday? Measuring blood pressure today tells us nothing, directly, about why a patient's blood pressure was low then.[10]

The prior two questions seek specific information about the *historical past*, not how natural processes generally operate in the *observable present*. Accordingly, doing a repeatable experiment is not a scientific methodology that works well, directly, for answering questions about historically past cause and effect questions.

Perhaps the best-known examples of this kind of inquiry are legal investigations, such as forensic autopsies used to understand murder crimes,[11] or courtroom cross-examinations of eyewitnesses that test witness reliability while trying to determine who proximately caused an accident by committing negligence in a traffic intersection.[12]

Such investigations of the past involve the specialized history analysis of forensic science because discovery and analysis of the past is vital to the forensic contexts of criminal and civil evidentiary proceedings. Forensic science methods—which include testing the probative value of eyewitness testimony and trial exhibits with process-of-elimination logic—are used to learn about past events that are historically and geographically unique. They can never occur again—they are singular events in history.

The beginnings of our cosmos, the heavens and the earth, and the beginnings of the human race, starting with Adam and Eve, are all unrepeatable and unique historical events. The methods of empirical science are *evidentiarily inadequate* to determine meaningful or accurate truth about what actually happened during those beginnings. Only God was there to witness it.

That is why Charles Lyell's uniformitarian assumption—that "the present is the key to the past"[5,13]—will never be adequate for learning about those eternally important beginnings.

In other words, when evolutionists preach that "the present" (cosmology) is the key to "the past" (cosmogony), they are blindly swallowing a camel of illogic.

## Past Events or Present Observations?

The forensic character of origins science, as opposed to the observational nature of empirical science, is routinely bungled and botched by uniformitarian evolutionists. They strain out "gnats" of empirical science data and analysis, yet they drink down whole "camels" of forensic science illogic, illustrating a kind of hypocritical foolishness—an intellectual blindness—that the Lord Jesus spoke of during His earthly ministry.

But God wanted us to know about our origins—the beginnings of the heavens and the earth, the beginnings of the human race (man and woman), the beginnings of sin and death, the beginnings of God's promised redemption in Christ, and much more.

God wanted us to know these important beginnings, so He took action to reveal this otherwise unknowable information in an error-free text of understandable words—the Holy Bible.

The book of Genesis tells us, *infallibly,* what empirical science cannot—the factual details of our real-history origins.

*Notes*

1. Swallowing refers to drinking rather than to eating. The word translated "swallow" in Matthew 23:24 is a form of the Greek verb *katapinô*, the same verb that appears in Hebrews 11:29 (referring to the Red Sea swallowing up the Egyptian army) and in Revelation 12:16 (referring to a flood being swallowed up). This verb is an accentuated form of a simpler Greek verb, *pinô*, which is translated 75 times as "drink."

2. Davis, B., M. Liston, and J. Whitmore. 1998. *The Great Alaskan Dinosaur Adventure: A Real-Life Journey Through the Frozen Past.* Green Forest, AR: Master Books, 23, 30.

3. According to an ancient Hittite inscription, a water carrier named Zuliyas was executed for his carelessness in allowing a hair to be found in the king's water pitcher. See Pritchard, J. B., ed. 1992. Instructions for Palace Personnel to Insure the King's Purity. *Ancient Near Eastern Texts Relating to the Old Testament,* 3rd ed. A. Goetze, transl. Princeton: Princeton University Press, 207.

4. Both gnats and camels were "unclean" (see Leviticus 11:4, 20-23), i.e., not *kôsher* for Hebrew cuisine purposes.

5. Morris, H. M. 2008. *The Biblical Basis for Modern Science*, rev. ed. Green Forest, AR: Master Books, 65-66, 282-286.

6. Guliuzza, R. J. 2009. *Made in His Image: Examining the complexities of the human body.* Dallas, TX: Institute for Creation Research, 32-33.

7. See the entries for "cosmology" and "cosmogony" in *New American Heritage Dictionary of the English Language*. 1976. Boston: Houghton Mifflin, 301. Unsurprisingly, this secular dictionary presupposes an evolutionary origin for the cosmos.

8. *Noah Webster's First Edition of an American Dictionary of the English Language.* San Francisco, CA: Foundation for American Christian Education (2006 reprint of 1828 edition), page COS-COS, 3rd column.

9. Ibid, COS-COS, 2nd column.

10. Physicians and surgeons are especially qualified to understand empirical and forensic sciences because they must use proper scientific methods to understand a patient's medical history (*past condition*) and his current symptoms (*present condition*) to promote health. Randy J. Guliuzza, P.E., M.D., who has often practiced medical science and engineering science in the real world, used just such a forensic science-oriented analysis to expose and refute the unscientific fallacies of so-called "natural selection" theory in his Darwin's Sacred Imposter series of *Acts & Facts* articles.

11. The slang for a crime mystery novel—whodunit—illustrates that the investigation and discovery of truth about the no-longer-observable past is a matter of forensic science, not a matter of repeated observations and experiments by a scientist with laboratory equipment.

12. Johnson, J. J. S. 2012. Tonsils, Forensic Science, and the Recent Fabrication Rule. *Acts & Facts.* 41 (6): 8-9.

13. The "willful ignorance" that 2 Peter 3:4-6 describes is perfectly illustrated in evolutionary uniformitarian thinking. Because God has revealed our beginnings to us in Genesis, there is no logical reason for the scientific community to endorse the forensically illogical Big Bang theory of Belgium's Monsignor Georges Lemaître, or to endorse the forensically illogical natural selection theory of England's Charles Darwin.

# 9

# ONLY BIBLICAL CREATION PROVES
# GOD LOVES YOU PERSONALLY

James J. S. Johnson, J.D., Th.D.

**Summary:** Some people accuse the God of the Bible of being impersonal. But one evidence of His personal love is that He chose to make each of us a unique, one-of-a-kind person.

Another evidence is that Jesus Christ our Creator came to Earth to die for our sins and reconcile us to God. We can rely on what the Bible says about God and about us because of Christ's recognition of the Scriptures as God's authoritative truth. The Bible provides the foundation for the unique worth of every human being.

Our Creator took special care to craft each person, plan their lives, and provide for them. He uniquely made you and loves you, and you can thank Him for being your personal Creator.

When was the last time you saw a bird—perhaps a common grackle or a pigeon—and shuddered with the scary realization: That could have been me! Maybe you have never thought about a grackle that way.

Yet, it is true; God did not need to make us just as we are. He had many other options. God could have created each of us as a bird, a butterfly, or a basalt rock. God could have made you (or me) a uranium-bearing rock, a nudibranch, an ice worm, a quince fruit, an ultraviolet ray, or an egret.[1] He deliberately chose otherwise. He chose to make us one-of-a-kind humans. What a fearful and wonderful reality!

Thinking about how God uniquely planned for us and how we are precious to Him is biblically logical. But it cannot logically fit the impersonal randomness of evolutionary thinking.

At a biblical apologetics conference hosted by a local church, a Genesis skeptic approached me and quickly displayed that he was "angry at the world." Likewise, he demonstrated hostility and disdain for God and His Word, attacking biblical truth and God's character. He accused "the Christian God" of being impersonal—of not "personally loving individuals."

Perceiving him as one with no stable assurance regarding his own personal worth as a valuable human individual created in God's image, I reminded him that God commended His love to all of us—even the skeptic—by having Christ voluntarily die for the sins of each of us, to pay the just price for personal forgiveness, reconciliation with God, and an abundant life here and later. That conclusively proves God's love for us individually, because Christ died for each of us.

When confronted with this truth, he coldly retorted, "But that is not really *personal*—the Bible teaches that Jesus died for all of humanity simultaneously, so it's not like He did it *just for me*; there is nothing personal about that. If I didn't exist, it would still be the same, so there is nothing personal about that kind of love."

**How would you reply to this skeptic's accusation that God is "not personal" in His love?**

This was my answer: "The proof that God cares about you, in an absolutely personal way, is in the obvious fact that He providentially, thoughtfully, and caringly made you. In fact, your very existence is proof of how personally God loves you. It doesn't get any more personal than God making you as the unique person that you are! If God had neglected to make you as you are or had made you something else, such as a lizard or a loon, you wouldn't even have the ability to falsely accuse Him of being impersonal! God had lots of options—He did not have to make you who you are."

At this point, the skeptic digressed into some excuses—what the Bible calls "science falsely so called" (1 Timothy 6:20, KJV)—that he had for disbelieving the truths of Genesis. None of the excuses were scientifically or logically sound (Romans 1:20), and all of them were logical fallacies flawed with arbitrariness, inconsistencies, and intelligibility precondition failures.

The skeptic had brushed aside the obvious truth that God made him as the unique person that he was, even though God could have made him as a gull or a gooney bird. The skeptic also rejected the example of Christ's recognition of the Scriptures as God's authoritative truth—the text of absolute truth (John 17:17). Though this skeptic professed to honor "the historical Jesus" (whom he "knew" could not be the Jesus described in the New Testament), he had no logical explanation for Christ's exemplary recognition of Genesis as the authoritative and trustworthy text God co-authored with Moses.[2]

The practical apologetics lesson should be obvious: If we deny the authoritative truth of Genesis, then we have no sure foundation for creation truth. And we, likewise, have no sure foundation for the unique worth of any one human being—you, me, or anyone else.

If Genesis is wrong about creation (which is impossible), I cannot prove that I am truly worth anything, much less precious to God, as the unique person that I am.

Five of our Creator's actions prove that He is worthy of our thanksgiving for making us exactly as we are: (1) God chose to make us; (2) God controlled how we were made; (3) God condemns ingratitude; (4) God cares for our needs; and (5) God cherishes our uniqueness, unlike most of the world around us.

## God chose to make each one of us a unique creation.

God made many careful and complicated decisions, literally thousands of years ago, in order to providentially and procreatively make each of us, personally, as who He wanted each of us to be.

Science fiction writers sometimes imagine alternative universes, qualifying their fanciful fantasies with the phrase "what if?" God, however, really can imagine other options, including *all* of the "what if" contingencies, all the possible domino-chain causality scenarios. God can truly tell us what consequences would have followed events that never really happened.

Christ, as omniscient deity, knows all of the past, present, and future. He even knows what would have and could have occurred if this or that detail of real-world history had been different. For example, Christ did not exaggerate when He described how Sodom and Gomorrah would have reacted to the miracles He powerfully performed in the region of Galilee (Matthew 11:23). Likewise, foreknowing literally all of the possible options and outcomes, our Creator purposefully chose to make you and me exactly as we are. Considering the "what if" scenarios is intellectually "fearful," yet appreciating God's actual choices is "wonderful."[3]

## God controlled how we each were made.

How did God mastermind our procreative origins? Consider Psalm 139—how we are "fearfully and wonderfully made," biologically and biochemically, inside the specific mother whom God selected, to make each of us who we are. That "fearful and wonderful" development did not stop at birth. God's biochemically programmed instructions equip and adjust our physical bodies throughout our lives.[4]

But God's control of our existence began thousands of years before we were physically procreated inside our respective mothers. Human life began on Day 6 of the creation week. Parental procreation began in Genesis 4. All of us descend—through literally hundreds of ancestral lines—from eight Ark passengers who sailed the one-of-a-kind high seas about 4,500 years ago. The social details of our genealogical ancestries thereafter—even ignoring the bio-genetics—are astounding beyond any fiction novel, more detail-laden than any supercomputer's database.

The family history facts unique to each of us are so detailed that we cannot learn them all during this earthly lifetime. The best that we can hope for, realistically, is to discover some informative family history records and to learn from them many examples of how God worked in human history to make us who we are.

How did God providentially orchestrate the circumstances of our parents' meeting each other, or their parents, or our great-great-great-great grandparents? What close calls with death did your ancestors encounter before they contributed to your personal genealogy? What if God had let someone die a few years earlier? Maybe you (or I) would have never existed![5]

## When we fail to thank God for His creation, God condemns our ingratitude.

When God condemns something, whether an action or inaction, that proves its importance. What about the ingratitude that we, as unique creations, demonstrate when we fail to thank Him as our Creator?

> Because, although they knew God, they did not glorify Him as God, nor were thankful, but became futile in their thoughts, and their foolish hearts were darkened. (Romans 1:21)

Obviously, we should thank God for making us, because failure to thank Him is wrong—so wrong that the integrity of our minds and hearts are at risk of becoming "reprobate" (Romans 1:28, KJV).

## God demonstrates how much He values us through caring for our needs.

Most Christians are well aware that the Lord is "our shepherd" (Psalm 23; John 10). He cares for our personal needs, like a good shepherd cares for every single sheep (Luke 15:4-7), not just 99% of them!

God's care for us displays our worth to Him—so much more than sparrows (Matthew 10:29-31; Luke 12:6-7) or field lilies (Matthew 6:28; Luke 12:27).

God cares for our physical and spiritual needs better than any human parent (Luke 11:11-13). God regulates climate dynamics that provide rain for both the just and the unjust (Matthew 5:45). Seasonal cycles and nourishing food are both continuing proofs of God's providential care for human creatures.[6]

## God cherishes our uniqueness.

Even more amazing than God's care for us—His human "sheep"—is how He cherishes our uniqueness. No one is exactly like you, and God designed you that way. God prizes variety. Even in something as supposedly simple as a snowflake (just a frozen water crystal!), God proves that He appreciates and values uniqueness. No two snow crystals are the same.

> Ice crystals are composed of simple, repeated internal patterns that produce beautiful, external shapes. And built into the laws that govern ice crystal growth patterns are temperature depen dencies that add filigrees to the basic hexagonal form. Columnar shapes, needle shapes, plate shapes, stellar shapes, and dendritic shapes are just some of the additional patterns in which snow crystals grow. In fact, because of the myriad of possible combinations of the millions of individual molecules that make up a single ice crystal, it can truly be said that *no two snow crystals are exactly alike!*[7]

Who sees and appreciates the countless snowflakes that fall on Earth? Only God. Yet, He treasures them (Job 38:22); each one is singularly fashioned by His artistic genius. Most of these fragile and ephemeral snowflakes are never seen by humans. The rare few that are observed by human eyes (and even fewer photographed by microscopists) are quickly forgotten, no matter how beautifully and carefully they were made by God.

And, sadly, so it is with human lives—most people will never know that you (or I) exist, and most of the few who see us, for a while, will not care much. Many will quickly forget us.

But, thankfully, not so with God!

While God appreciates the "simple," yet unique, snowflakes that are ignored by busy humans, God treasures our personal lives (created in His image) infinitely more, as if we were His precious jewels (Malachi 3:17). In fact, He providentially planned our lives to be exactly what they are, and if we belong to Him, He artistically "works together for good" the component details of our lives (Romans 8:28).

Surely we should thank Christ for being our very *personal* Creator.

So, the next time you see a grackle, think thankfully for a moment, "That could have been me!" And be grateful to your Creator, who made you a unique, one-of-a-kind creation.

### Notes

1. These six options produce the acrostic UNIQUE.

2. John 5:39-47, especially 5:46-47. For documentation on Genesis' Mosaic authorship, see Cooper, W. R. 2011. *The Authenticity of the Book of Genesis.* Portsmouth, UK: Creation Science Movement.

3. See Psalm 139:14 and Matthew 11:23, especially in light of Colossians 1:12-17 and John 15:16.

4. Guliuzza, R. 2009. *Made in His Image: Examining the complexities of the human body.* Dallas, TX: Institute for Creation Research, 32-33.

5. For example, see Johnson, J. J. S. 2011. Czech into Texas, at Last! From Bohemian Roots, to a Moravian Log Cabin, to the Lone Star State. *České Stopy* [Czech Footprints]. 13 (1): 15-22.

6. Isaiah 55:10-11; Matthew 5:45; Acts 14:17.

7. Vardiman, L. 2007. Microscopic Masterpieces: Discovering Design in Snow Crystals. *Acts & Facts.* 36 (12): 10. See also Libbrecht, K. 2003. *The Snowflake: Winter's Secret Beauty.* Stillwater, MN: Voyageur Press, 1-109.

# BIOLOGY

## CREATED KINDS
## OR COMMON ANCESTRY?

# 10
# A THEORY OF BIOLOGICAL DESIGN

Randy J. Guliuzza, P.E., M.D.

*Randy J. Guliuzza, MD*

**Summary:** Scientific theories contain a working framework that incorporates assumptions and provides a directional focus to drive the study process. Theories should be constantly refined, updated, or even abandoned if necessary. But that doesn't always happen.

Empirical studies indicate that evolution's basic assumptions are erroneous. A theory that starts with wrong assumptions prevents researchers from reaching truthful explanations for what they observe.

An alternate theory of biological design is needed that uses engineering principles to understand biological function. Living things possess innate features that require a research framework focusing on creatures' internal mechanisms rather than on external environments. This design-based, organism-focused approach will see creatures for what they are: active, problem-solving entities endowed with spectacularly engineered innate capacities.

How do living things work? Where did they come from? In what ways do they reflect their Creator? What principles emerge from studying them?

The current way of viewing life—through the lens of evolution by nature from particles to people—does not explain key features of living things. Biology is rife with design hallmarks. Living creatures have all-or-nothing features, adaptability, and self-repair. We need a new way to think about them.

## The Purpose of Scientific Theories

A theory is a working hypothesis of how a natural phenomenon happens. It tries to associate a number of observations and ideas to fill the gaps of our understanding. Science, therefore, is not merely a collection of data but the manner in which data are used. Theories usually develop slowly and always have a history of scholarly exchanges. The scientific activities of observation, interpretation, and application take place within a structure of ideas and assumptions defining a field of study.

"Structure" and "framework" are good similes to describe how scientific theories set boundaries. Theories endorse specific assumptions, approve certain ideas, are the context used to interpret natural phenomena, and establish and prioritize research programs. Since theories set boundaries, they are powerful in controlling scientific activities in any field.

A theory is supposed to be like a map that sets the starting point and direction of travel toward a destination called "truthful explanations" in the realm of natural phenomena. Thus, theories are supposed to be constantly refined, updated, or even abandoned if necessary.

But that does not always happen. Sometimes a theory, such as evolution, can start with wrong assumptions. This means that researchers cannot to get to truthful explanations. The theory should be dropped, but for reasons that may have nothing to do with science, it gets "hardened" in wrong ideas. Eventually, the accumulation of evidence contrary to the hardened theory gets to be so overwhelming that a revolution in the field happens and a new theory is accepted—which, of course, everyone knew was right all along.

Biological discoveries that are contrary to evolutionary theory and strongly support the inference that creatures are intelligently design have been in the scientific literature for decades. What would be useful is an alternative framework—a theory of biological design (TOBD)—that frames biological findings based on engineering principles.

Since Darwin was principally concerned with developing a theory to explain why creatures could exhibit features of incredible design without appealing to God's designing agency (see chapter 16), we should not be surprised if our TOBD fundamentally contrasts with the externalism and selectionism offered by Darwin.

## A Theory of Biological Design Concerns Biological Functions, Not Life Itself

The four main biological functions are recognized as: *metabolism, growth, adaptation,* and *reproduction.* These are produced by a creature's innate systems and together signify the defining characteristics of living entities. However, what we call "life" and consciousness seem to have attributes that are currently beyond the reach of scientific methods to explain. We don't know for sure how they originated, the basis for their distinctive characteristics, or what exactly they are. This is for good reason. No one currently knows if they come from biological functions, are independent of them, or if it is possible that they are not reducible simply to matter and energy. Tellingly, definitions of life describe what living things do—i.e., their functions—not what life actually *is*.

For research purposes we could, perhaps, hold "life" or consciousness in a unique category awaiting some way to research it. We can instead focus on explaining biomolecular, physiological, or anatomical functions that have proven to be decipherable. In fact, because these complex systems operate with such consistency, more researchers now explain biological functions using engineering or design principles. If diverse biological systems do seem to consistently operate by principles similar to human-engineered systems, then these observations could naturally flow into the development of a theory of biological design (TOBD).

Engineering principles are experimentally (or experientially) verified rules[1] that must be incorporated into designs in order to get them to work for an intended purpose or to achieve design characteristics such as efficiency, optimality, etc. For example, if an engineer wanted to maximize the heat transfer between two fluids flowing through adjoining pipes, then the engineering principle would stipulate that the fluids would flow in opposite directions by a principle known as *countercurrent flow*. Conversely, if an engineer observed a high transfer of heat between fluids in a biological setting, then their knowledge of engineering principles would guide them to suspect that a countercurrent flow system would be discovered.

Yet, knowing that organisms have functions operating by the same engineering principles as man-made things does *not* equate to saying that a living creature is "only a machine." Nor does it imply that bioengineers will inevitably create "life," since life might not emerge from either engineering principles or biological functions. Life could be something immaterial altogether that is not reducible to merely matter and energy.

Nevertheless, it appears that all biologists are going to face the inevitable rising tide of scientific literature from other disciplines that use engineering principles to more accurately explain biological functions. Creationists and intelligent design advocates should be at the forefront of this overdue change in the theoretical structure that frames biology.

## Should Engineering Principles Explain Biological Functions?

There are good reasons to explain biological functions with engineering principles. Despite their vastly different building blocks, living organisms use the same fundamental constraints that govern all regulatory and other mechanisms. They function within the same laws of physics as man-made designs.[2] Research demonstrates a remarkable correspondence in design, purpose, and function between many organs and biological systems and similar devices produced by human engineers.[3]

Just like human-engineered devices, organisms have organs and systems that often exploit the properties of natural laws such as gravity, inertia, magnetism, electromagnetism, and momentum. Thus, human engineers regularly copy systems found in living things and use them for inspiration in design, a practice engineers call *biomimicry*.[4] Some call for merging the fields of biology and engineering as "terminology and concepts from computer science and engineering are becoming more common in biology labs as scientists re-engineer the activity of cells for specific applications."[5]

Similarly, a professor at Stanford recently said, "An obvious approach to bring engineering into biology is to apply existing engineering disciplines—materials, chemical, electrical, mechanical, and so on—in the biological realm," adding "the question now isn't whether this is possible in biology or not...given where we are in engineering biology today."[6] Engineering-inspired fields such as integrative systems biology, biomedical engineering, and synthetic biology have more in common with engineering approaches than with traditional biological ones.[7]

Possibly the soundest justification for reframing the study of biology within the formal structure of engineering comes from how biological research is universally practiced. Biological research fundamentally reverse-engineers biological systems by methodically disassembling their components piece by piece to discover their operation.

Comparing the histories of biological research and engineering shows their extreme similarities. This should lead us to seriously question the accepted notion that biological functions operate from a fundamentally distinct realm. An undeniable case for the uniqueness of biological function could be made if researchers' progress was routinely hindered by observing biological phenomena that were so foreign to human experience that it's impossible to figure them out. If that were so, then by necessity biology would have to be treated separately from engineering.

But is there even a single published report in which researchers were totally baffled as to where to start reverse-engineering a biological system? Biological functions have been decipherable through reverse-engineering, which might explain why researchers have not encountered biological mechanisms that are impossible to model. At a minimum, conceptual models take into consideration that biological systems possess staggeringly intricate and voluminous information. They consistently craft models based on engineering principles. This means that it is current technological limitations that prevent humans from duplicating a biological function like reproduction, and not that reproduction operates outside the realm of engineering principles.

## Abbreviated Discussion of a Theory of Biological Design's Working Hypotheses and Tenets

A TOBD still seeks to answer the same three questions as current evolutionary theory discussed in chapter 16. The evidence would indicate that the realm of engineering could be the best place to begin explaining how biological functions operate. This relocation hardly suggests a tweaking of current biological theory. Starting from an engineering basis would produce a radically different theory. In fact, its major tenets would be the opposite of the anti-design tenets Darwin championed when he ushered in a revolutionary way to view the relationship of an organism to its environment (see chapter 16).

### Basic Premises

Theories always build on several basic assumptions or premises. But how are they derived? In addition to considering biology a branch of engineering, the basic premises of a TOBD are derived from associating these observations:

- The tight correspondence between the operations of biological systems and those of human-engineered systems performing similar functions,

- All creatures seem to exhibit purposeful outcomes in their biological systems and behaviors,

- And what humans have learned about the role of intelligent agency as it relates to purposeful design.

The TOBD's approach to biological research accords with the assumptions that (1) biological functions will be accurately explained by models developed utilizing engineering principles; and (2) studying human engineering practices can accurately inform biological research programs and can guide researchers to precise characterizations of phenomena.

## A Circle of Research

What this approach means to researchers is that the basic research of biological functions and their technical applications *both lie within* the domain of engineering practice. We see it as a misleading and false dichotomy to separate the practice of biology into the search for the knowledge of *how* biology works through reverse-engineering, and then a separate avenue of engineering as the *application* of that biological knowledge to solve problems. Within a TOBD, both basic research and engineering elements form a circle of research that can continually inform each other.

We often see biological discoveries providing ideas or inspiration to engineers. They incorporate the Great Designer's ideas into their designs for useful products, such as mimicking the properties of seed burrs for Velcro and dog feet for shoe-sole groove patterns. But ideas and insights need to flow from engineers back to biologists to assist them in their research and to complete the circle of research.

Thus, if biologists are reverse-engineering a biological system and it becomes apparent that an existing human-engineered system is performing a function similar to one they are working on, then taking note of how the human-engineered system operates could provide clues to where biologists should focus their research. Sara-Jane Dunn, a computational biologist, gave a fascinating example of this circle of research in her work at the interface between biology and computation.[8]

We see this as an acknowledgement of how biology will likely be practiced by succeeding generations of biologists. This explains why today many engineers must do basic research and many biologists are developing applications. Already researchers acknowledge that research is best handled by a multi-disciplinary approach. The future may foster more of a uni-disciplinary approach where the fields are merged and, as one research firm found out, "all the researchers say they had to learn a lot from outside their major field."[9]

## A Fresh Framework for Interpretation

Theory sets the research agenda by constraining which questions scientists may ask, the context for interpreting data, how they formulate explanations, and what they predict to find.

We'll illustrate this using evolutionary theory. Based on a premise that environments slowly mold relatively passive organisms through a series of life-or-death competitions, how do evolutionists explain the way a creature's traits are observed to change over time? These adaptations of organisms are interpreted as "imposed by the environment and that are external to the organism itself."[10] Similar traits between related but not identical organisms are interpreted as due to their descent from a common ancestor. This is called *divergent evolution*. But if common ancestry is highly unlikely, then similar traits are interpreted as diverse organisms converging on a similar trait due to pressures from similar lethal environmental conditions over time. This is called *convergent evolution*. So, we see that either way, the tenets of evolutionary theory always constrain how observations will be interpreted.

Likewise, a TOBD has internal structure, but its tenets contrast starkly with those of evolutionary theory. Based on the hypothesis that studying human engineering practices will direct researchers to precise characterizations of phenomena, at least three tenets provide an engineering-based context for interpreting biological observations.

## 1. Intentionalistic or Teleological

Goal-directed activity to specific ends is observed in creatures as essentially a continuum from the molecular level to the whole organism. Rather than contrive explanations to work around obviously purposeful events, a TOBD would characterize interpretations of biological systems in terms of their understood primary purpose.

A TOBD embraces the search for purpose as a useful guide to research agendas. TOBD expects purposeful systems within and between all biological functions in organisms. "Top-down" describes the goal-directed approach humans use when designing systems. Thus, within TOBD the "top-down" rule for interpreting biological findings is seen as essential to correctly analyze systems.

A fundamental change in research based on this tenet is that biological solutions to environmental challenges are largely expected to *precede* the challenge. This should prompt a search for innate biological systems that confer upfront capacity, as though the organism or its population anticipated environmental variations.

## 2. Internalistic

Until proven otherwise, operation of biological functions will be interpreted with the assumption that all biological operations for an organism arise from identifiable control systems innate to that organism. Innate systems govern both an organism's basic form and its adaptable capacity to modify that form.

Engineers design traits to confer capabilities. A TOBD thus assumes that for an organism all of its capabilities are determined by its traits. Theories guide interpretation of observations. Thus, when we observe what's happening between an organism and its environment, an internalistic perspective helps us interpret that the organism's traits—not conditions—successfully solve challenging exposures. Variability within those traits may lead to differential survival and reproduction in a population.

## 3. Individualistic

Like all engineered entities, organisms are discreet individuals delineated by definite and distinct boundaries that divide "self" from "non-self." Our proposed TOBD expects that innate engineered controls will regulate organism-environment relationships. An organisms' internal programing specifies (and restricts) certain internal or external conditions *to be* stimuli. Therefore, when interpreting how "self" relates to "non-self," individual organisms must be seen as *discreet elements* within ecosystems. An accurate understanding of the ecosystem as a whole is obtained by accounting for the individual role of each kind of organism as a distinct element that fits within that broader system.

ICR's approach contrasts with the view of many evolutionists such as Steven Rose of The Open University, who blurred the distinction between individuals and the ecosystem when he said:

> But what constitutes an individual is very much in the eye of the beholder. Genes are distributed across genomes within a population. There is no overriding reason why we should consider 'the

organism' as an individual rather than 'the group' or even 'the ecosystem.'[11]

A more functional TOBD recognizes that the characteristics of an ecosystem emerge from the contributions of each of its individual components. Therefore, within our proposed TOBD individuality is not obliterated by seeing creatures as one with an environmental collective.

Thus, no matter how closely two (or more) individuals may operate together in what engineers longingly call a "seamless operation," TOBD-guided interpretations recognize a real seam between them. TOBD-guided research into what is happening at the seam, where two individuals interface, expects to find that each individual organism will have a complex interface system that tightly controls how it relates to others. The innate control of these relationships by each organism individually determines the characteristics of the ecosystem.

## Making Useful Predictions

A viable theory should frame predictions of expected research findings. If engineering principles accurately explain biological functions, then a primary prediction of this TOBD is to discover corresponding system elements between human-designed contrivances and biological mechanisms performing similar functions.

Evidence has been described supporting this expectation. Guliuzza and Gaskill describe an organism-focused, design-based model to explain biological adaptation called *continuous environmental tracking*.[12] Hennigan and Guliuzza applied this model to explain seed dormancy and germination in forest ecosystems.[13] And Guliuzza and Sherwin found that body systems classified as defensive and labeled "immune" have a much broader purpose. They act as an interface that regulates the relationship primarily between host organisms and individual microbes.[14]

## Conclusion

A TOBD is not a simply a critique of the insufficiencies of adaptationism, random mutations, or selectionism. It is a new engineering-based, organism-focused model that flows from the latest findings from molecular biology. It incorporates the engineering principles that are likely essential to make correct cause-effect associations for biological functions. There is a notable trend among some evolutionists to infuse more engineering into biology. The evolutionists' current uncertainty over how new discoveries fit their theory provides a rare opening for non-evolutionists to frame these data into a novel, non-evolutionary theory that more accurately describes biology.

Most importantly, a TOBD fundamentally changes the way we perceive organisms. Evolutionary theory takes an externalistic approach that sees organisms as passive modeling clay for environments to mold. The design-based, organism-focused approach promoted by a TOBD sees creatures for what they are: active, problem solving entities endowed with spectacularly engineered innate capacities.

Creatures *drive themselves* through time as they detect, take on, and solve very challenging dynamic conditions whereby they continually "fill the earth"—all to their Creator's glory.

*Notes*

1. For an example of how engineering principles are experimentally derived and how these same are also observed in creatures, see Lucas, K. N. et al. 2014. Bending rules for animal propulsion. *Nature Communications*. 5: 3293. For how this discovery is framed within creationist explanations, see Guliuzza, R. J. Reverse Engineering Reveals Ideal Propulsion Design. *Creation Science Update*. Posted on ICR.org March 14, 2014, accessed October 16, 2019.

2. Khammash, M. 2008. Reverse engineering: the architecture of biological networks. *BioTechniques*. 44 (3): 327; Aoki, S. K. et al. 2019. A universal biomolecular integral feedback controller for robust perfect adaptation. *Nature*. 570: 533–537.

3. Kunkel, J., X. Luo, and A. P. Capaldi. 2019. Integrated TORC1 and PKA signaling control the temporal activation of glucose-induced gene expression in yeast. *Nature Communications*. 10 (1): 3558.

4. Socha. J. Snakes that fly–really. TEDxVirginiaTech. Posted on youtube.com December 6, 2012.

5. Savage, N. 2018. Computer logic meets cell biology: how cell science is getting an upgrade. *Nature*. 564: S1-S3.

6. Pande, V. How to Engineer Biology *Scientific American*. Posted on blogs.scientificamerican.com November 8, 2018 accessed December 21, 2018.

7. Synthetic biology. The Royal Society. Posted on royalsociety.org

8. Dunn, S.-J. The next software revolution: programming biological cells. TEDSummit 2019. Posted on ted.com.

9. Savage, N. 2018. Computer logic meets cell biology: how cell science is getting an upgrade. *Nature*. 564: S1-S3.

10. Denton, M. J. 2013. The Types: A Persistent Structuralist Challenge to Darwinian Pan-Selectionism. *BIO-Complexity*. (3): 1-18.

11. Rose, S. 2004. The biology of the future and the future of biology. In *Explanations: Styles of Explanation in Science*. J. Cornwell, ed. Oxford, UK: Oxford University Press, 138.

12. Guliuzza, R. J. and P. B. Gaskill. 2018. Continuous environmental tracking: An engineering framework to understand adaptation and diversification. In *Proceedings of the Eighth International Conference on Creationism*. J. H. Whitmore, ed. Pittsburgh, PA: Creation Science Fellowship, 158-184.

13. Hennigan, T. and R. Guliuzza. 2019. The Continuous Environmental Tracking hypothesis—application in seed dormancy and germination in forest ecosystems. *Journal of Creation*, 33 (2): 77-83.

14. Guliuzza, R. J. and F. Sherwin. 2016. Design Analysis Suggests that our "Immune" System Is Better Understood as a Microbe Interface System. *Creation Research Society Quarterly*. 53: 123-139.

# 11

# ALL-OR-NOTHING UNITY IN THE HUMAN BODY

Randy J. Guliuzza, P.E., M.D.

**Summary:** Evidence for design is found not only in how things work but also in how they must be put together. A minimum number of parts is required or nothing works. If even one vital part is missing, the system fails.

The process of human reproduction is an example of all-or-nothing unity. An entire organism is needed in order for it to reproduce. In addition to a man and a woman's contributions, the baby's own systems trigger many crucial functions needed to carry, deliver, and feed it afterward. It takes a baby to make a baby!

Evolutionists sidestep the origin of the vast amounts of biological information and all-or-nothing unity in living systems. The design in the living world was placed there in the beginning by the Creator.

The familiar question "which came first, the chicken or the egg?" illustrates a powerful but underutilized strength to design-based thinking—evidence for design is found not only in how things work but also in how they must be put together. Chicken/egg-like situations almost immediately let people see that there are a minimum number of parts—all necessary—to make things work... or *nothing* works. That phenomenon is called *all-or-nothing unity* (or by a more technical name, irreducible complexity, promoted in a popular book by Michael Behe[1]).

At first, a chicken/egg-like impasse looks like only a timing dilemma. That problem is real, but so is the quandary elicited if there were not the information in an egg for making a chicken that could then make an egg. And if

89

there is a failure in the controlling conditions for the parts—these being (1) available quantity, (2) localized together, (3) capable of functioning together, (4) for a purpose, and (5) at the right time—it doesn't matter if the goal is the chicken or the egg; the absence of the information, conditions, or any vital part is a definite showstopper.

Regarding function, design engineers need to know if all, some, or none of it is maintained without the full set of parts. They know that some aspects of their project can be built by increments, but at certain phases, all of those parts must be collected together and built together or none of that specific function can be obtained. In the living world, these are called *vital* parts. The chicken/egg scenario is really about the absolute unity of certain vital parts to vital functions.

When all-or-nothing unity exists, the known source is always real design. So, when it is found in the living world, it is reasonable to conclude that it is evidence of a real Designer's work.

## How to Explain the Vital Unity of Parts and Function

It is not difficult to present the case for all-or-nothing unity. A powerful, yet easily understood, statement is this: "In organisms, some parts are so important to the function of life that if they are missing, life stops." The difficulty is deciding on a great example.

Genesis 1:11 records God's formation of plants, each kind with its own "seed." It is notable that the first and foremost unified biological process—reproduction—is absolutely contrary to classic evolutionary origins of these vital systems. How do organisms "arise" by an iterative process until they can reproduce? For evolution to proceed, it is not enough just to attain some physiological function; what is needed is *reproductive* life. Fortunately, reproduction is a science topic of which almost everyone has some knowledge.

When you discuss reproduction from a design-based perspective, most listeners will hear for the first time something that totally defies evolutionary dogma. They will be astounded to learn that the minimum number of parts necessary for an organism to reproduce *is the organism itself.* The whole organism is vital. This is scientific fact. It doesn't mean that every part is vital, but it does mean that only the organismal unit encompasses all of the critical parts, information, and conditions necessary to reproduce itself according to the constraints of its life cycle. In order to produce a human baby, a man and a woman, and all of their vital interdependent parts, are the essentials—science has shown that it cannot be broken down to any smaller level.[2]

This fact is so indicting that evolutionists will push back with all kinds of arguments, but these explanations will all cheat. Every example given will always start and end by using some vital things from the organism itself, so be looking for this. For example—yes, there is in vitro fertilization, but that starts with donor egg and sperm, and the embryo is returned to the normal realm of development.

## Reproduction: A Perfect Example of All-or-Nothing Unity in Humans

A new life is started the moment a human sperm cell unites with a human egg. It may sound simple, but it isn't. In fertilization, a sperm is needed to fertilize an egg, but only a single sperm. How is that accomplished?

All-or-nothing unity is seen in human reproduction. The interrelated matching parts from father, mother, and baby must all be in place or the reproductive process will yield nothing in regard to offspring.

A sperm's head must be coated in proteins exactly matching a receptor on an egg—just like lock and key—since only human sperm can fertilize a human egg. In less than a second after sperm contact, many channels in the egg's membrane open, allowing an inrush of positively charged sodium ions. This creates an electrical charge across the outer surface of the egg, detaching any remaining sperm on the outside. Also, all remaining receptors on the egg are inactivated. Concurrently, substances inside the egg's cell membrane are released that bind water molecules. This causes the membrane to swell up to permanently block other sperm from fertilizing. These blocks prevent entrance of multiple copies of genetic material from any other sperm into the egg, which would be fatal to baby and maybe to mother as well.

Once united, tube-like structures in the egg rapidly build and then project from the egg and pull the nucleus of the sperm into the egg—the first cell of a new person.

From this point on, the real star of the show is the developing baby. This takes all-or-nothing unity to a level way past just male-female compatibility. Until recent times, the baby was viewed as simply a passive object being built by the mother's body. Nothing is further from the truth. In terms of guiding its own implantation into the uterus all the way to instigating labor and delivery, it is the baby-placenta unit orchestrating its own destiny. Mom's body, in great measure, is now under the control of a new person.

The baby has unique genetic material that expresses foreign markers on its cells that are not recognized as "self" by the mother. Her immune system could (and should) easily destroy the first cells of the new baby within just a few cell divisions. But substances secreted by those first cells suppress the maternal immune response. Later, the placenta will continue to modulate immune responses, though only at the uterine implantation site. The mother's body, therefore, accepts it. Without this immunological acceptance, no baby would ever survive.

A hormone produced by the earliest cells after fertilization travels in mom's bloodstream back to her ovary. Ovarian cells detect that hormone and respond by producing *progesterone*—the very important hormone that will calm uterine contractions for nine months and maintain the pregnancy. Later, the placenta will produce progesterone at even higher concentrations.

Other adaptations in mom's body that are absolutely necessary for its own survival begin after her body senses even more hormones produced by the baby. These changes include a sizable expansion of mom's blood volume, an increase in cardiac output, agents to modulate blood pressure, increases in blood flow to the kidneys, and cranking up mom's metabolism. The placenta will also extract nutrients from maternal circulation so efficiently that the baby's needs will always be met first—then the mother's.

In the last weeks of pregnancy, estrogen produced by the baby reaches a high concentration in mom's blood. This has two important consequences: Once detected, muscle cells of the uterus begin to express abundant receptors for the hormone *oxytocin*, and it slowly opposes progesterone's quieting influence. At term, certain cells of the baby begin to produce oxytocin, which is a powerful uterine muscle stimulant (man-made oxytocin is called Pitocin).

Since the uterus is now highly sensitive to oxytocin, labor begins. As the baby descends, a pressure sensor in the birth canal sends a signal to mom's brain and triggers her body to produce even more oxytocin—which causes stronger uterine contractions. Fortunately, for weeks before delivery, another hormone called *relaxin* has increased concentration. Augmented by placental production, relaxin facilitates pelvic ligaments and skin of the birth canal to relax, widen, and become more flexible. This increased motility expedites birth passage, for which the baby and mom are both thankful.

While the baby was still in the womb, placental hormones helped prepare mom's breasts to produce milk. After delivery, newborn suckling induces episodic oxytocin secretion by mom, which acts on breast ducts to cause milk let-down.

The reality clearly emerges that it is the mother who is in many ways passive, detecting and responding to signals emanating from the baby—even at times to her own detriment. Scientific research has shown that while mom's reproductive organs and body are indispensable, they are not enough. It takes a baby…to make a baby. This evidence is pretty compelling of all-or-nothing unity and should preclude wild evolutionary speculations about a step-by-step evolutionary process over many generations leading to the systems that produce a baby.

## Evolutionists Supply Insufficient Explanations

When reading evolutionary literature or listening to their programs, note that evolutionists will fail to explain the *origins* of biological information and reproduction. They simply start with reproducing entities. This is true not just for humans, but for any organism—even one-cell creatures.

Researchers with a prior bias forbidding consideration of non-natural explanations have addressed all-or-nothing unity in the best evolution-based journals,[3] but the argument has not been defeated.[4] These articles have all claimed that the solution to all-or-nothing unity is if researchers can imagine where similar—not always identical—parts could be borrowed ("co-opted," "pre-adapted," or "recruited") from existing objects. Even if borrowed parts could work, which is doubtful, only condition one—availability—is satisfied. The necessary information and the other four conditions are not even addressed. Thus, by taking an indirect path to all-or-nothing unity, these responses fail to engage the true issue and demonstrate how imagination cannot substitute for testable findings.

All-or-nothing unity, particularly in reproduction, is powerful in confronting evolution's attempt to chip away at prohibitive improbability and explain biological design.

- Reproduction is one of many entities revealing that *all* necessary conditions, parts, and information must come together or *nothing* of the function is achieved—an event distinctive of real design.

- Scenarios depicting organisms arising incrementally are implausible, since the minimum parts necessary for an organism to reproduce are the organism itself.

- Evolutionists' explanations cheat. Reproductive origins are not explained; they start with replicating life.

Why should anyone believe that the living world only looks like it is designed but really isn't? The design in the living world is such that it *resists* being explained by natural causes. All scientific evidence shows that creatures come programmed with innate abilities to reproduce after their kind, but not strictly identical offspring, in order to divide, multiply, and fill the earth.

The Bible not only clearly says that the Lord Jesus Christ designed life, but it also reveals how He did it: The chicken came "whose seed [egg or sperm] is in itself"—all at one time. These things were placed by the Lord in our first parents, Adam and Eve, fully functional right from the beginning.[5]

**Notes**

1. Behe, M. 1996. *Darwin's Black Box*. New York: The Free Press.
2. See Thomas, B. Have Scientists Created a Synthetic Cell? *Creation Science Update*. Posted on ICR.org May 27, 2010.
3. See Clements, A. 2009. The reducible complexity of a mitochondrial molecular machine. *Proceedings of the National Academy of Sciences*. 106 (37): 15791–15795.
4. See Thomas, B. 2009. Preadaptation: A Blow to Irreducible Complexity? *Acts & Facts*. 38 (11): 15; and Thomas, B. Pseudo-science Attacks Irreducible Complexity. *Creation Science Update*. Posted on ICR.org September 10, 2009.
5. Guliuzza, R. 2009. *Made in His Image: Examining the complexities of the human body*. Dallas, TX: Institute for Creation Research.

# 12

# UNMISTAKABLE EVIDENCE FOR GOD'S DESIGN: CELLS LEAD THE WAY

Brian Thomas, Ph.D.

**Summary:** Scripture clearly teaches God's majestic design right from the start. The inner workings of the cell point toward God's design like nothing else. This can be illustrated by comparing cellular function to building a skyscraper. It requires the right materials and energy, the application of those in the right forms, the right building plan, and the following of that plan at every turn.

Cells follow these steps in the building of a human from a single starting cell. But cells have all the necessary information encoded within themselves, not applied from outside. The super-intelligence behind the workings of the cell goes beyond anything humans could imagine or achieve.

Every living cell bears remarkable testimony to God's goodness and supreme intelligence in creating all life.

Did you know that the inner workings of the cell point toward God's design like nothing else? Do you know how it does so? Certain cell functions illustrate God's handiwork in ways that make creation conversations easy to begin.

Scripture clearly teaches God's majestic design right from the start. In Genesis 1:1, the statement "in the beginning God created the heavens and the earth" assumes that before anything was, God was. He is eternal, and nothing and no one existed in the beginning except God. No one else was there to compel Him to create or to give Him any ideas. Before the universe was, it existed only in His mind. Therefore, He alone knows everything about every molecule in every place.

Plus, according to Genesis, the way He intended each creation is exactly how it became. God looked on the results of His creative acts at the end of each creation week day and proclaimed them good. There were no mistakes, prototypes, or second tries when God designed. The Bible's account of creation loudly declares the incomparable glory of God in designing the universe!

In light of God's creative acts in Genesis 1, Scripture teaches us to expect abundant evidence of His design in creation. In Jesus, "all things were created: things in heaven and on earth, visible and invisible" (Colossians 1:16). He made humans "in the image of God." He told the first man and woman to "have dominion," and that requires creative design and engineering.

We can therefore anticipate that we will have the ability to recognize the design of the One whose ultimate design we are to mimic as we interact with and manage His created world. The New Testament puts it this way: "For since the creation of the world His invisible attributes are clearly seen, being understood by the things that are made, even His eternal power and Godhead" (Romans 1:20). Thus, everyone sees unmistakable evidence in creation for divine design—design more ingenious than any human achievement. Cell functions serve as just one set of examples of this design.

## How to Build a Cell? Try a Skyscraper First

Perhaps the easiest way to recognize the astounding evidence in the cell is by analogy to human engineering. Each human body represents a very large and complicated biological construction project. Building a human parallels building a skyscraper. The intelligence required to build a skyscraper illustrates the intelligence required to build the human body from a single cell.

At least four steps in skyscraper construction require knowledgeable intervention. First, someone must harness and transform the energy (i.e., sunlight) and raw materials (i.e., iron ore) before they can participate in the construction process. For example, despite enormous amounts of energy streaming down from the sun and sitting below the earth's surface in the form of oil, and despite plenty of raw materials present in the earth's crust, the hottest deserts do not spontaneously spawn skyscrapers.

Why not? For work to be accomplished, the energy and raw materials must be converted into useful forms, sizes, and shapes—such as electricity, gasoline, glass, or steel. Thus, intelligent human beings build solar panels, oil refineries, and glass and steel plants to transform energy and raw materials into useful forms. Sunlight does not build steel from rock.

The second step requires engineers to harness the transformed energy and materials toward useful work. Even if the raw materials are nearby, they cannot begin to assemble themselves. A pile of steel and glass next to an electrical outlet will, if left alone, never changes into the Willis (Sears) Tower. Rather, intelligent humans must build tools like welders and cranes that will harness the transformed energy to accomplish useful work.

The third step at which intelligence is absolutely required is organizing the useful work according to a plan for the final structure. Even if human workers are assigned tools and given raw materials, they will not automatically construct a skyscraper without a specified plan. Imagine the chaos that would ensue at a construction site not governed by a blueprint. One set of workers might begin to randomly connect steel beams, another would lay the wrong-size foundation, and another would wire the electricity however he saw fit!

The fourth step has already been assumed in the example above—the plan laid out in the blueprint must be enforced. Even if a blueprint is present at the construction site, it will never govern the process without intelligent human beings to read, interpret, and execute the plan. This step also assumes a means of communicating the steps to all involved. Without intelligent execution of the blueprint, the Empire State Building would still be a fancy drawing and not a reality.

Thus, skyscrapers exist only because creative and intelligent humans do. Whoever objects to this needs to explain why in the supposedly long evolutionary history of the universe energy and raw materials did not bring skyscrapers into existence on their own. And if they insist that skyscrapers did exist in the deep past, they should explain why they left no trace. Either way, how could any rational person deny that the world's tallest buildings came about only by intelligent planning and design?

## Constructing a Human Requires the Same Steps

A mother's womb must overcome the same four problems to build a single cell into the biological construction project we recognize as the human body. When sperm meets egg to form the first cell (the zygote), development will not proceed without some means to (1) transform energy into a form useful for cell growth, (2) harness the energy to useful work, (3) organize the work according to a plan, and (4) enforce the plan.

Though humans are involved in the initial act of procreation, mom and dad do not consciously instruct the zygote at any step of the developmental process. The mother-baby system solves these problems without human intervention. How?

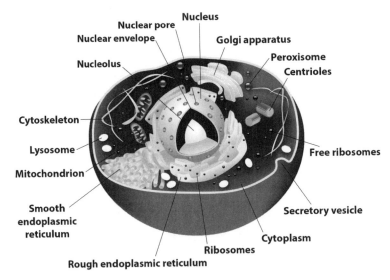

Each cell including the zygote maintains its own miniature power plants called *mitochondria*. These transform energy into the precise form that the cellular construction equipment (think tiny welders and cranes) run on. Inside the mitochondria, tiny protein machines harvest the energy present in chemical bonds of carbohydrates, fats, and proteins. These energy-rich molecules come from the foods that the mother consumes, digests, and provides to the developing baby.

The baby's growing cells transform raw yet mobile chemical food energy into energy in a more readily burnable chemical called *adenosine triphosphate* (ATP). In the cell, ATP functions as cellular "electricity," fueling most of its processes. Just like a power saw or drill are designed to run on electricity, most of the machines and tools inside cells are designed to run on ATP. The mitochondria solve the problem of producing the proper form of energy.

The cell also possesses tiny factories that manufacture the cell's own chemical building blocks such as proteins, phospholipids, and DNA. Like any manufacturing facility, those inside the cells use stringent quality control standards. For example, production pace protocols track the shifting needs of the relevant building project. Construction engineers do not order 10 times the required number of bricks for a building. That would waste space and energy. Similarly, cells manufacture or import just the right amounts of just what is needed. The chemical synthesis machinery solves the problem of raw material transformation.

Two major types of "tools"—proteins and RNA—perform much of the work in the cell. Both of these classes of molecules help perform required tasks like taking out the trash, synthesizing fat, copying cells, and processing information. The cell comes well-equipped with many molecular tools to execute a wide variety of biological tasks, including materials transport, quality control of both the blueprint itself and of the fit of the product to that blueprint, and intra- and extra-cellular communication.

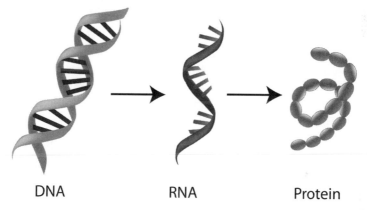

DNA                    RNA                    Protein

The cell organizes the work of development into a baby according to the "blueprint" encoded in its DNA. Our DNA comes packed as 23 separate lengths called *chromosomes* from the father and a separate 23 corresponding lengths from the mother. Prior to division, a cell builds a new set of all 46 chromosomes. The information in these chromosomes specifies nearly all the instructions for our anatomy and physiology.

Last, the cell enforces and manages that plan. How? RNA and proteins read and translate the DNA-encoded plan. They bring the plan out of the "office" and onto the various construction sites within each cell. At just the right times they build more cell components at just the right production rates. These molecules recognize specific sequences of DNA where they begin reading only the information they need at that moment. They interpret each sequence, partly by being regulated by dozens of additional associated molecules.[1] A complex interplay among a huge array of specific cellular molecules does the foreman's work of interpreting and enforcing the building plans stored in DNA sequences.

Does the absence of human intervention during the development process imply that intelligence is *not* required to construct the human body? Return to the skyscraper analogy. Everyone should recognize that designers and builders of the Empire State Building were intelligent and capable. If the designers instead programmed robots to perform all the tasks of the entire construction crew, would this have required more intelligence or less on the part of the designers?

Clearly, this would require much more. They would not only have had to specify the solutions for energy and raw material conversion, as well as a building blueprint and means to enforce it, but they would also have had to specify similar solutions for each robot! In one sense, cell systems act like robots, following instructions in the DNA without human intervention. Yet, the intelligence behind the workings of the cell goes beyond even this intelligence-confirming analogy.

## The Super-Intelligence Behind the Cell

To make our analogy more accurately reflect cellular reality, let's change it to something even more complicated. What if, this time, the designers programmed a computer chip with all the instructions for creating a skyscraper? What if all they would need to do is drop the chip on the construction site? What kind of chip would be able to use the surrounding raw materials and energy to build itself into the Empire State Building? Would this require more intelligence or less? Clearly, this would require intelligence that no human now possesses! But the intelligence in the cell exceeds even this analogy.

Extend the analogy beyond any conceivable human achievement to date. What if our designers programmed a computer chip not only to build the Empire State Building but to build an Empire State Building that possessed, *within itself*, the instructions to make *another computer chip* and begin the process all over again? Let's now have the designers also hard-wire an error detection and correction program into the same chip so that any mistakes at any step of the construction process would be identified and corrected. It builds itself, copies itself, repairs itself, maintains and corrects itself...and it can adapt itself to various surroundings. That's what creatures do, and what human engineers envy.

Clearly, we have far exceeded anything humanly realistic. Yet, the cell possesses, within itself, the instructions to make the next generation of cells, to detect errors, modify plans, and to correct problems. God's designs are not limited by humans' finiteness—He creates systems with efficiencies, capacities, and tiny scales that exceed our wildest imaginations!

Perhaps this fact lies behind often-heard exclamations about the miracle of birth. Human development from a cell points towards an Intelligence whose designs outpace anything within the realm of the best human achievements. This Super-Designer fits exactly what the Bible says about the nature of God the Creator, who deserves loud praises for what He has done![2]

Since every multicellular species on Earth is made up of cells, and since multicellular species populate every continent on Earth, the entire planet loudly proclaims unmistakable evidence for God's immeasurable, omnipotent, and omniscient design. Each cell bears remarkable testimony to God's goodness and supreme intelligence in creating all life.[3]

**Notes**

1. Thomas, B. 2010. Cell systems—what's really under the hood continues to drop jaws. *Journal of Creation*. 24 (2): 13-15.

2. Special thanks to the late A. E. Wilder-Smith for writing ideas that stimulated and extended some of the analogies in this chapter.

3. Tomkins, J. 2012. *Design and Complexity of the Cell*. Dallas, TX: Institute for Creation Research.

# 13

# EVOLUTIONIST VOCABULARY ON CELLULAR COMMUNICATION DISPLAYS FAULTY LOGIC

James J. S. Johnson, J.D., Th.D.

**Summary:** Espionage can involve elaborate systems of coding and decoding to ensure the effective transmission of a needed message. Communication within living cells is even more complex than any human-designed method. Evolutionists try to explain this cleverly coded communication as the product of natural selection, but the words they use prove they're describing a purposely programmed system.

The concept of natural selection is misleading because it ascribes a real power (selecting) to an abstraction (nature). Nature can't select anything because it has no mind. The interactive coded and encoded communication that occurs nonstop in our cells points to the infinite intelligence and engineering skill of our Creator.

Secret codes and ciphers are serious business—just ask Paul Revere.

Listen, my children, and you shall hear
Of the midnight ride of Paul Revere,
On the eighteenth of April, in Seventy-Five;
Hardly a man is now alive
Who remembers that famous day and year.

He said to his friend, "If the British march
By land or sea from the town to-night,
Hang a lantern aloft in the belfry arch
Of the North Church tower, as a signal light—

"One if by land, and two if by sea;
And I on the opposite shore will be,
Ready to ride and spread the alarm
Through every Middlesex village and farm,
For the country-folk to be up and to arm."[1]

Obviously, espionage relies on very precise and carefully crafted communication. Many spies and secret agents *die* when their messages are intercepted. Communications to and from spies, therefore, are often accomplished by using very clever codes to intelligently transmit valuable information. No one who honestly studies the use of coded information in clandestine espionage activities would attribute such carefully coded (and decoded) communications to mere chance or accident.

## Coding and Decoding at the Biomolecular Level

Illogically, however, many look at the more cleverly coded communications that are sent and received inside living cells and explain what they see as products of blind chance and "evolutionary accident." Yet, genetic code-based communication is informationally more complex and detailed than any system humans could create, and it displays engineering complexity beyond our wildest imagination. And these biomolecular communications are being sent and received all the time, every millisecond! How can this be?

Evolutionists describe this remarkable communication system's supposedly "accidental" parts and processes using vocabulary that sounds like the cryptographic vocabulary of spies and secret agents, thus demonstrating the inexcusable illogic[2] of crediting the system to "natural selection." In other words, evolutionists use words that prove they are observing providentially programmed biomolecular communication at work. How is this?

When accurately describing the organized activities that routinely occur inside a eukaryotic cell's nucleus or mitochondria, evolutionary geneticists routinely use terms like code (e.g., genetic code, protein coding, coding regions, encode, decode, codon, anti-codon), transcription, translation, blueprint, program, information, instruction, edit, decipher, messenger, reading, proofreading, signal, alphabet, letter, language, gene expression, surveillance (for detecting nonsense), etc. It is important to recognize that these genetic message-oriented terms were not imposed on the evolutionists by the creationists.

The details of how immeasurably ingenious all of this biochemical information machinery is—and it is!—have been documented, at least to some degree, by many who have honored God, intentionally or unintentionally, by their respective research in the related fields of microbiology, molecular biology, biochemistry, and genetics.[3]

The main point of the lengthy vocabulary list above is to illustrate how scientists have chosen to describe the micro-world of DNA, RNA, ribosomes, mitochondria, endoplasmic reticula, protein synthesis, etc., in vocabulary that befits intelligent and purposeful communication.

Specifically, genetic science reveals God's purposeful encoding of genetic messages, with mind-bogglingly complex instructions on how to build living things from the biomolecular level upward, with those same encoded messages being efficiently decoded and recognized with sufficient accuracy to produce responsive compliance with those biomolecular instructions![4]

## Unintelligible Messages Are No Good

In the world of spies and counterspies, intelligent agents use codes with language that is designed to be recognizable by the intended recipient. Codes have been employed from time immemorial to prevent messages from being intelligible to unintended recipients.

However, a coded message is no good at all if the intended recipient cannot understand its encoded meaning. Accordingly, every code-based message must be informationally devised (i.e., created), encoded, and sent to the intended readers. The readers must then decode the message, recognize the information it contains, and act on that information in a way that corresponds to the original purpose of the message's creator. It is vital that the intended recipient understand the sender's meaning, because the message itself is unrecognizable unless both sender and receiver share a common understanding of what the words (or other symbols) mean.

Consider the following message: "One if by land, two if by sea." What does that sequence of words signify? Because that message used a language shared by the sender (Robert Newman, with the help of John Pulling) and receivers (those awaiting word on the movement of British troops), it provided a recognizable warning that "the Regulars [British soldiers] are coming" by water, not by land. Two lanterns lit in the Old North Church on the night of April 18, 1775, provided a signal—but it was recognizable as such only to those who knew the "language" shared by Paul Revere and his allies.

This principle of coded information transfer is illustrated at the subcellular level. If a protein-coding "message" borne by a portion of DNA cannot be transferred by RNA and translated on ribosomes providentially fitted for the task, the DNA's instructions cannot be complied with, and that would mean no protein synthesis—which can be a fatal failure for whatever life form is involved, whether girl or gecko, boy or bacterium.

## Metaphors Describe Genetic Information Transmittal

In short, genetic realities must be expressed using human communication metaphors, because only such metaphors accurately portray the underlying realties of biochemical information processing.

It is quite proper to use metaphors to talk about natural science topics if they accurately assist in communicating truth. DNA and RNA are heavily involved in encoding and decoding information, and the biochemical "language" used truly exhibits transcription, translation, editing, and the like.

## Some Metaphors Are Misleading, Even Deceptive

The genetic code metaphors listed above are helpful because they help communicate *real truth* about how biomolecular information is sent and received at the subcellular level.

However, not all metaphors employed by scientists are helpful for conveying truth. The term "natural selection" is a metaphor that has often been used by evolutionists to promote their model of biodiversity origins. Creationists have long admired how living creatures are superbly designed for their various environmental niches, so creationists rhetorically ask, "How could this possibly be without a Designer?" It is all too common for the evolutionists to respond, "Natural selection is the answer. Nature 'selected' those organisms with such traits, catalyzing organisms to adapt to their environment."

But such an answer is horribly misleading. It falsely attributes a real power to an abstraction ("nature"). This commits both the reification and personification fallacies, to say the least. Nature cannot literally "select" anything because nature has no mind. Even some evolutionists recognize this and are embarrassed:

> The answers that have been suggested so far have not been convincing. In particular, though there is no end of it in popular

accounts of adaptationism, it is a Very Bad Idea to try and save the bacon by indulging in metaphorical anthropomorphisms. It couldn't, for example, be literally true that the traits selected for are the ones Mother Nature has in mind when she does the selecting; nor can it be literally true that they are the traits one's selfish genes have in mind when they undertake to reproduce themselves. There is, after all, no Mother Nature, and genes don't have, or lack, personality defects. Metaphors are fine things; science probably couldn't be done without them. But they are supposed to be the sort of things that can, in a pinch, be cashed. Lacking a serious and literal construal of "selection for," adaptationism founders on this methodological truism.[5]

It is a good thing that Paul Revere did not wait on nature to "select" a code-message about the British, because there is no intelligent, decision-making "Mother Nature" who can select anything or anyone.

There is, however, a Creator who used infinite intelligence and engineering skill to provide the providential programming that is observed in the interactive coded and encoded communication that occurs, non-stop, in nuclear and mitochondrial DNA, RNA, and ribosomes.[6] That Creator is the God of the Bible. He has revealed Himself in and through the Lord Jesus Christ, and He is the one we should gratefully revere.

### Notes

1. Longfellow, H. W. 1863. Paul Revere's Ride (a.k.a. The Landlord's Tale). In *Tales of a Wayside Inn*. Boston: Ticknor and Fields. Paul Revere historically said "river" (alluding to the Charles River) and not sea, but Longfellow apparently wanted a noun to rhyme with the word "be." The poet also took a few liberties with the actual details of that night's events.

2. Romans 1:18-25, especially verse 20 (literally "without apologetic").

3. See, generally, Gitt, W. 2007. *In the Beginning Was Information*. Green Forest, AR: Master Books, 15-254; Wilder-Smith, A. E. 2003. *The Natural Sciences Know Nothing of Evolution*. Costa Mesa, CA: The Word for Today, 5-100, 137-163; Sanford, J. C. 2005. *Genetic Entropy and the Mystery of the Genome*, 2nd ed. Lima, NY: Elim Publishing, 1-151, 185-188. See also unintended admissions from a famous evolutionist geneticist in Sykes, B. 2002. *The Seven Daughters of Eve*. London: W. W. Norton, 22-62.

4. An example of highly detailed research on DNA coding as it relates to human hearing is Ahmed, Z. M. et al. 2011. Functional Null Mutation of MSRB3 Encoding Methionine Sulfoxide Reductase Are Associated with Human Deafness DFNB74. *American Journal of Human Genetics*. 88 (1): 19-29. The article analyzes protein-coding exons, transcription, translation stop codons, translation initiation codons, the encoding of a mitochondrial localization signal, and other examples using communication terminology, showing that information transfer terminology is needed to aptly describe the content and function of DNA sequences that code for construction of proteins needed for human hearing.

5. Fodor, J. 2007. Why Pigs Don't Have Wings. *London Review of Books*. 29 (20):19-22.

6. For more information on the remarkable processes of living cells, see Tomkins, J. 2012. *The Design and Complexity of the Cell*. Dallas, TX: Institute for Creation Research.

# 14

# THE MISTAKES IN EVOLUTIONARY ARGUMENTS AGAINST LIFE'S DESIGN

Randy J. Guliuzza, P.E., M.D.

**Summary:** Evolutionists admit living creatures appear designed, but they claim this "design" is an illusion.

One argument they use is that certain parts are poorly designed and therefore couldn't be the work of a deity. But this assertion reflects an ignorance of the full function of the parts in question and of the principles governing design. In reality, creatures in their prime normally exhibit breathtaking fit and finish.

Evolutionists also imagine that complex living systems could be cobbled together from pre-existing parts, but where did those parts come from? And how could this work when each part must fit its individual "machine" precisely in order to maintain function?

None of these and other arguments against design is an argument *for* evolution. Living organisms appear designed because they *were* designed.

In chapter 12, obvious attributes of design in living things are detailed. The Bible says, "For since the creation of the world His invisible attributes are clearly seen, being understood by the things that are made" (Romans 1:20).

Is design clear even to atheists? It certainly is. Consider the remarks of the atheist Dr. Jerry Coyne of the University of Chicago:

> If anything is true about nature, it is that plants and animals seem intricately and almost perfectly designed for living their lives.... Nature resembles a well-oiled machine, with every species an in-

tricate cog or gear. What does all this seem to imply? A master mechanic, of course.[1]

However, when Coyne says that animals "seem" intricately designed, he means they *look* or *appear* like they were designed but really weren't. Thus, life's "design" is only an illusion. What arguments do evolutionists use to dismiss design?

## The Argument of Bad Design Is an Assertion from Ignorance

Evolutionists argue that all sorts of creatures' parts are poorly designed, ranging from nerves, to the retina found in vertebrate eyes, and even to the way testicles descend from the abdomen in the human male fetus. They contend that these could not be designed by an infinitely wise deity. However, this argument against design reveals ignorance. This doesn't mean these evolutionists are stupid; it means they generally are ignorant of the full function of the parts they criticize and are ignorant of principles governing design.

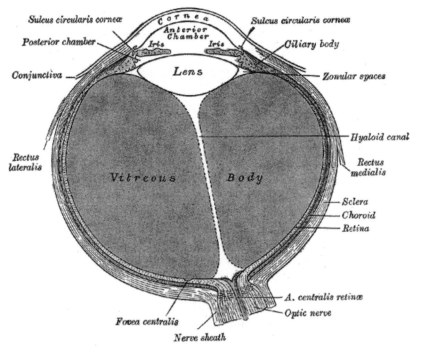

You decide—does the human eye show evidence of great design, or is it a classic example of poor design that argues against an all-wise Creator? That debate is theological in nature, but the main question really is, does the eye show evidence of design? Credit: *Grey's Anatomy* plate 869

There is absolutely no need from the outset to ever concede that any part of a creature is poorly designed. In reality, creatures in their prime normally exhibit breathtaking fit and finish. For most people, the complexity and near-perfect function in living things are amazing. It would be one thing if evolutionists could show a single loss of function in the origins of the parts they criticize, but they cannot. So, claims that something is poorly designed are not equivalent to data-supported facts.

Critics usually demonstrate a profound lack of knowledge of the parts they fault, since that criticism is not backed up by other people who conduct research on those parts. For example, evolutionary biologist Frank Zindler claims, "Although the human eye would be a scandal if it were the result of divine deliberation, a plausible evolutionary explanation of its absurd construction can be obtained quite easily"[2] from evolutionary trial-and-error. However, a biophysicist eye researcher noted:

> Yet for all these apparent flaws, the basic building blocks of human eyesight turn out to be practically perfect. Scientists have learned that the fundamental units of vision, the photoreceptor... are not just good or great or phabulous [*sic*] at their job. They are not merely exceptionally impressive by the standards of biology....Photoreceptors operate at the outermost boundary allowed by the laws of physics, which means they are as good as they can be, period.[3]

A similar criticism is summed up in "I think it would make more sense to design [whatever] another way; thus, an infinitely wise deity could not have designed it." The late evolutionary biologist George Williams argued that there is no functional explanation for humans having specifically two eyes. "To begin at the grossest level, is there a good functional reason for having two eyes? Why not one or three or some other number?"[4] He's convinced that since humans do not have a third eye on the back of their heads, the visual system was clearly not designed.

Though these critics may not know what they are talking about in regard to function, there are other problems with their arguments. First, their attack is not scientific but theological. Their perception of a design does not fit their perception of a deity. Meaning what? They could be in error on both accounts. Questioning *how* something was designed has nothing to do with the question of *whether* it was designed.

Second, they may be ignorant, from a design perspective, of the need to balance several competing interests—i.e., obtaining an optimized design that satisfies conflicting needs-based design requirements. Whether a design maximizes the performance of the one particular trait capturing their interest is irrelevant to the question of whether the entity as a whole was designed. They may be ignorant of good reasons for design tradeoffs between various traits, and others may yet be discovered. Design tradeoffs are actually a better indicator of intelligence behind a design.

Third, the claim of poor quality does not disestablish design. Items designed by humans range in quality from careless to extremely fine. Words describing quality such as "seamless," "blemish free," "consistent," or "durable" are qualifiers that add weight to correctly perceiving patterns of design—but so do words like "crude" or "sloppy." Quality in itself is not the sign of intellectual activity. Genuine design does not demand anything be of the best quality.

Finally, none of the arguments against design are actually arguments *for* evolution. From the most current experimental understanding of environments, environmental elements alone do not achieve even shoddy design—since they have not been shown to produce *any* design.

## The Argument That Nature Designs by Repurposed Pre-existing Parts Is Pure Imagination

How do evolutionists explain the arrival of fundamentally distinct parts in molecular machines? They turn to imaginatively simplistic scenarios where "the necessary pieces for one particular cellular machine...were lying around long ago. It was simply a matter of time before they came together into a more complex entity"[5] upon which "natural selection" tinkered away at cobbling together borrowed parts for millions of years. Aside from the magical whimsy, this explanation is like saying cars originated when an engine was coupled to a transmission that was mounted to a chassis and so forth, leaving another major unanswered question—where did the engine, transmission, and chassis come from?

Individual parts between molecular machines may be almost like each other, but each *fits precisely* into each specific machine to maintain function. There are great gaps of information in the evolutionary path that depicts molecular parts as stripped from their primary original functions to self-assemble as new machines—making a plausible iterative evolutionary transition unbelievable.

These weaknesses are merely dismissed. Lacking experimental evidence supporting their explanations, evolutionists turn to a firm belief that if it can be imagined, it could happen. Dr. Coyne says, "It is not valid, however, to assume that, because one man cannot imagine such pathways, they could not have existed."[6] In conversation, highlight this disconnect, but recognize that Coyne's type of response cannot be satisfied with scientific answers.

## The Argument That Nature Generates Complex Entities Is Irrelevant

Meteorologists and geologists analyze naturally occurring convoluted relationships that puzzle human understanding, such as the interplay of atmosphere and ocean conditions that produce hurricanes, or processes underlying the current understanding of plate tectonics and mountain building. While some natural processes might indeed be intricate, using them as illustrations to validate a natural origin for biological complexity is off-target since they do not produce any precisely arranged parts and their interrelationships are not close to what is found in biological complexity.

## The Argument That Order Spontaneously Arises from Chaotic States Is Irrelevant

Evolutionists correctly assert that natural processes alone can produce ordered arrangements. After molten aluminum cools, atoms do naturally align into ordered lattices. But only after being worked into specifically shaped and precisely arranged parts could aluminum become a *complex* engine. While an ordered status does have more structure than a chaotic one, it is far from the status of many intricately arranged parts. Thus, comparing order to biological complexity is inappropriate.

## The Argument of Vestigial Structures Is an Assertion from Ignorance

The term *vestigial structure* is applied by evolutionists to a part in an organism they consider to be an evolutionary "leftover" whose function is diminished or totally lost from the part's original function in the ancestors of that organism. The main point to make in replying to this argument is that the list of vestigial organs used today to support evolution is only useful as a historical record of today's current knowledge and ignorance. "Vestigiality" is not a real thing; rather, it is a concept that exists only in the mind of the beholder.

Given the fact that many organs on these lists have been an embarrassment to evolutionists since they have been found to have important functions (e.g., spleen, tonsils, appendix), one would think this argument would be abandoned. As addressed in creationist literature,[7] certain organs may not be vital for life, but they still perform important functions. (As a medical doctor discussing organ donation with patients, I wondered if I could accentuate that fact by asking them if they would like to donate their "vestigial organs" today.)

## Be on Guard for Other Ploys Related to Design

Evolutionists use the following gambits to shore up their unwarranted dismissal of design in living things.

**Changing designs is simple.** The approach that evolutionists would have everyone adopt is this: Attach the word "simple" to biological processes, anatomy, and, especially, presumed evolutionary changes. Why? Because simple changes made to simple creatures are more easily believed.

Note this approach toward nature, starting in 1859 with Charles Darwin, who said:

> I can see no very great difficulty...in believing that natural selection has converted the simple apparatus of an optic nerve merely coated with pigment and invested with transparent membrane, into an optical instrument.[8]

In May 2010, the current authority, Dr. Coyne, stated:

> Bats evolved from small four-legged mammals, probably resembling shrews....How could they possibly evolve wings? And yet they did: selection simply retooled the forelegs into wings, along with modifying the animal's weight, shape, musculature, nervous system and bones for flying (no feathers needed). One of the great joys of being a biologist is learning about the many species in nature whose evolution would appear, a priori, impossible.[9]

That bats are designed to fly is clearly seen, but seeing that is not the challenge. Evolutionists would have people replace their natural understanding that bats are very complicated—and thus designed—with a belief that changing shrews to bats is simple, meaning bats only look designed but really aren't.[10]

**Appealing to an organism's design to explain its own origination.** The existence of complex biological features allows a test for their origins. This test only needs careful observation. However, it must be done right. Since the origination of how living things operate—especially their ability to generate diverse offspring—is the issue in dispute, ensure that the ability in question isn't used as part of the explanation in any way. Thus, for creationists the original cause of biological complexity is an intelligent mind, versus the chance coupled to environmental elements (sunlight, wind, rain, gravity, etc.) claimed by evolutionists. They can't start by using already-existing DNA, proteins, etc., in the context of a cell…that's cheating.

**Extraordinary extrapolations.** When looking at the evolutionist's best scientific journals for explanations on origins (e.g., molecular machines), stay alert for conclusions extrapolated far beyond what the evidence will bear.[11] The exaggeration is assured. Why? Since researchers find only one fully functioning machine or another, evolutionary *conclusions* of how, in the remote past, parts from one molecular machine morphed into another will always be conjectures inferred greatly beyond what the findings support.[12]

*Notes*

1. Coyne, J. 2009. *Why Evolution Is True*. New York: Viking Press, 1.

2. Quoted in "Does an Objective look at the human eye show evidence of creation?" posted on 2think.org/eye.shtml. See also Sherwin, F. 2005. That Troubling Laryngeal Nerve? *Acts & Facts*. 34 (5).

3. Angier, N. Seeing the Natural World With a Physicist's Lens. *The New York Times*. Posted on nytimes.com November 1, 2010. See also Thomas, B. Eye Optimization in Creation. *Creation Science Update*. Posted on ICR.org November 23, 2010..

4. Williams, G. 1998. *The Pony Fish's Glow: And Other Clues to Plan and Purpose in Nature*. New York: Basic Books, 9.

5. Report on reference 1 in Keim, B. More 'Evidence' of Intelligent Design Shot Down by Science. *Wired Science*. Posted on wired.com August 27, 2009.

6. Coyne, J. A. 1996. God in the details. *Nature*. 383 (6597): 227-228.

7. See Thomas, B. A Vocal Vestigial Organ? *Creation Science Update*. Posted on ICR.org July 25, 2008; Bergman, J. and G. Howe. 1990. *"Vestigial Organs" Are Fully Functional*. Terre Haute, IN: Creation Research Society Books.

8. Darwin, C. 1859. *On the origin of species by means of natural selection, or the preservation of favoured races in the struggle for life*. London: John Murray, 218

9. Coyne, J. The Improbability Pump: Why has natural selection always been the most contested part of evolutionary theory? *The Nation*, May 10, 2010.

10. For a reality check, see Madrigal, A. C. To Model the Simplest Microbe in the World, You Need 128 Computers. *The Atlantic*. Posted on theatlantic.com July 23, 2012.

11. For example, Clements, A. 2009. The reducible complexity of a mitochondrial molecular machine. *Proceedings of the National Academy of Sciences*. 106 (37): 15791–15795.

12. For further information, see Guliuzza, R. 2012. *Clearly Seen: Constructing Solid Arguments for Design*. Dallas, TX: Institute for Creation Research.

# 15

# HOW CREATURES ADAPT

Randy J. Guliuzza, P.E., M.D.

**Summary:** Darwin saw creatures as passive entities that were randomly pressured by external conditions to develop features and traits in response to environmental change. Instead, creatures actively respond to such change rather than being passively shaped by it, and this is only possible if they are already fully equipped with the necessary innate mechanisms.

They do this in ways that correlate with human-engineered tracking systems. Sensors detect external conditions, and internal logic segments and actuators process the situation and select and execute the best response.

ICR has devised a new theory of biological design that incorporates an engineering paradigm to understand biological function. It forms the foundation for a design-based, organism-focused model called *continuous environmental tracking* that holds much promise for our understanding of how creatures adapt.

Charles Darwin envisioned evolution proceeding through a long string of small adaptations imposed on organisms through deadly struggles to survive in changing environments. Thus, he deliberately directed his theory toward the process of adaptation. He astutely recognized that securing the conceptual high ground in the battle over evolution's validity depended on controlling the explanation of how adaptation happened.

Darwin visualized random processes in the environment exercising designing agency over organisms from outside of them, which was in lieu of God's designing agency—as expressed through purposeful self-adjustments originating from within organisms. By stressing the governing role played by changing environmental conditions in producing biological adaptations, he proposed a revolutionary reversal of what causes adaptation (see chapter 16).

Chapter 10 hashes out a new theory of biological design (TOBD) that is based on premises and assumptions that are the opposite of those Darwin assumed for his theory. Actually, premises for the TOBD go back to the ones biologists simply took for granted prior to the late 19th-century Darwinian revolution. These assumed that creatures were engineered by God, as evidenced by the tight correspondence between parts of creatures and human-engineered devices that perform similar functions. The eminent natural theologian William Paley wrote about this correspondence in the early 19th century.[1] He famously argued, for example, that if one were to discover a watch on the beach, one would infer that a person, not wave action, created it and left it there.

A good theory should be able to frame observed biological phenomena into a model that has a mechanism to explain how the phenomena happen and can make predictions of anticipated findings to guide research. ICR has developed a model opposing Darwin's to explain how biological adaptation happens. It is both design-based and organism-focused, and has the descriptive title *continuous environmental tracking* (CET).

A basic premise of a TOBD incorporated into CET is that "the engineering paradigm in modern biology" is fundamental, and, therefore, engineering principles should guide biological research.[2] In terms of adaptation, a new concept was proposed: Engineering principles underlying how human-designed things self-adjust to changing environments is the most accurate way to explain how organisms adapt themselves.

Before we jump into the observations and scientific findings that led to the development of CET, we need to address some important biblical and theological reasons why we can make a correlation between a creature engineered by God and a human-engineered device.

## Human Engineering Principles Correlate with God's Designs

What if the biological function of organisms turned out to be totally foreign to human design experience? How would it impact God's general revelation of Himself to humanity if deciphering how creatures operate completely eluded the human mind? Someone could claim that organisms were designed, but they could not back that up if they were unable to compare a creature's traits or functions to any standards of design known to humans. Other people could be just as convinced that organisms emerged from chaotic struggles to survive, or maybe it was magic, or maybe something else.

Though God has total freedom, and it was within His prerogative to design His systems to differ with man-made designs or to operate through different laws of nature, He didn't. The Bible teaches that God's creation is the "work of His hands," "His handiwork," and "His workmanship." The Bible says that this workmanship is clearly seen and understood by everyone (Romans 1:20). The *only* way that humans could immediately recognize God's engineering handiwork in living things as "workmanship" is if His devices worked somewhat like human devices.

Thus, making sense of biomolecular, physiological, or anatomical functions is not mysterious. Just like man-made things, creatures and their systems operate within the laws of nature. Neither group defies properties of natural law such as gravity, inertia, and momentum. Rather, design mechanisms utilize those properties—as seen in the motion-sensing maculae and semicircular canals of our inner ears.[3]

This is a godsend for human engineers because this makes possible, say, designing aircraft after studying birds. If engineers want an entity to respond to an external condition, they will specify the condition of interest and build a triggering sensor designed exclusively for that condition *into* the entity—a construction practice that is true of God-designed things.

Creationists, therefore, should be confident to use engineering-based frameworks to explain biology. Biological functions are incredibly complicated. But with hard work, researchers can eventually reverse-engineer biological systems by methodically disassembling them piece-by-piece to discover their operation. If people *could not* readily correlate features of living things with human design, they would remain either clueless or in need of God to reveal additional knowledge of Himself.

If we begin by assuming that biological functions are best explained by engineering principles, then we can see biological phenomena differently—and ask fresh questions.

## Continuous Environmental Tracking Model Summarized

If engineers, not Darwinists, hypothesized how creatures spread into diverse niches (and possibly undergo speciation), they might have produced *On the Origin of Species by Means of Continuous Environmental Tracking*. Many new discoveries on biological adaptation should make design advocates realize that it is not enough just to identify the features of design in biological systems. These findings must also fit into a conceptual framework.

A framework is a plausible working hypothesis about an underlying principle that links together, or may actually cause, a diverse range of biological phenomena. Frameworks help researchers ask appropriate questions, interpret data, and set research agendas. CET is a model developed from a theory of biological design to explain adaptation.

How does ICR begin to develop a design-based model? We start with observations. In this case, as environments change, creatures soon deploy suitable traits. An extensive review of recent literature describing adaptations reveals findings that do not seem to fit scenarios in which genetic variability is fractioned out trial-and-error style through struggles to survive. Rather, these innate mechanisms yield results that are regularly described as "regulated," "rapid," very often "repeatable," and, surprisingly at times, even "reversible"— words that fit the outcomes of engineered systems.

Thus, adaptability appears to arise from engineered controls within organisms. Creatures make innate self-adjustments appropriate to fit and fill changes in their surroundings. This leads to the conclusion that creatures somehow track environmental changes. If that is true, and if biological functions operate by engineering principles, then we next look for a corresponding human engineered mechanism(s) that may explain the observation.

For changing conditions, tracking systems are regularly used to detect and maintain surveillance of moving targets. Could God have designed organisms with the ability to continuously track environmental changes and self-adjust within their own and their offspring's lifetimes through their innate ability to express variable heritable adaptive traits? Thus, one hypothesis is that creatures use internal tracking systems to initiate their adaptive features.

We find that for most of the documented adaptations, creatures use underlying elements that match well with the self-adjustable property of human-designed tracking systems. These are:

1. Input **sensors** to gather data on external conditions.

2. Internal programming specifying reference values, and **logic segments** that compare input data to a reference and select a suitable response. Note that in this model trait selection happens through internal pro-

gramming, not through nature.

3. Output **actuators** to execute responses. In addition, the route from detected condition to specific adaptation runs through these components. The systems exhibit the engineering principle of *functional coherence*. This means that key elements must be available at the right times, places, and amounts to attain function.

From June 2017 through August 2019, ICR published a series of articles explaining the CET model under the heading "Engineered Adaptability" in its *Acts & Facts* magazine. The following paragraphs sum up an article from the series on how to develop an organism-focused, design-based model.[4] The series highlighted diverse mechanisms of how organisms express traits that enable them to closely track changing conditions. The articles included dozens of examples of how creatures use the following system elements to track environmental changes and make suitable self-adjustments. These recently outlined internal mechanisms have some surprising characteristics.

Sensors play a vital role at the organism-environment interface even though some research papers omit them in their causal explanations of adaptation. How creatures utilize sensors highlights the purpose-oriented, internal nature of engineered design. A fundamental engineering principle is that an adjustable system will have a trigger as an *integral* part. That "trigger," be it mechanical, electronic, etc., will be a sensor, and *the* initiating element of self-adjusting processes. Creatures respond to a select few out of a myriad of exposures. Why? First, sensors are exquisitely designed to be sensitive to specific environmental conditions. Second, internal programming *specifies for itself* what conditions will be "signals," "cues," or "stimuli."

Data collected by sensors is processed by innate logic mechanisms that also direct a response. Human-engineered logic mechanisms imitate the conscious logical intentions of the person who programmed it. Basic "if-then" logic is usually achieved by a switching mechanism, e.g., on and off switch.

Many biological switches are incorporated in gene regulatory networks yielding a type of logical cellular "cognition" used in adaptation. Remarkably, cells possess specific mechanisms to optimize their genomes in response to their environments. Consistent with a design-based approach, recent findings indicate that mathematical models and engineering principles could potentially explain *all* intracellular regulatory networks.

When organisms respond, their self-adjustments may so suitably target the condition that often they are described as "predictable." Selectionists will assert that the environment "selected for" the trait. But lacking a real selection event, the only place selection is happening is in their minds. A realistic approach recognizes an organism's programmed "if-then" logic (reflecting in program language the intention of the programmer's real mind) that enables an *internal* selection of the correct solution to different challenges. This logic-based selection comes from an anticipatory adaptive strategy. Innate solutions *precede* environmental challenges and are not "due to" them. Therefore, we may have a reasonable explanation for why diverse organisms use similar traits when facing the same exposure. Perhaps they simply share the same internal programming for adaptive responses.

Three unique mechanisms show tight correspondence to what a human engineer would design. They enable us to better understand engineered biological adaptability. To meet an abrupt environmental challenge, some mechanisms enable a very rapid change in the expression of genes without changing the genes themselves. These are called *epigenetic* mechanisms.

Two characteristics achieve enviable design outcomes. Epigenetics allows a population to "flex" when handling sudden stresses. The early generations rapidly express suitable traits, but then a future generation typically returns to "baseline" after the stress passes. Also, engineers must factor time considerations into any adaptable design. Epigenetic mechanisms perfectly fill a crucial time gap right between very rapid physiological self-adjustments and full multi-generational genetic changes.

An exciting research topic focuses on creature's internal predictive models that seem to couple information about themselves and their environments to confer "foresight" of future conditions. These "anticipatory systems" give vital "look ahead" response capability to any tracking system and are a key element to CET.

The reality of anticipatory systems refutes evolutionary theory, which holds that adaptations must be "blind" with respect to the future needs of the organism. Details of anticipatory systems are not yet known in biology. However, by knowing key elements of human forecasting systems, a theory of biological design lets us make useful predictions and guide scientific research into how biological anticipatory adaptive systems may operate.

Finally, entire populations might track changing environments. An engineering-based model could see a population like an array of unique problem-solving entities that function like a human-designed distributed computing system. Cutting-edge blockchain technology illustrates how this non-random process may work.

This model expects rapid convergence on optimal solutions rather than slow, gradual evolution. Whereas evolutionists emphasize competition in which a few emerge victorious at the expense of the many, the CET population model refreshingly emphasizes cooperation over competition. Both the individual and the population are valuable.

## Pulling it All Together

The design-based model of adaptation postulates that organisms continuously track environmental changes. If this is correct, it would emphasize organisms as active, problem-solving entities—not passive modeling clay. It's a creature's self-adjusting innate mechanisms that adjust traits. These mechanisms precede, and are not due to, changing conditions. Creatures actively track changing conditions—and are not passively "pressured" by them—while driving themselves through time to fill new niches.

When researchers see recurrent, similar categories of changes described as being regulated, rapid, and repeatable, they should recognize these as corresponding with known designs. With human-engineered things, all engineered causality for their function originates internally, and it seems this should be true for organisms.

Therefore, a framework that postulates that creatures were designed is reasonable. This would imply that both internal form *and adaptability* are governed by internal systems. Rapid, repeatable, and reversible creature features challenge the validity of Darwin's externalistic theory itself, not merely its insufficiency. CET makes better sense of what we see in biology.

### Notes

1. Paley, W. 1802. *Natural theology: or, Evidences of the existence and attributes of the deity, collected from the appearances of nature*, 2nd ed.. London: R Faulder. Chapter xii, 227-258.

2. Guliuzza, R. J. 2017. Engineering Principles Should Guide Biological Research. *Acts & Facts.* 46 (7): 17-19.

3. Guliuzza, R. J. 2009. Made in His Image: Beauty in Motion. *Acts & Facts.* 38 (5): 10-11.

4. Guliuzza, R. J. 2019. Engineered Adaptability: Continuous Environmental Tracking Wrap-Up. *Acts & Facts.* 48 (8): 17-19. To read the entire Engineered Adaptability series, use the link at the bottom of this article posted on ICR.org.

# 16

# HOW DARWIN CHANGED BIOLOGY

Randy J. Guliuzza, P.E., M.D.

**Summary:** Charles Darwin radically changed biology by replacing God's agency as Creator with a materialist, externalist explanation of nature as the force that acts on and changes living creatures through natural "pressures."

From Darwin's time on, biologist saw creatures as passive, moldable objects, and attributed causality to nature. Godlike ability was attributed to nature, as though it wields power and choice in and of itself. This essentially removed God from the picture—no Designer is needed if natural selection makes things happen.

But living entities are active, not passive, and they predictively respond to the environment because God designed them with innate abilities to do so. Instead of the worshipful idolatry of nature, we can honor the Lord Jesus Christ as life's incredible Engineer.

What would biology be like without the influence of Darwinism? To envision that, one should first understand the fundamental changes that Darwin brought to biological research—the study of living things. No doubt, many people think Darwin's theory flows from observations of nature. It doesn't. Darwin developed a story to help answer three observations about nature:

1. **Apparent Design**. How do we account for the apparent design of organisms, as seen in their purposeful behaviors and the exquisite fit of their traits to their circumstances?

2. **Apparent Designer**. Can nature function as an agent sufficient unto itself to explain design, or is an intelligent agent needed?

3. **Adaptation**. How do living things relate with their surroundings? Specifically, do adaptations arise from an internal dynamic within or-

ganisms, or does the external environment set the course of change?

Secular scientists herald Charles Darwin for his great feat of eliminating any need for God's selective agency to explain how creatures adapt. He invoked a totally materialist mechanism. His supposed mechanism to replaces God's actual selection he called *natural selection*. How did one man make such a radical change? He began by focusing his readers on how living and Earth systems interact.

## Darwin Understood and Targeted Essential Characteristics of Design

Stephen Jay Gould's *The Structure of Evolutionary Theory* expertly chronicles the history of evolutionary intellectual discourse. He quotes Darwin's 1859 letter to his neighbor John Lubbock to emphasize how thoroughly Darwin understood the most renowned intelligent design advocate of his day, William Paley. Darwin wrote, "I do not think I hardly ever admired a book more than Paley's 'Natural Theology.' I could almost formerly have said it by heart."[1] Gould notes that after re-reading Paley that Darwin's style of argument, his examples, and even his words closely matched Paley's. Gould wrote, "I was struck by the correspondences between Paley's and Darwin's structure of argument (though Darwin, of course, *inverts the explanation*)."[2]

Darwin applied his knowledge about how engineers use fundamental principles to design distinct entities. But he substituted the environment for the designer. To Darwinists even today, environments exercise designing agency over organisms through random processes instead of through God's agency.

### Environments as Intelligent Agents?

Gould lauds Darwin's trailblazing approach, saying:

> Darwin's theory, in strong and revolutionary contrast, presents a first "externalist" account of evolution....Darwin overturned all previous traditions by thus granting the external environment a causal and controlling role in the direction of evolutionary change.[3]

Gould chose his words carefully, for he prefaced his conclusion by saying:

> I proceed in this way for a principled reason, and not merely as a convenience. All major evolutionary theories before Darwin... [are] presenting a fundamentally "internalist" account, based

upon intrinsic and predictable patterns set by the nature of living systems, for development or "unfolding" through time.[3]

Early in his career, Gould discussed this debate. He categorized externalists as holding "that evolution proceeded when changes in the physical environment established selective pressures for new adaptation....I will refer to the belief in external control as *environmentalist* and to claims for an inherent cause of change as *internalist*." Externalists, therefore, "identified the agent of change not within organisms themselves, but in a fluctuating external environment."[4]

Harvard geneticist Richard Lewontin incisively describes how Darwin's externalistic approach fundamentally changed the way biologists see organisms:

> For Darwin, the external world, the environment acting on organisms was the cause of the form of organisms. The environment, the external world with its autonomous properties, was the subject and the organism was, again, the object acted upon....It is from this view of environment as the cause of organism that the entire corpus of modern biology arises. We cannot fully appreciate the nature of the change in biology wrought by Mendel and Darwin unless we understand the historical importance of the objectification of the organism.[5]

Similarly, science philosopher Trevor Pearce wrote, "The new dichotomy of organism and environment proved both useful and portable. By the 1890s, it was already operating as an essential framing device in scientific and philosophical arguments." He continued, saying, "In biology and psychology, the environment was seen as a causal agent, highlighting questions of organismic variation and plasticity."[6]

Another theoretician, Marta Linde Medina, refined the view, saying, "The term 'internalist' makes reference to the nature of the originating organizing principle of biological form (in true 'externalism' the originating organizing principle is imposed from without, regardless of how it may become inscribed in the organism)."[7]

Non-Darwinian biochemist Michael Denton explained how externalists see *all* traits as "the result of specific adaptations built additively by selection during the course of evolution, to serve particular functional ends, ends that

127

are imposed by the environment and that are external to the organism itself."[8]

The overarching premise that active environments mold passive "objectified" organisms—meaning that nature as a substitute intelligent agent *can* create the diversity of life—seems to elude most evolutionary biologists, according to Gould. In an exclamation turned to lament, Gould says:

> I regard this passage [from *The Origin* where Darwin explains his externalist approach] as among the most important and portentous in the entire *Origin*, for these words embody Darwin's ultimate decision to construct a functionalist theory based on adaptation as primary....Yet this passage, which should be emblazoned into the consciousness of all evolutionary biologists, has rarely been acknowledged or quoted.[9]

People fixate on "no Designer needed" but don't recognize how that started when Darwin accomplished the profound shift in understanding organisms.

Darwin was a profound forerunner in a vital area of biological enquiry. He pioneered a way to conceptualize *nature* as the agent of design for organisms. British evolutionist M. Hodge acknowledged "that no one would easily or inadvertently slip into talking of nature as a realm where anything like selection was located; and, indeed, we find few authors before Darwin making that transition."[10] Darwin's concept credits nature as the cause of creature adaptations. He reversed 18th-century thinking about organisms as adapting themselves to environments to today's thinking of organism as clay for environments to model.

## Natural Selection

Both atheistic and theistic selectionists agree that environments can mold the diversity of life, though they may differ on the extent of potential change. As we will see below, this inherently mystical agency animates Darwinian explanations of living systems.

Selectionism begins with the projection of volitional "selective" capacity onto nature to do something like "favor" or "weed out" organisms. Scientists should find this unsettling. Some religious practitioners ascribe volition to inanimate things like a statue or graven image. How can science practitioners legitimately ascribe selective powers to an immaterial concept like "natural selection" or a mindless entity like nature?

Intelligent design advocate William Dembski explains how Darwin ushered in an illegitimate projection of selective capacity onto nature. Darwin deflected the power of selection from within organisms to something outside them. According to Dembski:

> In short, evolutionary biology needs a designer substitute to coordinate the incidental changes that hereditary transmission passes from one generation to the next, and there's only one naturalistic candidate on the table, to wit, natural selection. Indeed, it's no accident that the word *selection* and the word *intelligence* are etymologically related—the *lec* in *selection* has the same root as the *lig* in *intelligence*. Both derive from the same Indo-European root meaning "to gather" and therefore "to choose." Before Darwin, the ability to choose was largely confined to designing intelligences, that is, to conscious agents that could reflect deliberatively on the possible consequences of their choices. Darwin's claim to fame was to argue that natural forces, lacking any purposiveness or prevision of future possibilities, likewise have the power to choose via natural selection. In ascribing the power to choose to unintelligent natural forces, Darwin perpetuated the greatest intellectual swindle in the history of ideas. Nature has no power to choose.[11]

As Dembski observed, "Before Darwin, the ability to choose was largely confined to designing intelligences, that is, to conscious agents that could reflect deliberatively on the possible consequences of their choices."[9] Colleagues of Darwin resisted his injection into science of these mystical volitional powers to nature. Hodge explained why, saying:

> One source of trouble was that Darwin liked the term "natural selection" because it could be "used as a substantive [a mental concept] governing a verb" (F. Darwin, 1887, vol. 3, p. 46). But such uses appeared to reify, even to deify, natural selection as an agent.[10]

Reification refers to a fallacy whereby one ascribes personal powers to impersonal objects, like talk about the kindness of Mother Nature.

Externalists designate certain conditions as "selective pressures." They believe these cause the precise match of an organism's trait to that particular outside "pressure." However, one evolutionist noted that nobody measures this pressure. He said the work nature supposedly does is a phantom that he calls "a metaphorical external agent."[12] One evolutionist named Stephen Talbott sought to extricate naturalist theory from the mysticism of selectionism. He objected, "Natural selection becomes rather like an occult Power of the pre-scientific age."[13]

Talbott went into detail to reveal to his fellow evolutionists why Darwin's selectionism did not deliver biology from superstition—just the opposite. He identified it as mystical. Talbott wrote:

> Natural selection is *always doing things*....We learn that natural selection shapes the bodies and behaviors of organisms, builds specific features, targets or acts on particular genomic regions, favors or disfavors (or even punishes) various traits....This sort of language is all but universal. I think it is safe to say that relatively few references to natural selection by biologists fail to assert or imply that we are looking at something like a humanly contrived mechanism with the well-designed power to do things, beginning with the activity of selecting....Some evolutionists are uncomfortably aware that their use of a phrase *intentionally* evoking the breeder's "artificial selection" invites mystical belief in a breeder-like agent supervising adaptive evolution. And so they assure us that "natural selection", despite its *explicit* suggestion of a selecting agent, is "just a metaphor"....But it is hard to see this as anything but subterfuge. There is a reason why no *effective verbal alternative* to the painfully tendentious [biased] "selection" has taken hold. The idea of a selecting power is deeply rooted and seemingly ineradicable [incapable of removal] from the modern biologist's thinking about evolution.[14]

Just as Darwin intended, this selectionist approach revolutionized biology. It produced four radical results in how we view God, organisms, and the world.

### Result 1: Nature the Tinkerer

Who can establish scientifically that any change within creatures happens without a purpose? Similarly, those who so often assume that most genetic changes associated with adaptations occur at random rarely show evidence for it. These assertions merely convey the anti-design essentials of naturalist philosophy. Ironically, they leave no doubt that they contrast the distinctive practice of engineers to their concept of a non-purposeful natural world. Evolution is supposed to describe an interplay of accidental genetic changes and directionless environmental fluctuations. Libermann and Hall wrote in 2007:

> Evolutionary change occurs because phenotypic variation within populations is generated through random alterations to existing pathways or structures. This point has been made many times, including by Darwin (1859), but perhaps was made most clearly by F. Jacob's (1977) useful and brilliant analogy between evolutionary change and tinkering ("bricolage" in French). Unlike engineers who design objects with particular goals in mind based on *a priori* plans and principles, tinkers create and modify objects opportunistically by using whatever happens to be available and convenient.[15]

If we look closer at Francois Jacob's often-quoted comparison, he contrasts personification of natural selection as capable of doing work versus actual engineers, saying:

> However, if one wanted to play with a comparison, one would have to say that natural selection does not work as an engineer works. It works like a tinkerer—a tinkerer who does not know exactly what he is going to produce.[16]

## Result 2: Passive, Moldable Creatures

In the real world, engineers design problem-solving capabilities into self-adaptable machines. In contrast, externalism posits environments—not engineers—that accidentally mold passive organisms. Two researchers summarize Darwin's externalism:

> He [Darwin] accepted the view that *the environment directly instructs the organism* how to vary, and he proposed a mechanism for inheriting those changes....The *organism was like modeling clay*, and remolding of the clay meant that each of the billions of little grains was free to move a little bit in any direction to generate new form....If an organism needed a wing, an opposable thumb, longer legs, webbed feet, or placental development, any of these would emerge under the proper selective conditions with time.[17]

Linde Medina expresses her agreement with Lenoir, saying:

As a result, organisms are as passive as the matter that forms them: "Surprisingly, in spite of language like 'struggle for existence', for Darwin, organisms are far more passive and less tenacious in their grip on life; they simply vary—spontaneously. Natural selection does all the work of adapting populations of descendants to their changing circumstances."[18]

Gould adds that biologists treat "organisms as inert substances, buffeted by an external environment and reacting immediately to physical stress without counteracting, intrinsic control or even temporary resistance....i.e., stimulus leads to immediate and passive response."[19] Clearly, Darwinism's insistence of creatures as moldable clay leaves no place for designed systems that could detect, direct, or deploy adaptive features from within creatures.

## Result 3: Anti-Designer

People intuitively link a Creator God to the features of living things. And it makes sense. Living things show the same features found in human workmanship. Gould notes that "the word adaptation did not enter biology with advent of evolutionary theory." But historically, "the British school of natural theology used 'adaptation' as a standard word for illustrating God's wisdom by the exquisite fit of form to immediate function. Darwin, in borrowing this term, followed an established definition while *radically revising the cause* of the phenomenon."[20] Who or what caused creatures' fitted forms? Surely not an actual person.

Darwin radically inverted the cause of adaptation from a person to impersonal forces. While adaptations actually depend on the innate capability of creatures to self-adjust, he attributed self-adjusting features to an imaginary molding process from outside. The switch in causes for adaptation from internal to external is more than mere semantics. Darwin's shrewd twist essentially helps justify a world without God.

This sets the context for possibly the most perceptive—and important—analysis of Darwin's anti-designer shift. Again, according to Gould:

> Now suppose, as a problem in abstract perversity, that one made a pledge to subvert Paley in the most radical way possible. What would one claim? I can imagine two basic refutations. One might label Paley's primary observation as simply wrong—by arguing that exquisite adaptation is relatively rare, and that the world is

replete with error, imperfection, misery and caprice. If God made such a world, then we might want to reassess our decision to worship him. An upsetting argument indeed, but Darwin chose an even more radical alternative.

With even more perversity, one might judge Paley's observation as undoubtedly correct. Nature features exquisite adaptation at overwhelming relative frequency. But the unkindest cut of all then holds that this order, the very basis of Paley's inference about the nature of God, arises not directly from omnipotent benevolence, but only as a side-consequence of a causal principle of entirely *opposite* import—namely, as the incidental effect of organisms struggling for their own benefit, expressed as reproductive success. Could any argument be more subversive? One accepts the conventional observation, but then offers an explanation that *not only inverts* orthodoxy, but seems to mock the standard interpretation in a manner that could almost be called cruel. This more radical version lies at the core of Darwin's argument for natural selection.[21]

Perverse indeed. In sum, evolutionary theory teaches that nature's beauty and complexity arise from the incidental byproducts of a cruel, self-oriented, death-filled world where every creature acts out its own ultimately purposeless existence instead of from God's engineering genius, wisdom, and kindness.

## Result 4: All Hail Nature

Selectionism is how Darwin reintroduced veneration of nature into science.[22] Leading science journals even give credibility to Gaia—an unabashed personification of nature.[23] Talbott noted above that evolutionists are trapped in a selectionist perspective. Thus, if they were to shift faith from Gaia, its replacement would still require nature to create itself.

Romans 1:25 teaches that those who fail to credit the creation to the Creator have "exchanged the truth of God for the lie (or 'exchanged the true God for the false god')." The false god is viewing nature as self-creative, and now we see how the false agency ascribed to nature through the concept of natural selection facilitates the way. Some evolutionists further imagine Earth, moon, stars, galaxies, etc. like a massive organism, "acted on" by "cosmic natural selection."[24] This would mean that "the universe could be further understood as a self-coherent and self-creating whole, without the need for anything outside itself to give it law, meaning or complexity."[25]

The Bible can read human behavior perfectly, even atheists like Carl Sagan who add "adoration and reverential service" to nature, saying:

> A religion old or new, that stressed the magnificence of the universe as revealed by modern science, might be able to draw forth reserves of reverence and awe hardly tapped by the conventional faiths. Sooner or later such a religion will emerge.[26]

## How to Restore Biology

Getting our theory right matters more than answering every latest evolutionary claim. It is time to restore credit to our Creator for crafting creatures that can navigate an ever-changing world over multiple generations. We therefore propose a design-based, organism-focused model called *continuous environmental tracking*. It centers on innate capabilities of organisms to actively track environmental changes.

Evidence for this model comes from so many purposefully engineered systems in creatures. These systems produce highly regulated responses to specific challenges, like cave fish that quickly swap chemical and touch senses for eyesight, and mice that pass fear of a smell down several generations. Even the evolutionary biologists who encounter these features call them predictable—that's not random.

So, did Darwin explain how nature can explain biological design without the need for a real intelligent agent? Not at all. He slipped an alternative pseudo-agency into the operation of nature. He cleverly cloaked the agency within an analogy. Few people spot the illegitimacy of analogy for a real person.

But atheistic evolutionist Jerry Fodor and his coauthor, bothered by Darwin's duplicity, pulled back the curtain when they wrote:

> Familiar claims to the contrary notwithstanding, Darwin didn't manage to get mental causes out of his account of how evolution works. He just hid them in the unexamined analogy between selection by breeding and natural selection.[27]

Darwin's pseudo-agent, natural selection, opens the door to wholesale personification of nature as acting in God's stead. In contrast, whoever acknowledges adaptation inside creatures finds new ways to honor the Lord Jesus Christ as life's incredible Engineer.

**Notes**

1. Gould, S. J. 2002. *The Structure of Evolutionary Theory*. Cambridge, MA: Belknap Press of Harvard University Press, 116. November 1859 letter in F. Darwin, 1887, volume 2, 219.

2. Ibid, 119. Emphasis added.

3. Ibid, 161-162.

4. Gould, S. J. 1977. Eternal metaphors of palaeontology. In *Patterns of evolution as illustrated by the fossil record*. A. Hallam, ed. Amsterdam: Elsevier, 2-3. Emphasis in original.

5. Lewontin, R. C. 1983. Gene, Organism, and Environment. In *Evolution from Molecules to Man*. D. S. Bendall, ed. Cambridge: Cambridge University Press, 273-274.

6. Pearce, T. 2014. The Origins and Development of the Idea of Organism-Environment Interaction. In *Entangled Life: History, Philosophy and Theory of the Life Sciences*. G. Barker et al, eds. Netherlands: Springer, p.13.

7. Medina, M. L. 2011. Reply to the Comments on "Natural Selection and Self-Organization: A Deep Dichotomy in the Study of Organic Form. *Ludus Vitalis*. 19 (36): 387.

8. Denton, M. J. 2013. The Types: A Persistent Structuralist Challenge to Darwinian Pan-Selectionism. *BIO-Complexity*. (3): 1-2.

9. Gould, *The Structure of Evolutionary Theory*, 251.

10. Hodge, M. J. S. 1992. Natural Selection: Historical Perspectives. *Keywords in Evolutionary Biology*. Cambridge, MA: Harvard University Press, 213.

11. Dembski, W. A. 2004. *The Design Revolution*. Downers Grove: Intervarsity Press, 263. Emphasis in original.

12. Reid, R. G. B. 2007. *Biological Emergences: Evolution by Natural Experiment*. Cambridge: MIT Press, 393.

13. Talbott, S. L. Can Darwinian Evolutionary Theory Be Taken Seriously? Posted on natureinstitute.org May 17, 2016, accessed September 14, 2018.

14. Talbott, S. L. 2019. Let's Not Begin With Natural Selection. Posted on natureinstitute.org July 19, 2019, accessed November 7, 2019. Emphasis added.

15. Lieberman, D. and B. Hall. 2007. The evolutionary developmental biology of tinkering: an introduction to the challenge. In *Tinkering: The Microevolution of Development*. G. Bock and J. Goode, eds. Chichester, UK: John Wiley & Sons Ltd., 4.

16. Jacob, F. 1977. Evolution and tinkering. *Science*. 196: 1161-1166.

17. Kirschner, M. and J. Gerhart. 2005. *The Plausibility of Life*. New Haven: Yale University Press, 3, 31. Emphasis added.

18. Medina, Reply to the Comments on "Natural Selection and Self-Organization," 389, quoting Lenoir, T. 1987. The eternal laws of form: morphotypes and the conditions of existence in Goethe's biological thought. In *Goethe and the Sciences: A Re-Appraisal*. F. Amrine, F. Zucker, and H. Wheeler, eds. Dordrecht: Reidel, 27.

19. Gould, S. J. 1977. Eternal metaphors of palaeontology. In *Patterns of evolution as illustrated by the fossil record*. A. Hallam, ed. Amsterdam: Elsevier, 21-22.

20. Gould, S. J. 2002. *The Structure of Evolutionary Theory*. Cambridge, MA: Belknap Press of Harvard University Press, 116. November 1859 letter in F. Darwin, 1887, volume 2, 117. Emphasis added.

21. Gould, S. J. 2002. *The Structure of Evolutionary Theory*. Cambridge, MA: Belknap Press of Harvard University Press, 116. November 1859 letter in F. Darwin, 1887, volume 2, 120-121. Emphasis added.

22. Guliuzza, R. J. 2011. Darwin's Sacred Imposter: Natural Selection's Idolatrous Trap. *Acts & Facts*. 40 (11): 12-15.

23. Guliuzza, R. J. 2020. Gaia and Selectionism's Nature Worship. *Acts & Facts*. 49 (2): 17-19.

24. Smolin, L. 2004. Cosmological natural selection as the explanation for the complexity of the universe.

*Physica A.* 340: 705-713.

25. Rifkin, L. The Logic and Beauty of Cosmological Natural Selection. Posted on blogs.scientificamerican. com June 10, 2014 accessed December 1, 2019.

26. Sagan, C. and A. Druyan. 1994. *Pale Blue Dot: A Vision of the Human Future in Space.* New York: Ballantine Books, p. 50.

27. Fodor, J. and M. Piattelli-Palmarini. 2010. *What Darwin Got Wrong.* New York: Farrar, Straus and Giroux, 162.

# 17
# IS THE EVOLUTIONARY TREE OF LIFE REAL?

Brian Thomas, Ph.D., Jeffrey P. Tomkins, Ph.D., and Frank Sherwin, M.A.

**Summary:** Darwin's tree of life depicts life emerging from a single-cell creature and developing into more complex kinds over millions of years. There are both biblical and scientific problems with this concept.

Recent research has shown the evolutionary tree of life to be erroneous—creatures don't fit neatly into places on the tree. Evolutionists need to force the data to make the tree appear to work. And different trees are produced depending on what criteria are used.

The fact that it has been impossible to objectively establish evolutionary relationships among living organisms reflects an underlying reality: Evolution never occurred. The observed scientific data agree with the biblical record that creatures were created as distinct kinds around 6,000 years ago.

Evolution is often depicted in a tree-like structure with single-cell organisms at the bottom and more complex forms of life progressively emerging as the tree branches upward. The individual branches represent lineages and new lines of evolution that terminate with either living organisms or organisms that are now extinct (Figure 1). This tree represents the supposed evolution of increasingly complex organisms during millions and billions of years of "deep time."

Evolutionary trees were first popularized by Charles Darwin, who drew a picture of one in 1837 in what is known as his B notebook, along with the comment "I think" (see Figure 2). This drawing visually depicted his idea that all of today's species arose from a single common ancestor. Darwin's thinking lies at the heart of evolutionary dogma, and his fictional tree-like images have since been embellished, making them effective indoctrination tools.

There are both biblical and scientific problems with this concept. If today's creatures (as well as those that are now extinct) evolved from other creatures millions or billions of years ago, then the biblical account in Genesis must be abandoned. Scripture indicates that the creation of all the "kinds" of biological life occurred in the latter days of the creation week. Thus, millions of years were *not* involved in their creation. The Bible does not support the concept of vertical Darwinian "descent with modification" with one kind changing into another.

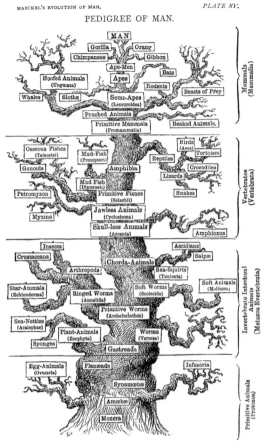

Figure 1. A graphical illustration of an evolutionary tree showing what is often called macroevolution, or vertical evolution.

Interestingly, many scientific discoveries since the time of Darwin now fully support and confirm the biblical concepts outlined in Genesis. These discoveries have been bad news for both evolutionary trees and evolutionary theory in general. Attempts to mathematically build evolutionary trees (also known as phylogenetic trees) have resulted in many inconsistencies that cast doubt on the Darwinian paradigm. An article in *New Scientist* magazine titled "Why Darwin Was Wrong About the Tree of Life" reflected this frustration among evolutionists.[1]

## Molecular vs. Morphological Trees

Traditional phylogenetic trees show the relatedness of organisms to possible ancestors based on data measurements taken from morphology. Morphology refers to observable physical traits that can be measured, like brain size, skull shape, or arm length. Measurements of such features are taken from multiple organisms. Scientists use a computer algorithm to compare similarities between these measurements, then position each organism in an evolutionary hierarchy. The result is then graphically represented by a tree diagram, similar to Darwin's original concept.

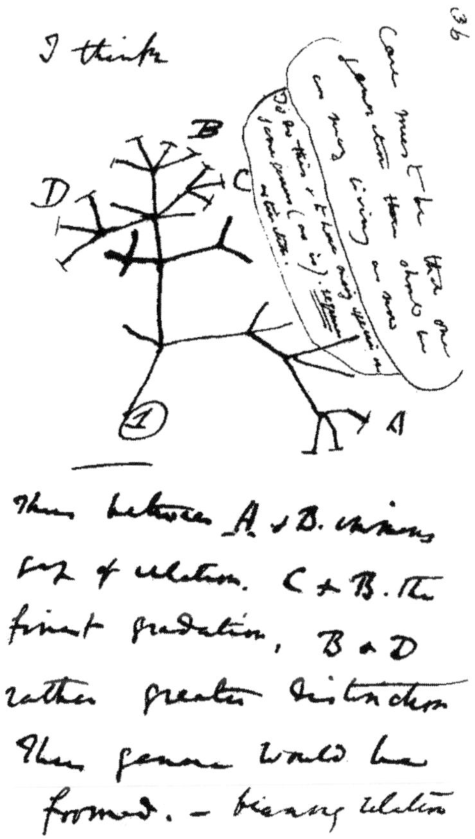

Several serious problems immediately became apparent with this type of evolutionary analysis. First, evolutionists quickly realized that the phylogenetic trees they obtained depended upon the trait being measured, and that these trees often contradicted the expected evolutionary lineage.

For example, no evolutionist suggests that octopi are closely related to mammals, and yet both have

Figure 2. Charles Darwin's first graphical representation of vertical evolution.

very similar eyeball structure and function. Did mammals inherit octopus eyes but not their tentacles? A phylogenetic tree based only on eyes would place mammals and octopi on very close branches. But another analysis based on body structure, counting the fact that octopi have no skeleton, would place them on opposite sides of the tree!

## Contradictory Trees from DNA and Proteins

In an attempt to settle the issue of conflicting phylogenetic trees, evolutionists began using protein and DNA sequences instead of morphological data. Researchers had hoped that digital comparisons of protein or DNA sequences would result in the construction of authoritative phylogenetic trees that would finally show consistent evolutionary patterns among the categories of life. However, these new techniques only solidified the problem of discordant trees.

Study after study has revealed even more problems with the evolutionary lineages derived from molecular data than with lineages derived from morphological data.[2,3] Furthermore, lineages based upon biological sequence data often contradict lineages based upon morphological data.[4] In these studies, evolutionists will select sequences that lend themselves to evolutionary interpretations and reject sequences that have no apparent evolutionary explanation. However, even this technique still produces discordant phylogenetic trees.

For example, in one study on human evolution, a large pool of human, chimp, orangutan, rhesus, and gorilla DNA sequences were fitted into an evolutionary tree format.[5] The original pool of DNA sequences went through several levels of selection for optimal DNA comparisons. First, a set of 30,112 sequences that shared similarity between humans and all the apes were selected. Dissimilar sequences were ignored. These hand-picked sequences were further evaluated for their evolutionary utility. Only those that produced ≥300 base alignments were retained for another series of alignments, and only the sequences that produced superior statistical probabilities (> 95%) were used in the final analysis. This filtering process removed over 22% of predetermined highly similar DNA sequence. Despite this DNA cherry-picking designed to produce the most favorable evolutionary trees, the results did not show any clear evolutionary connection between humans and chimps (or with any of the other apes). Instead, the data showed a mosaic of unique human and ape DNA sequences. Perhaps the most revealing features of the research are found in the author's own words:

> For about 23% of our genome, we share no immediate genetic ancestry with our closest living relative, the chimpanzee....Thus, in two-thirds of the cases a genealogy results in which humans and chimpanzees are *not* each other's closest genetic relatives. The corresponding genealogies are incongruent with the species tree. In accordance with the experimental evidences, this implies that there is no such thing as a unique evolutionary history of the human genome. Rather, it resembles a patchwork of individual regions following their own genealogy.[5]

The authors added that the lack of support for a consistent and clear evolutionary relationship between humans and apes is due to the "inclusion of alignments with no clear phylogenetic signal."[5] This is a remarkable admission, given that the researchers did a great deal of data filtering and cherry-picking in an attempt to show a relationship between humans and apes. However, even with this biased selection of the data, they could find no clear evidence of such a relationship!

Indeed, the situation is prevalent across the spectrum of life. British evolutionist Michael Benton said, "Relationships among living and extinct sarcopterygians [Sarcopterygii include all tetrapods], and their relationships to early osteichthyans have been controversial"[6] and that "relationships between coelacanths, lungfishes, and tetrapods are debated. It has been surprisingly difficult to resolve the three-clade problem within Sarcopterygii."[7]

Evolutionary biologists Andrea Feller and S. Blair Hedges compared the DNA sequences of four mitochondrial genes and found a sister-group relationship of salamanders and caecilians, with frogs as the outgroup.[8] This contradicts the pairing of frogs and salamanders based on their similarly amphibian life cycles. Benton states, "The position of Testudines (turtles) is debated, but here we show the assumed consensus view from current molecular analyses."[9] But "assumed consensus view" is hardly scientific. The same problems popped up when cartilaginous fish were investigated: "Assignment of the fossil clades [chondrichthyans] is more contentious."[10] When it comes to the neoselachii (modern sharks), "Their early history is hard to track."[11] Sharks have always been sharks.

Examples of this widespread disharmony continuously emerge across all forms of animal life examined. Nor is this issue restricted to the animal kingdom: "Only rarely have phylogenetic studies of morphology and DNA data agreed in plant studies, even in well-studied groups."[12]

In the 21st century, the subtle undercurrent of confusion still persists in the eukaryote tree of life.

> Integrating the results of phylogenomic analyses and the main lineages added over the past 15 years, the current consensus tree has been shuffled to the extent that most of the original supergroups have either been subsumed into new taxa or disappeared altogether.[13]

The authors appeal to the unscientific idea of consensus to make their questionable case for the eukaryotic tree of life. But as evolutionist Alan Feduccia said, "There is no such thing as consensus science. If it's consensus, it isn't science. If it's science, it isn't consensus. Period."[14]

## No Detected Evolutionary Relationship—the Implications

Evolutionary trees typically contradict one another. Examples are plentiful, and many more could be shown. The best explanation for this observed discordance is that the data do not fit evolutionary origins. Evolutionists must force the data—whether they are physical traits or molecular sequence differences—into their preconception and then make excuses for why it produces so many problems.

This widespread embarrassment is still not widely acknowledged outside the secular scientific community. General biology texts still typically depict outdated and mythical evolutionary trees with smooth progressions of creatures evolving into "higher" forms. Of course, these fictional depictions completely ignore the rampant disagreement found at every level in the technical literature. Perhaps this is because many scientists are unwilling to face the glaring implications of all these studies. They know they must find support for vertical Darwinian evolution to justify their denial of a Creator and His Word. The total lack of support for vertical evolution from actual creatures also refutes the erroneous idea that God used evolution as a means of "creation."

The fact that it has been impossible to objectively establish evolutionary relationships between so many creatures reflects an underlying reality: Evolution never occurred. Darwin's tree of life and the generations of more and more intricate versions of phylogenetic trees published over the past 150+ years are merely man-made fictional illustrations of a long macroevolutionary past that never really happened.

Like junk DNA and vestigial organs, Darwin's tree of life was a roadblock, misleading students and scientists for over a century. Is it any wonder that evolutionist Michael Rose stated, "The tree of life is being politely buried—we all know that."[15] Instead, the science confirms what God's Word says. The progenitors of today's living creatures were created as distinct kinds around 6,000 years ago according to the biblical record—in strong agreement with the observed scientific data.

**Notes**

1. Lawton, G. 2009. Why Darwin Was Wrong About the Tree of Life. *New Scientist.* 2692: 34-39.

2. Degnan, J. H. and N. A. Rosenberg. 2009. Gene Tree Discordance, Phylogenetic Inference and the Multispecies Coalescent. *Trends In Ecology & Evolution.* 24: 332-340.

3. Dolgin, E. 2012. Phylogeny: Rewriting Evolution. *Nature.* 486 (7404): 460-462.

4. Patterson, C., D. M. Williams, and C. J. Humphries. 1993. Congruence Between Molecular and Morphological Phylogenies. *Annual Review of Ecology and Systematics.* 24: 153-188.

5. Ebersberger, I. et al. 2007. Mapping human genetic ancestry. *Molecular Biology and Evolution.* 24 (10): 2266-2276. Emphasis added.

6. Benton, M. J. 2015. *Vertebrate Paleontology.* Malden, MA: Blackwell Publishing, 71.

7. Ibid, 73.

8. Feller, A. E. and S. B. Hedges. 1998. Molecular evidence for the early history of living amphibians. *Molecular Phylogenetics and Evolution.* 9 (3): 509-516.

9. Benton, *Vertebrate Paleontology*, 150.

10. Ibid, 178.

11. Ibid, 179.

12. Frohlch, M. W and M. W. Chase. 2007. After a dozen years of progress the origin of angiosperms is still a great mystery. *Nature.* 450 (7173): 1184-1190.

13. Burki, F. et al. 2020. The New Tree of Eukaryotes. *Trends in Ecology & Evolution.* 35 (1): 43-55.

14. Feduccia, A. 2012. *Riddle of the Feathered Dragons Hidden Birds of China.* New Haven, CT: Yale University Press, 5.

15. Lawton, Why Darwin Was Wrong About the Tree of Life.

# 18

# DOES BIOLOGICAL SIMILARITY PROVE EVOLUTIONARY ANCESTRY?

Randy J. Guliuzza, P.E., M.D.

**Summary:** Darwinian evolution claims all living things came from a universal common ancestor, and evolutionists offer similar creature features as proof. But common design is a better scientific explanation for these similar features.

Claiming that different creatures—over long periods of evolutionary time—somehow converged to develop similar intricate features while also diverging into wider varieties of creatures amounts to speculation.

The missing links between kinds that would help demonstrate evolution aren't found in the fossil record. Instead, we see similar body plans and stasis throughout the record, with some matching living creatures. The Genesis narrative describes God creating a wide variety of living forms instantly during the creation week, and the abrupt appearance of fully formed creature kinds throughout the fossil record supports this position.

A common designer, not a common ancestor, is the best explanation for similar features.

Children tend to look like their parents. They definitely share similar DNA sequences. Without a doubt, humans, chimpanzees, and other organisms share some similar features, like hair, heads, and humeri. So, can similar looks or DNA sequences establish relatedness? If different causes equally account for similar features, then looks alone can be deceiving.

Nature-only advocates insist that all organisms today descended from the same single ancestor. We call this concept "universal common ancestry." This

Darwinian tale tells of creatures slowly changing from one basic kind to another through their struggles to survive ever-changing conditions over eons. This supposedly produced the diversity of life on Earth. Naturalists see similar features on different creatures as remnants from evolutionary history. For example, many very different mammals have the same number of finger bones. Surely they all inherited that number from the first mammal ancestor, right? This makes one of the most popular arguments for evolution.

A take-home message from this is that evolution is a theory about how transformation happens where similarities are evidence. It is not a theory about similarities as evidence showing that transformation happens.

Logically, however, creatures might share similar features for reasons other than ancestry. Perhaps they reflect similar designs that serve similar purposes. This common design (as opposed to common ancestry) inference makes good sense in light of the way that parts fit and work together in human-designed systems. Man-made machines were definitely designed, and they share the same design features as creatures' features.

For example, a heart that pumps blood corresponds to the size, shape, and strength found in human-made fluid pumps. Also, where does one see that the random coursings of nature craft exquisite details into working machines? Nature does not craft cardiovascular systems today (nor does it take the first baby step toward that, but it does break systems down), so it probably didn't make them in the past. People open to God have long acknowledged that common design makes good sense.

Evolution's nature-only dogma constrains the way researchers think about biology. Each naturalistic idea in turn reinforces the dogma. This amounts to circular thinking, not science. Thus, it is important to understand how naturalists think.

## The Circularity of Homology

Before Charles Darwin, common attributes among different types of, say, fish or birds helped early scientists classify living things. Darwin and his followers later layered the common descent concept across these common attributes as though evolution is the only way to account for them. For them, this is an axiom—an obvious truth—that needs no experiment to confirm it. Darwin's explanation sounded just as dogmatic as his followers do today. He wrote in 1859:

The similar framework of bones in the hand of a man, wing of a bat, fin of the porpoise, and leg of the horse...and innumerable other such facts, at once explain themselves on the theory of descent with slow and slight successive modification.[1]

Not long ago, evolutionary authority Stephen Jay Gould similarly wrote, "Why should a rat run, a bat fly, a porpoise swim, and I type this essay with structures built of the same bones unless we all inherited them from a common ancestor?"[2] To them, common ancestry explains common attributes, and common attributes show common ancestry. They argue in a circle to self-certify their ideas.

This circular argument has even advanced to the point of definition. Evolutionary biologist Michael Donohue wrote, "Although ancestry was at first viewed only as an explanation for homology [similar features], it soon was incorporated into the definition."[3] These ideas all ignore the logical possibility for another way—for example, common design—to explain similar features.

## Making Inferences into Facts

An evolutionist searching her genealogical record could discover that she's related to George Washington. She could also believe that she is closely related to chimpanzees. "Related" needs to be defined for each conversation.

Records verify fact-based relationships. For example, a line of connected birth certificates can tie one back to George Washington. What about comparing similar features or DNA? Uncertainty enters without Washington's own DNA. Thus, the best one can do with DNA is to infer a probability of relatedness. It will range high to zero. Yet, evolutionists claim that 99% of Earth's species are extinct, so how can they verify their inference of universal common ancestry? They also tend to leave behind common design. Without common design, common ancestry starts to look like a fact.

## Flies in the Common Ancestry Ointment

"Inconsistent" describes how evolutionists treat similar features in their ever-changing branching family tree diagrams. Workers can always fit similar features into different supposed relationships. It all depends on which feature, protein, or gene the investigator chooses to emphasize and the order of evolution he or she imagines for each chosen element. The options are endless. Speculation runs rampant and passes as science.

How do you explain why organisms with essentially no common ancestry have extraordinarily similar features? For example, both squids and humans have camera-like eye designs. The evolutionist who believes that similar features arose from a common ancestor must now make an exception to their *divergent evolution* rule. The new story invokes the opposite, called *convergent evolution*. In fact, many very different creatures possess eyes made up of similar parts. Naturalists must claim that similar environments constrained these various creatures to "converge" on comparable complex features. In the case of camera eyes, they had to have evolved independently at least 40, and more probably 65, times.[4]

Meanwhile, nobody has seen natural processes even begin to make even a component of these kinds of eyes. A creation perspective explains all these data. If a wise Creator was the common designer of all these creatures, then no wonder they all share similar eye types. (And no wonder each of their eye systems comes fully formed and functional, fully integrated into each very different body form.)

Students of evolution should recognize these counterintuitive claims as red flags. Millions of years of genetic tinkering supposedly propel organisms to *diverge* into increasingly different classes, while simultaneously cobbling their traits to *converge* upon the same solution to problems. Convergent evolution is not a scientific observation. It is a bare declaration based on an assumed evolutionary past.

What about the opposite cases? Organisms presumed to be very closely related have stark differences. For example, humans have a muscle to move their thumb's tip that chimpanzees don't have. Naturalists skip these details. Clearly, explanations for the presence or absence of similar features can be totally arbitrary.

Whales illustrate the situation. Evolutionists assert that the whale body shape evolved from land mammals that slowly readapted to life at sea. Consider how authors in the leading journal *Science* selected between conflicting features, whether molecules or body parts (called *morphology*), to support their theory:

> Despite this evidence that cetaceans [whales] evolved from artiodactyls [even-toed mammals like deer, sheep, pigs], substantial discrepancies remain. If cetaceans belong to artiodactyls, then similarities in the cranial and dental morphologies of mesony-

chians [extinct carnivorous mammals] and cetaceans must be a result of convergent evolution or must have been lost in artiodactyls. Furthermore, molecular data favor a sister-group relationship between whales and hippopotami. This conflicts with the conventional view based on morphology that hippopotami are closer to other artiodactyls than they are to whales.[5]

Common design easily accounts for these features that confound common descent. Now consider a report that tries to explain the origins of similar echolocation genes in both bats and whales:

> The discovery represents an unprecedented example of adaptive sequence convergence between two highly divergent groups… It is generally assumed that most of these so-called convergent traits have arisen by different genes or different mutations. Our study shows that a complex trait—echolocation—has in fact evolved by identical genetic changes in bats and dolphins…. If you draw a phylogenetic [relationship] tree of bats, whales, and a few other mammals based on similarities in the prestin [a hearing gene] sequence alone, the echolocating bats and whales come out together rather than with their rightful evolutionary cousins….We were surprised by…the sheer number of convergent changes in the coding DNA.[6]

So, are deer, sheep, pigs, extinct wolf-like animals, hippopotami, or bats the bona fide relations to whales? Conflicting similarities in body parts, fossils, and genes leave common descent in the dust.

"Divergence," "convergence," "character reversals," "vestiges," "rudiments," "independent losses," "one-time gains," "parallel derivatives," and other jargon reveal the subjectivity of evolutionary speculations. Fossil comparisons based on similar features suffer from the same trap of circular reasoning. Gene sequence comparisons suffer from the same prejudices, inconsistencies, and excuses. These labels reveal how plastic evolutionary theory is. It can absorb any observation—even ones that are totally contradictory—in the minds of its defenders.

## The Mystery of Similar Features in Different Fossils

Trying to explain similar features between fossil specimens can suffer from the same biases that taint explanations for living creatures. But fossils present unique challenges. They must answer these four basic observations:

1. **Diversity**. How can each creature kind show such diverse features, and how can so many different basic kinds show similar features between kinds?

2. **Stasis**. Why do fossil forms retain their same body plan throughout the fossil record and in many cases up to their *living* counterparts?[7]

3. **Abrupt appearance**. A fossil kind just shows up fully formed. Why do evolutionary experts disagree over the status of all proposed evolutionary ancestors?

4. **Discontinuity**. Organisms fit *only one* phylum, class, and order. Why don't most fossils show a continuous connection between creature kinds instead of discrete (discontinuous) kinds?[8]

## Common Design Works

Biblical creation relieves these evolution-inspired strains. According to Scripture, "for in six days the LORD made the heavens and the earth, the sea, and all that is in them, and rested the seventh day" (Exodus 20:11). If "the LORD made," then He deserves credit, not natural processes. Nature describes the way things are, not necessarily the way they came to be. And who has seen nature design new organisms, body systems, organs, or their required gene networks from scratch? All this means that we no longer need to fit all creatures onto a big family tree.

Dogs represent a separately created kind from macaws. Why do both share camera eyes, hearts, and bones, while completely different eggs, hair, feathers, and streamlined bodies? A common designer between the two—whom the Bible identifies as God—accounts for these similarities and differences. But mysteries remain. For example, dogs come in a wide range of sizes, shapes, and colors. Most of them can interbreed, but none of them are compatible with a macaw. So many dog varieties descended from the few that survived the Flood in Noah's care. A creation model of ancestry accounts for this ancestor-descendant relationship.

The illustration conveys a general model of creature ancestry through Earth history. It shows time progressing from creation at the bottom up until today. As creatures multiply and fill the earth's ever-changing habitats, they can deploy discrete trait variations. Sometimes they go extinct. Fossils show that most marine creatures went extinct during Noah's Flood. But even many land creatures went extinct, especially because of Ice Age climate change after the Flood. This scriptural basis avoids evolutionary confusion, accounts for the designed variations within each kind, provides a common designer to explain similar features on very different creatures, and accommodates the stasis or stable body forms seen in both fossil and living animals.

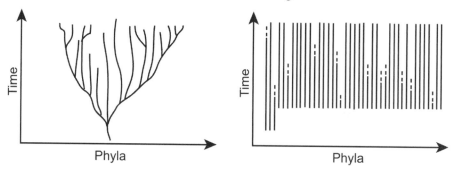

## Conclusion

Evolutionists assert that similar features prove evolutionary relationships. By assuming the truth of a claim that they should be proving, evolutionists end up in this inescapable tangle of circular thinking: Common ancestry caused similar features, and similar features are the best evidence for common ancestry. Darwin disregarded this circularity, just as his followers do today. And circular reasoning is a poor substitute for science.

Similar features between different creatures may fuel the best arguments for evolution, but they turn out to be big problems for that view. Nobody can point to a tidy thread of traits that track from a particular common ancestor down all the paths to its supposed descendants. This forces evolutionary biologists to choose which traits to show or to excuse.

In truth, creatures share some traits with other creatures, whether or not they may look related. Comparing organisms' traits actually shows patchwork similarity. That is why humans have some traits that are similar to chimpanzees but other traits just as—or more—similar to orangutans, gibbons, guinea pigs, other animals, and even plants.

If all organisms had completely different features, there might not be any discussion of them being related by common descent. However, evolutionists have effectively sold the idea that when people see similarities they can actually "see" remnants of their common ancestry. Seeing something carries emotional links. So, persuading an evolutionist, who feels deep down inside that all life is somehow connected, to replace their inference-based account of similarities with a design-based explanation is challenging.

Similar looks and features can be very deceiving. A common designer—not a common ancestor—is the best explanation.

*Notes*

1. Darwin, C. 1872. *The Origin of Species by Means of Natural Selection*, 6th ed. London: John Murray, 420. Emphasis added.

2. Gould, S. J. 1994. Evolution as Fact and Theory. *Hen's Teeth and Horse's Toes*. New York: W. W. Norton & Company, 253-262.

3. Donoghue, M. 1992. Homology. *Keywords in Evolutionary Biology*. E. F. Keller and E. A. Lloyd, eds. Cambridge, MA: Harvard University Press, 171.

4. Land, M. and R. Fernald. 1992. The Evolution of Eyes. *Annual Review Neuroscience*. 15:1-2, referencing Salvini-Plawen, L. and E. Mayr. 1977. On the evolution of photoreceptors and eyes. *Evolutionary Biology*. 10: 207-53.

5. Rose, K. 2001. Evolution: The ancestry of whales. *Science*. 293 (5538): 2216-2217.

6. In bats and whales, convergence in echolocation ability runs deep. Cell Press via *ScienceDaily*. Posted on sciencedaily.com January 27, 2010, accessed January 2020.

7. See Werner, C. 2008. *Evolution: The Grand Experiment. Living Fossils*, vol 2. Green Forest, AR: New Leaf Publishing Group.

8. Guliuzza, R. 2010. Similar Features Show Design, Not Universal Common Descent. *Acts and Facts*. 39 (10): 10-11.

# 19

# COMMON DESCENT VS. COMMON DESIGN: HEAD-TO-HEAD

Brian Thomas, PhD., and Randy J. Guliuzza, P.E., M.D.

**Summary:** Evolutionists long assumed that random changes over millions of years would have altered or obliterated genetic similarities that different creatures inherited from a common ancestor. But empirical research has shown there is common genetic information within diverse organisms, and this points to a common Designer who engineered all living things in the beginning.

Contrary to Darwinian predictions, this common genetic information underlies and explains similar physical structures that perform common functions found in creatures as diverse as fruit flies and mammals. Creatures appear engineered in all aspects because they are. Evolutionists' predictions have failed as genetics knowledge has advanced, and this should drive life science research from a design-based approach rather than an evolutionary one.

Evolutionists hypothesize that all organisms today share a universal common ancestor. They perceive the similar features between organisms as indicating actual descendants with modifications. Many people take this as the most persuasive evidence for Darwin's hypothesis. Others who believe that organisms look engineered because they were designed by God recognize that although common ancestry can account for some similar features, a real Designer would employ similar designs to serve similar purposes—especially for very diverse creatures.

There is solid evidence for the existence of underlying common information in diverse organisms. This design-based concept better explains the similar features that perform similar functions in sometimes very different creatures. The data have been available for decades, but it just needed to be framed with an engineering mindset. In fact, the history behind these data provides a fascinating story of successful and failed predictions for creationists and evolutionists. Read on to better evaluate each theory of life's diversity.

## Design-Based Predictions: Common Central Design—Unique Details

We know that similarity extends past body parts to genetics. Decades in advance of the current genetic analysis techniques, creationists and evolutionists published expectations based on either supernatural design or natural evolution. One test of the accuracy of a scientific model is its ability to make accurate predictions of results from future research. What did each group predict before the light of new genetic information?

In 1975, prior to detailed genetic analysis, creation scientist Dr. Henry Morris asserted common underlying design patterns would explain similar structure. He said:

> The creative process would have designed similar structures for similar functions and different structures for different functions...
> In the creation model, the same similarities are predicted on the basis of a common purposive designer.[1]

Creation-based thinkers knew that organisms, per their kind, must have traits to thrive on the same planet but occupy diverse niches. They therefore sought design-based explanations with: (1) similar features to fulfill similar purposes based on similar information, and (2) extreme multistep specified regulation over thousands of details to alter certain organisms' traits while retaining their similar overall plans.

## Evolution-Based Predictions: Initially Not Common Ancestry

Prominent evolutionists rejected basic common designs, but their rationales differed among them. Darwin, for theological reasons, doubted "that it has pleased the Creator to construct all the animals and plants in each great class on a uniform plan" and derided the concept of underlying common information as "not a scientific explanation."[2]

Regarding genetics, Henry Morris' 1975 prediction can be compared to an evolutionary prediction in 1963 by Dr. Ernst Mayr, who was Harvard's leading evolutionary theorist. He predicted that looking for similar DNA between very diverse organisms would be pointless. He believed that random genetic changes over millions of years obliterated genetic similarities.

> Much that has been learned about gene physiology makes it evi-
> dent that the search for homologous genes [similar codes due to
> common ancestry] is quite futile except in very close relatives.
> If there is only one efficient solution for a certain functional de-
> mand, very different gene complexes will come up with the same
> solution, no matter how different the pathway by which it is
> achieved. The saying "Many roads lead to Rome" is as true in
> evolution as in daily affairs.[3]

Unfortunately for Mayr, geneticists routinely discover similar genes in organisms whose ancestors supposedly diverged eons ago. This failed prediction
forced evolutionary theoreticians back to the drawing board. They cooked up
a new twist called *convergent evolution*. It refers to natural evolution accidentally crafting the same genes or traits in very different creatures. It boils down
to an entirely circular argument where the only reason to conclude convergent
evolution is because of the assumption of evolution in the first place. As an
example, evolutionists rejected common underlying information in diverse
creatures for eye formation and claim that eyes evolved independently at least
40 times.[4]

Creationists remained skeptical that highly complex structures "evolve independently" over and over again. Instead, they maintained their expectation
of finding a link between similar features to similar genetics.

## Evolutionary Predictions Were Spectacularly Wrong

The reality of a common genetic basis for similar structures across diverse
organisms was confirmed in landmark discoveries between 1978 and 1984.[5-8]
For example, one class of genes with regulatory and developmental functions
responsible for core design patterns in developing embryos is called *Hox* genes.
The name is a contraction of the longer descriptive words *homeotic* and *homeo-
box*. Similar *Hox* genes perform similar tasks in fruit flies and mammals.

This astounding finding so opposed the evolutionists' notions that it con-
stituted a spectacular blunder. Evolutionary developmental biologist Sean
Carroll describes the implications of the stunning details. He wrote in a 2005
book *Endless Forms Most Beautiful*:

> When the sequence of these homeoboxes were examined in de-
> tail, the similarities among species were astounding. Over the 60

amino acids of the homeodomain, some mice and frog proteins were identical to the fly sequences at up to 59 out of 60 positions. Such sequence similarity was just stunning. The evolutionary lines that led to flies and mice diverged more than 500 million years ago, before the famous Cambrian Explosion that gave rise to most animal types. No biologist had even the foggiest notion that such similarities could exist between genes of such different animals. The *Hox* genes were so important that their sequences had been preserved throughout this enormous span of animal evolution.[9]

Why can't a common Designer explain the origin of these critical *Hox* genes common to so many different creatures? Carroll also wrote:

The discovery that the same sets of genes control the formation and pattern of body regions and body parts with similar functions (but very different designs) in insects, vertebrates, and other animals has forced a complete rethinking of animal history, the origins of structures, and the nature of diversity. Comparative and evolutionary biologists had long assumed that different groups of animals, separated by vast amounts of evolutionary time, were constructed and had evolved by entirely different means.[10]

And they were wrong. Yet, evolutionists remain closed to a common designer. They somehow feel little need to concede they were greatly mistaken. Instead they just feel "stunned" at the appearance of, guess what…new, unexpected evidence for evolving *Hox* genes.

Yet, the only "evidence" that *Hox* genes can be "preserved throughout this enormous span of animal evolution" is the belief that life evolved from a common ancestor. All of the stories about convergence get promptly scrapped. Firmly held prior accounts like convergent evolution are run through the magic tunnel of evolutionary belief, and, *voila*, *Hox* genes instantly turn into "preserved" ancient DNA, which is now used—with equivalent certainty—as evidence of common ancestry.

## Design-Based Expectations Confirmed

It is now factually confirmed that similar genetic regulatory information is common to many classes of organisms and aids in helping achieve similar function. Many have remarkably similar designs. Carroll again relates the confounding weight of this finding:

It was inescapable. Clusters of *Hox* genes shaped the development of animals as different as flies and mice, and now we know that includes just about every animal in the kingdom, including humans and elephants. Not even the most ardent advocate of fruit fly research predicted the universal distribution and importance of *Hox* genes. The implications were stunning. Disparate animals were built using not just the same kinds of tools, but indeed, the very same genes![11]

What about the teaching of 40 independent evolutionary events of eyes? That manifested into another incredible evolutionary blunder and validation of creationists' design-based expectations. As Carroll candidly continues, "Natural selection has not forged many eyes completely from scratch; there is a common genetic ingredient to making each eye type, as well as to the many types of appendages, hearts, etc."[12] Common genetic ingredients suggest a common genetic engineer.

## Is Common Design More Plausible than Common Ancestry?

*Hox* genes could be considered the "smoking gun" of common design expected by supporters of intelligent design for decades. Consider this: If engineers were tasked to detect common design in any other area, how would they proceed? They would study various sets of plans and specifications, identify any common features, and verify if there was, in fact, common underlying information. Genetic research has identified this common information across diverse groups of organisms prescribing traits with the same general function. In other areas of research, this fact would be ascribed to common engineering instructions.

Evolutionary theory predicted the opposite of common underlying information for similar traits. The fact that it was dogmatically taught as evidence for evolution and was found to be profoundly wrong catalogs it as a spectacular blunder. This repressed prediction-evidence mismatch connects to ever-changing evolutionary explanations like "convergence" or "conservation." These come across scientifically as a mishmash of improvised, after-the-fact stories aimed at forcing observations into an evolutionary view.

Creationists can say with credibility that in creatures as diverse as bacteria, insects, and humans, the same information controls the formation and utilization of many key anatomical or molecular structures seen performing broadly similar functions. Applying organism-focused, design-based analysis to biology brings clarity. Common genes are clearly the common designs creationists had been looking for during the last 200 years.

## Conclusion

The history behind the discovery of *Hox* genes is important for at least three reasons. First, *Hox* genes are the common underlying information in diverse creatures. They specify a common design for common features that perform common functions, like telling tissues when to turn on and off limb production. This evidence is undeniable.

Second, they serve as a lesson to creationists. Even though creationists held a belief in common design, we, like others, were still interpreting evidence through the evolutionary paradigm—just a lighter version that did not extrapolate as much change. If creationists scrap all vestiges of Darwinian thinking and fully move to an organism-focused, engineering-based theory to interpret data, then the meaning of findings like *Hox* genes becomes immediately apparent.

Third, evolutionary and creationary theories had a head-to-head test of predictions about the existence of common underlying information for similar structures. Predictions are a good gauge for the strength of a theory. In this case, the discovery of the same regulatory DNA confirmed the creationist prediction of common DNA from a common Designer. It also showed that the evolutionary prediction was stunningly wrong.

The premise that structures in many life forms are manufactured for similar purposes but applied in different environments is both intuitive and plausible. Electric motors that power a toy train or a real subway train operate by the same principles. They may have similar parts made from the same materials. But it is the specification that regulates manufacturing of unique shapes, controls, and arrangements of parts that allow them to fit specific applications. Specifications demand a person to do the specifying.

We see the same engineering principles in creatures. Organisms are programmed to adapt to fill environmental niches. Genetics and developmental pathways help control embryonic development of similarity in form from flies to elephants. But flies are flies because of uniquely specified developmental controls. This information is previously encoded in the entire organism—not just the genes—to control embryonic development. Reproduction transmits the entire system to the next generation.

### Notes

1. Morris, H. 1975. *The Troubled Waters of Evolution*. San Diego, CA: Creation-Life Publishers, 84-85.

2. Darwin, C. 1872. *The Origin of Species by Means of Natural Selection*, 6th ed. London: John Murray, 383.

3. Mayr, E. 1963. *Animal Species and Evolution*. Cambridge, MA: Harvard University Press, 609.

4. Land, M. F. and R. D. Fernald. 1992. The Evolution of Eyes. *Annual Review of Neuroscience*. 15: 1-29, referencing Salvini-Plawen, L. V. and E. Mayr. 1977. On the evolution of photoreceptors and eyes. *Evolutionary Biology*. 10: 207-263.

5. Lewis, E. 1978. A gene complex controlling segmentation in *Drosophila*. *Nature*. 276: 565-570.

6. Wakimoto, B. 1981. Analysis of larval segmentation in lethal genotypes associated with the Antennapedia gene complex in *Drosophila melanogaster*. *Developmental Biology*. 81 (1):51-64.

7. Scott, M. and Weiner, A. 1984. Structural relationships among genes that control development: sequence homology between the Antennapedia, Ultrabithorax, and fushi tarazu loci of *Drosophila*. *Proceedings of the National Academy of Sciences*. 81 (13): 4115-4119.

8. Slack, J. 1984. A rosetta stone for pattern formation in animals? *Nature*. 310: 364-365.

9. Carroll, S. 2005. *Endless Forms Most Beautiful*. New York: W. W. Norton & Company, 64.

10. Ibid, 71.

11. Ibid, 65.

12. Ibid, 72.

# 20
# THE ORIGIN OF PARASITES

Frank Sherwin, M.A.

**Summary:** Our world is full of death, disease, and parasites. Would a good God have designed a world like this?

Evolutionists see death as part of the natural order. But death, evil, and suffering weren't part of God's original creation. Our world came under the Curse of humanity's sin, and as a result nature became corrupt and now contains predators, parasites, and pathogens.

Creation scientists and theologians research the Curse to understand how this alteration might have occurred. It appears today's "bad" viruses and bacteria could have had neutral or even beneficial functions before the Fall and became corrupt afterward, possibly through mutations.

Though sin brought death and disease into God's perfectly designed world, He offers redemption to all who put their trust in Jesus Christ.

Perhaps no area of biology has raised more questions than the issues of predator/prey relationships, diseases, and parasites in a world God created. This chapter will address some of these.

We start with the two opposing worldviews on origins. While evolutionists have unscientific ideas regarding all life coming from a single cell that somehow developed from non-life, creationists turn to the book of beginnings—Genesis. In this historical, God-breathed document, we read of an idyllic creation, with God the Creator proclaiming, "It was very good" (Genesis 1:31).

Christians see natural evil and physical death as not being part of God's original plan (Deuteronomy 32:4). In Genesis 3, we read of the fall of Adam and Eve, followed by God cursing the earth: "Both thorns and thistles it shall bring forth for you, and you shall eat the herb of the field" (Genesis 3:18). We can see that something changed at the Curse.

Thankfully, although Genesis 3 graphically shows the Curse and its effects on the world, it also gives the first prophecy of redemption. We read in verse 15 God's pronouncement to the serpent:

> And I will put enmity between you and the woman, and between
> your seed and her Seed; He shall bruise your head, and you shall
> bruise His heel.

Our creation and Curse are there in Genesis—but so is the blessed hope we have with the first promise of salvation and renewal in Christ.

Evolutionists see the evil and pain in the world and, not surprisingly, attribute it to the evolutionary paradigm. Charles Darwin stated in the closing paragraphs of *Origin of Species*:

> Thus, from the war of nature, from famine and death...the pro-
> duction of higher animals, directly follows.[1]

We read in Romans 8:19-21 that the creation is subject to "futility" (v. 20) and that the universe is subject to death and deterioration. In verse 21, Paul uses the word "corruption," which is equivalent to decay. But this dreadful cycle of disease and death was never part of God's original plan, despite evolutionists' attempt to make it seem a part of the "natural" order.

## Thorns and Thistles

Creation scientists and theologians research this area called the Curse to understand the mechanisms by which this alteration from God's perfect creation occurred. It would not be theologically accurate to say that God created thistles and thorns at this time since Genesis 2:2 indicates that "on the seventh day God ended His [creation] work." Perhaps He allowed the beneficent structures and processes He created previously from His "very good" creation to deteriorate. This deterioration was due to humanity's sin (Isaiah 53:6). Some animals and plants now have a physically changed form (such as thorns) that would require genetic modifications to pass on the changes to future generations.

Another theory regarding the function of thorns and thistles prior to the Fall involves a concept called *exaptation*. God could have designed a trait with a specific function that subsequently came to serve another purpose after the Fall.

Creation scientists also suggest there was hidden or latent genetic information contained within a person, plant, or animal's genome that could be phenotypically (physically) expressed at a later time.

## Bacteria and Viruses

Today there are increasing discoveries indicating that "bad" (pathogenic) bacteria, parasites, and viruses may have had a more neutral or even beneficial function prior to the Fall. For example, *Escherichia coli* (*E. coli*) bacteria can either be good or bad depending on the subspecies and where it is found in the body. In the colon, the bacteria make important B vitamins and vitamin K, but if the colon is ruptured, *E. coli* escaping into the body cavity can have fatal consequences.

If the creation science model of deterioration (or alteration) after the Fall is true, it raises the possibility that under different conditions, disease-causing bacteria in nature, for example, might have had beneficial applications. This can be seen with the Hawaiian bobtail squid, which hosts the otherwise pathogenic bacteria called *Vibrio cholera*. The bacteria secrete a deadly toxin that can cause cholera. Perhaps this toxin had an alternative function in the beginning?

A very similar toxin is produced by *V. fischeri*, a curious light-emitting symbiotic bacterium found in the Hawaiian bobtail squid. The creature uses the luminescent properties of the bacteria to evade predators in the clear water where it feeds. Although the squid are good hunters, they are preyed upon by large, nocturnal predators. Seen from below, the dark squid would ordinarily be framed against the moonlight, making an easy target. But the bottom (ventral) side of the squid contains a light organ containing *V. fischeri* surrounded by an ink sac that operates much like a camera's diaphragm. Light from the bacteria, plus a reflector, is radiated downward in a way that counters the moonlight, putting the squid in a "stealth mode." When the bacteria get hungry, they secrete the cholera-like toxin, which doesn't *sicken* the squid but rather *informs* it—they need food, which the squid then provides.

Indeed, one evolutionist suggested, "Maybe when we've been studying cholera pathogenesis we've been studying an aspect of a normal conversation that's gone wrong."[2] Creation scientists suggest this may be a result of the Curse. The example above indicates that biological compounds and organisms are not evil in themselves but have different functions depending on the perspective.

Non-cellular viruses have protein-DNA coding design showing they were created. Dr. Gary Parker suggests a non-Darwinian explanation for the originally created viruses:

> It seems to me that in God's originally perfect creation, the interlocking of docking and receptor proteins was designed to allow viruses to insert their DNA (or RNA) into only those cells in which gene transfer would be beneficial. In properly programmed receptor cells, some viruses can splice their DNA into the cell's genome, and the added (pre-existent, pre-programmed!) genetic information multiplies along with the cell....Perhaps God, the ultimate Genetic Engineer, designed viruses as gene carriers, especially for bacteria.[3]

## Parasitism

A parasite is a type of animal (or plant) that lives in close, non-mutual association with another, usually larger animal (or person) called the host. The word parasite comes from the Greek word meaning a person who eats at another's table. For example, malaria parasites are single-cell animals that live in the liver and red blood cells of a victim after the person is bitten by an infected mosquito. The tiny parasites eat the red pigment in the blood cells, reproduce, and are shielded from the person's immune system. Well over 650 million people are currently infected, with hundreds of thousands dying yearly.

Parasites may have been free-living in the environment as complete animals that became parasitic after the Fall and Curse. Their complexity as to how they evade our immune system, as well as their incredible life cycles, shows God's creative hand.

The evolutionary community knows very little regarding parasites' origin, evolution, or complex biology. "Complex life cycles remain one of the most baffling features of parasites, and there is still much to be learned about their evolution."[4] Creationists maintain that evolutionists will never come to a full knowledge regarding parasites because they begin with a faulty premise—the parasites' supposed evolution.

Evolutionists ignore Genesis 1–3, so they ignore God's role in creation and its corruption due to sin. It is a given that parasites today such as malaria, along with genetic mutations, were not part of God's very good creation.

At the Curse, could God have allowed beneficent structures in creatures that were non-parasitic to deteriorate into the devastating parasites we have today (including weeds, poisons, and pathogens)?

Creation scientists have some intriguing ideas regarding the origin of parasites from a biblical context. Could parasites (post-Fall) such as the malaria organism be slight genetic variations of non-parasite ancestors (pre-Fall)? After Adam sinned, God possibly cursed the animals by design modification. Genesis 3:14 says that God told the serpent he is cursed above all cattle and every beast of the field, the implication being that these animals were cursed as well, though to a reduced extent. God did this with plants (thorns and thistles) so that they now cause pain. The vector of malaria—the female mosquito—has needle-like structures (stylets) specifically designed to allow it to obtain a blood meal. God may have adjusted the design of creatures such as the mosquito at the time of the Curse to allow it to feed off of other creatures. The originally created malaria parasite itself seemed to have a photosynthetic capability (using sunlight to make food). Conceivably, at the time of the Fall the group lost this complex food production capacity and became parasitic.

Parasites as well as pathogens were possibly created as neutral or even beneficial but became destructive. Because of sin, there was an easing of biological controls that would have kept them beneficial. Genetic mistakes (mutations) might have contributed to parasites and the suffering they cause. Creation zoologists do not have all the answers regarding parasite origin and their interesting, convoluted life cycles. However, we use a priori creation thinking to ask or hypothesize what the origin and advantage of, for example, parasite life cycles might be. Some creation zoologists suggest free-living creatures (i.e., non-parasitic) became parasitic after the Fall. This is hardly far-fetched. As one evolutionist stated, "Parasitic species have retained some morphological resemblance with their free-living counterparts."[5] The step to a parasitic mode after the Fall could have been a small one. "In fact, free-living species could become parasitic without substantial anatomical or physiological changes."[6]

Another concept to consider is that parasites may have had a beneficial function prior to the Fall (exaptation). One evolutionist stated:

> Parasitism usually implies that some harm is done to the host, but this interpretation must be qualified. Effects on the host range from almost none to severe illness and eventual death, but even where such obvious immediate harm accrues to the individual host it does not follow that the relationship is harmful to the host

species in the long term or in an evolutionary context (e.g. it might favour beneficial adaptation in the host species population).[7]

If the relationship may not have been harmful to the host in the long run, then perhaps this may point to a time prior to the Fall when there may have been commensalism (one party gains some benefit) or mutualism (both parties benefit, e.g., lichens).

Those who ignore Genesis 1 and 3 cannot understand the nature of disease and parasites.

Although parasites still show God's glory, before the Fall they were evidently a complete, non-parasitic animal. Many parasites today are little more than protoplasmic bags of reproductive structures with an attachment (hooks or suckers) on one end. It has been suggested they have lost much of their genetic information as a result of the Curse.

Creation scientists have an explanation for parasites based on the written record of One who was there. Parasites are mostly ugly reminders that the law of sin and death (the Curse) is operating today. Death is God's enemy, but death is doomed. As fallen creatures, we see parasites as a reminder of how today's world is still "good yet groaning" as we await the ultimate redemption of creation promised in Romans 8:20-22.

## Conclusion

The Curse is the key to understanding the presence of disease and death in today's world. It is man, not God, who is to blame for sin and death. To say that God is the author of death and suffering is to say He either does not care to solve this dilemma, He is not powerful enough to do so, or that He doesn't exist at all. The Bible, however, teaches that natural evil and physical death came into existence only after the Fall. One should remember that the design came first, and disease and devastation are an example of a breakdown of these ingenious and created systems. Yes, there are details that require further research, but the model of creation, the Fall, and the Curse is superior to the strange science of Darwinism.

The Curse answers the accusation by secularists that a loving God could not have created the world we see today. It was God, however, who provided a means of total forgiveness in the sinful world into which humans are born. Jesus Christ made the blood atonement for our sins for those who put their trust in Him, promoting them from a world groaning with sin to eternity with

Him (Luke 23:43). Christians await the ultimate redemption of creation that is promised in Romans 8:20-22, when He will wipe away every tear (Revelation 21:4).

### Notes

1. Darwin, C. 1964. *On the Origin of Species*. Cambridge, MA: Harvard University Press, 490.

2. University of Wisconsin-Madison biologist Margaret McFall-Ngai, quoted in Weird Wonders of Biology. The Why? Files. Posted on whyfiles.org December 29, 2011.

3. Parker, G. 2006. *Creation: Facts of Life*. Green Forest, AR: Master Books, 140.

4. Poulin, R. 2006. *Evolutionary Ecology of Parasites*, 2nd ed. Princeton, NJ: Princeton University Press, 40.

5. Ibid, 13.

6. Miller, S. and J. Harley. 2010. *Zoology*, 8th ed. New York: McGraw Hill, 226.

7. Allaby, M. 2014. *Oxford Dictionary of Zoology*. New York: Oxford University Press, 454.

# 21

# CAIN, HIS WIFE, AND THE ORIGIN OF RACES

Frank Sherwin, M.A.

**Summary:** Creationists are often asked, "Who was Cain's wife?" The likely answer is a sister or niece. Today this inbreeding is risky because of the buildup of genetic mutations, but the first humans didn't have degraded genes. Interbreeding wasn't a problem in Cain's time. In fact, God didn't prohibit it until the Mosaic law.

Modern people possess much variation in size, skin color, and other attributes, but we are all one human race created in the image of God. The Tower of Babel is a key to understanding these variations, as well as the 70 main language groups on Earth. Because of the people's rebellion at Babel, God confused their language, forcing them to migrate. Earth's early history as presented in Genesis makes sense of the world we see today.

As Christians, our thinking about Earth's early history is based on the events listed in the critical opening chapters of Genesis—the book of beginnings. Scripture presents us with the proper interpretation of the past versus the fictitious view of evolution and uniformity that rejects the biblical record. The origin of people groups and nations are critical events, so we must get it right.

One of the premier questions the materialist often asks the Christian is, "Who was Cain's wife?" This trivial question was presented in the movie *Inherit the Wind*, a fictionalized portrayal of the Scopes "Monkey" Trial with Spencer Tracy playing Henry Drummond, a character patterned after the infamous Chicago lawyer Clarence Darrow. A frustrated Matthew Harrison Brady (based on William Jennings Bryan and played by Fredric March) was not surprisingly unable to answer Drummond's bullying query. At the end of the film, secular reason prevailed, and audiences through the decades have been left with the impression that the Bible had—and has—no answer, or that it supports immorality by condoning incest.

This is a typical "heads I win, tails you lose" argument with supposedly no decent possible answer. So, how is a Christian to respond to this challenge?

We should start "in the beginning." Eve was the first woman, the mother of all peoples, and there were no other women at the start of creation. Genesis 3:20 states, "And Adam called his wife's name Eve, because she was the mother of all living." They were commanded by God to "be fruitful and multiply" (Genesis 1:28), so it is not beyond reason to suppose they had many children—especially when Adam lived for 930 years and Eve for a presumably similar period. Indeed, the Jewish historian Josephus said, "The number of Adam's children, as says the old tradition, was thirty-three sons and twenty-three daughters."

Cain was Eve and Adam's first child (Genesis 4:1), and he had two recorded brothers, Abel and Seth. It should be noted that Adam and Eve also had other offspring. Genesis 5:4 says, "After he begot Seth, the days of Adam were eight hundred years; and he had sons and daughters." So, who was Cain's wife? She was a descendant of Adam/man—or, Cain's sister.

Skeptics maintain there must have been people other than Adam and Eve, because Cain went to the land of Nod after killing Abel. But the Bible makes it clear there was only one man and one woman from whom came all other human beings. In the pre-Flood world, women and men lived to be hundreds of years old, and populations grew rapidly. Cain had enough time to marry his sister (or a niece perhaps), move to Nod, and build a city for his own descendants and others. Originally, there was nothing wrong with marriage between sister and brother. Indeed, how else was the world going to be populated except by these unions? God did not condemn the marriage of Abraham and his half-sister, although this was later forbidden in the Levitical laws.

Today, interbreeding is dangerous because of the genetic load or genetic burden that a species carries.[1] Purebred dogs, for example, always carry a hidden genetic defect (deafness, hip dysplasia, or other imperfections) that often manifests itself physically (called *phenotypic expression*). In the days of Adam and Eve, there were virtually no mutations built up, and intermarrying could occur without genetic harm. Indeed, in that first generation all marriages had to be brother/sister marriages. As the centuries progressed, mutations began to accumulate in the human genome. Therefore, God, in His infinite wisdom, prohibited incest, as we read in the Mosaic laws (Leviticus 18–20). For example, "none of you shall approach anyone who is near of kin to him" (Leviticus 18:6). These new laws were introduced by God for our sake, because of our sin. Today, the more closely related two people are, the greater the chances that they will have the same mutation on the same chromosome. With a brother/sister union—even first cousins—the offspring would inherit the two gene sets (for example, Aa in the sperm and Bb from the egg) and very likely phenotypically express one or more of the mutations. Today, people are now subject to at least 5,000 mutational conditions that our first parents and their offspring didn't encounter. It is no wonder God implemented the Levitical laws.

## The Origin of People Groups

> And He has made from one blood every nation of men to dwell on all the face of the earth, and has determined their preappointed times and the boundaries of their dwellings. (Acts 17:26)

Genesis 1–11 takes the reader through creation, the Curse, and the global Flood (catastrophe) of Noah's day. We will never comprehend human origins, migrations, genetics, or languages without considering Babel. "From there the LORD scattered them abroad over the face of all the earth" (Genesis 11:9). The events at Babel give us the key to understanding the origin of modern nations and peoples. We are descended from those confused and scattered at Babel after the Flood. Babel was the breakup of the languages and the dispersion of families into all parts of the world.

After the Flood, God instructed Noah and his family (eight people in all) to "be fruitful and multiply, and fill the earth" (Genesis 9:1). Instead, in the years to follow their descendants assembled at Babel under the leadership of a defiant Nimrod, who no doubt was under demonic influence.

They proceeded to build a tower "lest we be scattered abroad over the face of the whole earth" (Genesis 11:4), and it became an astrological worship center to praise the creation rather than the Creator (Romans 1). Except for a faithful remnant (e.g., Noah, Shem), the disobedient populace had united in rebellion against God.

But God separated their one language into many, preventing their communication (and therefore cooperation). This confusion of language caused them to disperse throughout the earth (Genesis 11:6), as He had commanded earlier (Genesis 9:1).

In the Table of Nations (Genesis 10), we discover a documentation of 70 nations/family groups migrating to fill the earth after Babel. Not surprisingly, linguists have found the number of separate language groups is basically the same as the 70 listed in Scripture. The Ice Age that extended for centuries after the Flood resulted in global changes such as severe climates in Europe, a lush Egypt, and a reduced sea level that allowed migration across the Siberia/Alaska land bridge, as well as others. Genesis 13–50 mentions physical locales, towns, and cities that have been verified through the centuries by archaeology, confirming these basic details and identifying major locations and people groups. Sadly, history has been rife with conquests of uninhabited lands and wars between tribes who spoke different tongues.

Regardless, since the dispersion at Babel we have seen only variation within the created kind of people. If this is true, then there are no separate races but only one race—the human race (as we read in Acts 17:26). Creationists would call the different groups of people we see throughout the world not "races" but people groups. We are all humans, but quite variable in function and form.

One creation scientist has called this the law of conservation of genetic variability. The human genome is composed of at least six billion nucleotides (a nucleotide is the functional unit of DNA composed of a sugar molecule, a phosphate molecule, and a nitrogenous base). Evolutionist Francisco Ayala has said the human genome is 6.7% heterozygous (different alleles at a specific gene locus or location) for a variety of the genes.[2] Translated, this means that of every 100 genes, six or seven pairs of genes for a given trait differ, such as eye color or the ability to roll the tongue. So, a human couple with this kind of variety can—according to Ayala—produce 10 to the 2,017th power children that would be unique before producing an identical twin. How big is that number? Physicists estimate there are "only" 10 to the 80th power atoms in the universe. God has created us with an amazing variation potential.

Take skin color, for example. Physically and genetically, we find people of the world with different skin colors and shades. In fact, we all have the same pigments or skin-coloring agents—just different shades or combinations of them. This is due to cells called *melanocytes* located in the lower epidermis (skin) that produce melanin (dark pigment) granules. Melanin is injected by the melanocytes into adjacent cells. The question is, how long would it take to get all the skin color variation we see in people today? The answer is—a single generation. In 2006, a medium-dark-skinned man and woman produced fraternal twins; one was quite light, while the other was quite dark. How could this be?

Geneticists have found that four to six genes (DNA) control the type and amount of melanin formed (melanin also gives us our different eye colors). Although Scripture doesn't say, the Punnet Square used in basic genetics indicates the skin color of Adam and Eve was very probably a middle-brown shade (AaBb). Each parent having these four alleles (different sequences of genetic material) could produce offspring from very dark (AABB) to very light (aabb) in just one generation due to crossing over of chromosomes and gene segregation. As people broke up into isolated groups, some groups would develop limited variability—only dark (many parts of Africa), only medium (such as Orientals, Polynesians, and Native Americans), or only light (much of the Scandinavian population). This variation of skin color—as well as variation in height and all other forms of human function and form—has been built into humans by God, starting with our first parents. Variation within the created kind is consistent with what we observe—not only with people since Babel, but also in plants and animals.

To conclude, the Christian should be equipped with biblical knowledge to "give a defense to everyone who asks you a reason for the hope that is in you, with meekness and fear" (1 Peter 3:15), whether it concerns Cain's wife, the origin of people groups, the Genesis Flood, or the resurrection of our Lord.

### Notes

1. Sanford, J. C. 2014. *Genetic Entropy and the Mystery of the Genome.* Waterloo, NY: FMS Publications; Parker, G. 2006. *Creation Facts of Life.* Green Forest, AR: Master Books, 118-119.
2. Ayala, F. 1978. The Mechanisms of Evolution. *Scientific American.* 239 (3). 56-69.

# 22

# THE EROSION OF GENES CONFIRMS GENESIS HISTORY

Brian Thomas, Ph.D.

**Summary:** Human bodies grow old and wear out. Their genes wear out, too. Some 100 mutations occur in each generation, leaving humanity on a genetic "countdown" to zero. According to current estimates, the human race could last fewer than 500 generations before mutational overload ends it.

This confirms the biblical record in a number of ways. DNA's complicated, tightly packed biological information points to an ingenious Creator. The ongoing loss of genetic function reflects the Curse placed on the world due to sin. And the human race's continued existence fits the biblical timeline of thousands of years but totally derails evolution's millions of years.

Also, data indicate that human genetic diversity began to accelerate only about 5,100 years ago, a scientific finding that is in lock-step with the biblical record.

Nobody lives forever. Most of us are aware that our individual bodies are engaged in a relentless countdown called aging. If we are fortunate enough to avoid lethal violence and disease, our biological countdown will eventually reach zero and our bodies will simply stop working.

The death of an individual is a sad fact of life, but it gets worse. Many are unaware that biological decay overtakes not just individuals but whole species. The entire human race is on a countdown to zero. And the countdown is occurring rapidly. The only reason we have not yet reached the end must be because we began our journey as a species recently—only thousands of years ago.

Let's examine how this genetic countdown happens. DNA contains densely packed, highly regulated, and mind-bogglingly complicated biological information. That kind of functioning intricacy could only come from an ingenious Creator, and it matches a creation that was originally "very good" (Genesis 1:31).

The world we live in is no longer very good. Genesis 3 tells why the world was cursed—the reader learns that the penalty for Adam's sin is death. And sure enough, each new body cell undergoes a process of programmed death.[1] When enough cells in any vital system die, then the whole body ceases to function.[2]

Even without programmed cell death, another process would eventually cause bodily death. Every time a cell divides, a small number of its 3.2 billion DNA chemical building blocks fails to copy correctly. These copying errors, or mutations, build up over time. Not only do they accumulate in an individual's body during their one lifetime, contributing to system failure leading to diseases and death, but they also accumulate over many lifetimes, passing from generation to generation. Fortunately, the believer in Christ will receive a new body, and its "flesh shall be young like a child's, he shall return to the days of his youth" (Job 33:25).

Geneticists use powerful new technology to count the exact number of single DNA differences, often called *single-nucleotide variants* (SNVs), between two individuals. This permits them to track mutations, many of which occur as SNVs. A few recent studies counted the accumulation of SNVs within direct descendants. Their results confirm what geneticists had suspected. Over 100 brand-new SNVs occur every generation. That means every person alive today is a mutant! It also means that every person alive today carries more mutations than their parents, grandparents, and all ancestors all the way back to Adam, whose genes were perfect. Fortunately, the vast majority of these SNVs have an immeasurably small effect. But over hundreds of generations, thousands of nearly harmless individual mutations add up to become harmful in total. And these mutations are counting down to the end of the entire human race. The fact they're still "counting" must mean that we are still young.

Nearly neutral mutations accumulate and slightly garble genetic information. This type of mutation far outnumbers any that could in theory construct new and useful information, and likewise those few that cause severe harm.[3]

This process is like copying an encyclopedia every 20 years (the approximate length of a human generation) by hand. Each time the encyclopedia is copied, only a few errors—simple typos—creep into the text. At first, and for thousands of years, the information in each article can still be understood, even with the copying errors. But eventually, after many thousands of years, the articles become so riddled with mistakes that the encyclopedia becomes totally useless.

Similarly, cells are left to interpret the damaged genetic information like scholars who must try to reconstruct text from tattered and marred ancient scrolls. Cells can decipher enough information even from inferior DNA sequences to continue functioning for many generations, but eventually core coding will become corrupted. Genetic information is garbled just a tiny bit more with each generation. This ongoing "erosion" of genes and supporting DNA sequences confirms a corrupted creation, just like Paul described in Romans 8:22: "For we know that the whole creation groans and labors with birth pangs together until now."

The decay of DNA's biological data also confirms biblical creation by limiting the total possible number of human generations to far fewer than evolutionary history requires. Since each generation accumulates about 100 more mutations than the prior generation—and since each mutation is so nearly harmless that no cellular or natural process can detect or remove it—the total number of mutations continues to mount unimpeded. This sets a finite total threshold for number of generations. Currently, the best estimates show that mutational overload will doom the whole of humanity in fewer than 500 generations.[4]

According to the genealogy of Jesus through Mary provided in Luke 3, and the genealogy of Jesus through Joseph shown in Matthew 1, the total number of human generations from creation to Christ averaged about 100. Assuming a new generation every 20 years, the 2,000 years that have elapsed since Christ should have yielded another 100 or so generations.

Two hundred total generations multiplied by 100 mutations per generation equals 20,000 more mutations than were in the genome of Adam, who had none.[5] Evolutionary ideas insist that modern humans evolved about 2.5 million years ago. Such a vast time would have produced about 125,000 generations and many thousands of mutations. Where are all the expected human SNVs? Or, as one evolutionary human population geneticists candidly asked, "Why have we not died 100 times over?"[6]

One recent genetics study has provided particularly clear confirmation of biblical history. In it, the authors counted genetic diversity within a group of over 2,400 people.[7] They discovered that each person harbors very recently formed DNA differences (SNVs) within their genes. The study authors modeled the rise of genetic diversity through time, finding that it exactly paralleled historical population growth. Their data indicated that human genetic diversity began to accelerate only about 5,100 years ago.

Of course, 5,100 years falls right in line with biblical creation but presents big problems for evolutionary history. Anyone who defends human evolution now needs to explain why the human population failed to grow for 2.5 million years, only to begin exponential growth in just the last 5,100 years. In other words, they should explain how each family produced, and how nature maintained, no more or less than two children per generation—one to replace the father and one to replace the mother—for about 125,000 consecutive generations!

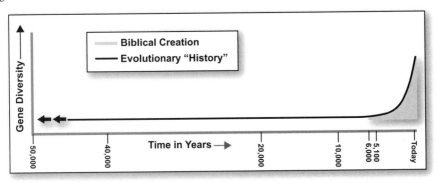

Human gene diversity over time, after Tennessen et al. Genetic data show that genes diversified beginning about 5,100 years ago. This presents a significant challenge to an evolutionary timeline, which must now explain why humans waited for millions of years before beginning to diversify. The results, however, are quite consistent with a biblical timeline.

Evolutionists reason that humanity's long delay before the population exploded stemmed from their supposedly long wait until agriculture had evolved. But this merely begs the question—it assumes evolution to prove evolution. In reality, the weight of archaeological evidence shows that humanity has always been as smart, or smarter, in the past than today. For example, the world's oldest temple, Gobekli Tepe in Turkey, has expertly carved animal and human figures on its still-straight stone pillars. And artifacts that include spears in an Ice Age German coal mine, Neanderthal jewelry, axe glue, butchered bones in Africa, and ancient stone animal pens in Arabia all show that people have always been fully capable of manipulating their environments much like today's people do. Thus, in contrast to the false picture of human evolution that invokes invented "rescuing" devices like agriculture evolving, biblical history fits the genetic diversity and archaeological data straightforwardly.

Overall, genetics clearly confirms biblical creation in at least three ways. First, high-tech gene organization could only be the product of a Mastermind. Second, the breakdown of genes both within and between generations is consistent with the Bible's description of a fallen creation. Last, two observations from genetics confirm the Bible's timeline: The human genome would accumulate too many copying errors to survive more than 500 generations, fitting well with the Bible's inferred 200 or so elapsed generations. Also, genetic diversity only began accelerating about 5,100 years ago, a scientific finding that is in lockstep with the biblical record.

### Notes

1. Specifically, the cell division process has a counting mechanism that appears to be related to the fact that telomeric DNA shortens after each cell division. After about 40 divisions, cells cease dividing and eventually turn themselves off through a process called *apoptosis*. See Hayflick L. and P. S. Moorhead. 1961. The serial cultivation of human diploid cell strains. *Experimental Cell Research*. 25: 585-621.

2. "When the same kind of molecular mischief occurs in the cells of vital organs, leading to an increase in vulnerability to disease or pathology, treatment is required because life may be threatened." Hayflick, L. 2007. Entropy Explains Aging, Genetic Determinism Explains Longevity, and Undefined Terminology Explains Misunderstanding Both. *PLoS Genetics*. 3 (12): e220.

3. Sanford, J. S. 2005. *Genetic Entropy and the Mystery of the Genome*. Lima, NY: Ivan Press, 150.

4. "Assuming an additive model, the result is that our species goes extinct in roughly 300 generations." Ibid, 113.

5. Actually, any two people have many more than 20,000 SNVs. But the majority of DNA differences were likely placed into Adam's genome on purpose. After all, Adam had two each of 23 chromosomes, one with certain gene variations and the matching chromosome with other variations. God designed Adam's body to produce future generations that could produce future trait variations that would successfully multiply and fill the earth's ever-changing environments. God "has made from one blood every nation of men to dwell on all the face of the earth" (Acts 17:26).

6. Kondrashov, A. 1995. Contamination of the genome by very slightly deleterious mutations: why have we not died 100 times over? *Journal of Theoretical Biology*. 175 (4): 583-594.

7. Tennessen, J. et al. 2012. Evolution and Functional Impact of Rare Coding Variation from Deep Sequencing of Human Exomes. *Science*. 337 (6090): 64-69.

# 23

# THE JUNK DNA SCAM

Jeffrey P. Tomkins, Ph.D.

**Summary:** Some evolutionary proponents use the concept of junk DNA to support Darwinian evolution. They propose that non-protein-coding DNA in the genome represents evolutionary "leftovers." However, researchers have discovered that virtually the entire genome is functional, negating the idea that it contains junk.

Non-protein-coding DNA sequence can be classified into several functional categories. The first is regulatory, which involves many switches, signals, and other control features that regulate gene and genome function. Another category involves long non-coding RNA genes, which produce an RNA molecule as a final gene product instead of a protein. The functional and structural products of these numerous RNA genes perform a huge array of functions in the cell associated with gene expression, growth, development, and physiology.

Other regions and features thought to be nonfunctional are now proving to serve key roles in genomic function. Each new discovery demonstrates that the genome is a masterful marvel of incredibly complex engineering and design.

One of the greatest evolutionary frauds in biology is the idea that plant and animal genomes contain vast amounts of meaningless "junk" DNA sequences that serve no practical purpose. However, many researchers working in the vast field of genomics now realize that virtually the entire genome is functional in some respect.

Nevertheless, a handful of influential evolutionists still authoritatively proclaim the fraudulent concept of junk DNA to perpetuate the overall myth of Darwinian evolution.

The general idea behind junk DNA is that the large percentage of the genome that does not directly code for protein represents the evolutionary vestiges of viruses, defunct genes, and other repetitive sequences dragged along through evolutionary history like some sort of excess baggage. These so-called junk DNA regions are postulated to be "neutral" in regard to the magical forces of "natural selection" as some sort of explanation for why they still exist.

One of the more common arguments from some of the evolutionary propagandists is that a Creator God would never have filled genomes with such large amounts of seemingly useless DNA. Of course, this presupposition is based on the false idea that these regions of the genome serve no purpose. However, as will be shown, science now abundantly proves that this is not the case.

Because literally hundreds of research citations would be required for this chapter, only a few key papers will be cited. For the advanced reader who is interested in exploring this material in more detail, please see the book on this subject by Jonathan Wells, *The Myth of Junk DNA.*[1]

## The Coding of Noncoding DNA

The non-protein-coding parts of genomes can be divided into a number of categories. One category contains segments of so-called junk DNA that are very similar across a wide variety of creatures.[2-4] These are called highly conserved noncoding regions. According to evolutionary reasoning, these should be heavily mutated and variable. Since they are supposedly nonfunctional and not actively undergoing any type of natural selection, they should freely mutate. However, the high level of similarity in these noncoding DNA segments among many types of organisms is actually a strong indicator of the functionality of these sequences. They serve a common and important design purpose across various classes of life.

Another major argument indicating the functionality of so-called junk DNA is the fact that diverse classes of non-protein-coding DNA are used as templates to make a wide variety of RNA molecules that help regulate gene activity throughout the genome. One significantly large component of this noncoding DNA that is copied into RNA (transcribed) is produced by a diverse class of genes that do not code for proteins, called *long noncoding RNAs* (lncRNA). These lncRNA genes, which outnumber protein-coding genes by at least two to one, perform a wide variety of functions in the cell.[5,6]

Interestingly, many RNAs are transcribed from the reverse (anti-sense) strand of the double-stranded DNA helix to produce RNAs that will base-pair in a complementary fashion to protein-coding RNAs transcribed from the forward (sense) strand.[7,8] This can provide rapid regulation in several ways. First, it can keep messenger RNAs (mRNAs) from being degraded, preserving their presence in the nucleus. Secondly, it keeps messenger RNAs from being translated to make proteins.

In fact, the regulation of gene expression by a wide variety of RNAs produced from non-protein-coding DNA sequence is now also perceived as an important target of study in addition to the actual protein-coding sections of the genome. The wide diversity of noncoding RNAs (ncRNAs) in a cell affects virtually all aspects of growth, development, and physiology, and is one of the key features of life.

For example, the protein-coding sections of the human genome, which comprise less than 5% of the DNA sequence, are somewhat analogous to the raw materials (bricks, boards, wire, etc.) used in a construction project. It is the intelligent oversight, implementation, and usage of these raw materials that makes the building take shape and function. To a major degree, that's what the noncoding parts of the genome do, and ncRNAs appear to play a major role in this.

## The Amazing Splicing Code

Another major feature of the genome that destroys the junk DNA scam is the splicing code. This genetic paradigm has been progressively developed over the past several decades but has recently come together in more detail. Researchers claim that the number of human protein-coding genes is about 21,500 to 23,000. However, the public databases currently contain about two million different human protein sequences.

The amazing thing is that the number of protein variants greatly outnumbers the total number of protein-coding genes. Obviously, something very complicated is going on in a regulatory sense, roughly akin to the way a computer programmer utilizes code optimization and re-use. However, what has been described through the discovery of the splicing code is much more complicated than any computer system developed by man.

Plant and animal genes are interrupted by noncoding areas that are spliced out after RNA transcripts of the gene are produced. These are called *introns*.

The coding regions are called *exons*. Scientists discovered early on in the genomics era that some genes exhibit alternative splicing, where exons are either omitted or added in the linear sequence of a transcript, allowing for the production of different proteins from the same sequence (see the illustration in Figure 1). The great disparity between the number of protein-coding genes and the number of proteins produced appears to be the result of the amazing splicing code.

So-called junk DNA plays a comprehensive and immense regulatory role in the process of alternative splicing. Not only does noncoding DNA contribute to exon selection and placement decisions, but it also controls the recognition and usage of alternative transcriptional start sites, splice site recognition, transcriptional and translational cues, transcript processing and transport, genome architecture, and nuclear membrane architecture.

The actual triggers or predictors for the splicing code consist of a large list of protein, DNA, RNA, tissue type, and cell physiology factors combined in complex sets of configurations to produce different transcript and protein production activity in the cell. If there ever was a foolproof example from the world of biology to unequivocally prove intelligent design, the function of the genome is it.

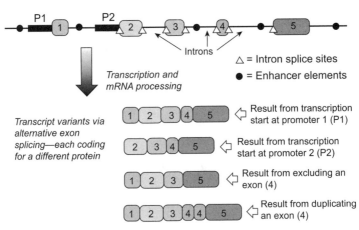

Figure 1. Diagram of a gene with five exons (protein-coding regions) showing some features that allow for the splicing code. The gene has alternate controlling (promoter regions) labeled P1 and P2. These provide variable control of the gene, along with alternative start sites for the production of a messenger RNA transcript. The different protein-coding regions (exons) can also be used to create different proteins. Special controlling sequences called enhancer elements also play an important role in up-regulating the gene.

184

## Pseudogenes Are Functional

Another critical topic related to the whole junk DNA scam is the commonly misunderstood subject of pseudogenes. The false idea that pseudogene regions of the genome represent dysfunctional genes or nonfunctional copies of genes has been a key argument in evolution.

Pseudogenes are supposedly partial or dysfunctional copies of genes that are fully functional in other parts of the genome. When these sequences were first discovered, evolutionists immediately assumed that they were the products of hypothetical naturalistic processes and served no immediate functional purpose. They were thought to be the cryptic remnants of once-functional genes or copies of genes that are in the process of evolving.

However, a slew of contemporary research is showing that pseudogenes are fully functional and critical control features of the genome.[9,10] Indeed, in some cases when they are disrupted in genetic studies, their mutation is harmful or lethal to the organism. In fact, their disruption in many cases causes severe problems in gene expression and disease. Obviously, these are critical features of the genome required for life, and changing their sequence causes problems.

Pseudogenes have also been proven to be actively transcribed via both the minus and plus strands of the DNA molecule, so their regulation in the genome is quite complex. These types of transcripts play a diversity of critical roles in both the up and down regulation of a wide variety of functional protein-coding genes with which they share similarity.

## Transposable Elements

Another class of so-called junk DNA that has also been the target of evolutionary propagandists is the diverse group of DNA features called *transposable elements* (TEs), sometimes referred to as "jumping genes." Many scientists have stated that all of the subclasses in this diverse group of DNA elements were merely genomic baggage conferred by ancient ancestral viruses that maliciously infested our DNA and have served no other purpose than to bloat and expand our poor hapless genomes with meaningless DNA fragments. However, the past several decades of research now show that every identified class of TEs (LINEs, SINEs, ERVs and DNA-transposons) has an important role in the function of the genome during development, growth, and day-to-day physiological activity.[11-14]

In *The Myth of Junk DNA*, Jonathan Wells discusses the history of these discoveries, along with detailed information about each subclass of TE and its currently known functional characteristics. Interestingly, all of these TEs are now known to have multiple functions depending on the type of cell and its activity. Rather than cryptic viral genome contaminants, it is now clear that TEs are absolutely critical to genome function and survival. TEs apparently also play important roles in cell stress responses and other protective measures. Wells' book clearly shows how the various classes of TEs present in the genome are not useless trash but indispensable functional features that contain numerous critical control features that regulate gene expression and genome formatting.

Computer hard drives have specialized code to format the arrangement and function of files. One of the key functions of transposable elements has been described as serving a similar purpose.[15] They literally format the genome for proper gene function and expression.

## Noncoding Structural Genomic Information

Another important aspect of noncoding DNA is the architectural purpose it serves in genome structure. It is now known that DNA is not randomly strewn about the nucleus but packaged into distinct, highly controlled organizational areas depending on what type of cell it is and the genetic processes involved.[16-18]

Chemical modifications not associated with actual base changes also affect the DNA molecule itself. These include nucleotide methylation and histone protein acetylation and methylation. Histones are proteins that stabilize and package the DNA molecule. Histones can be modified as well as the DNA molecule to affect genome and gene function. This field of research is called *epigenetics.*

The levels of DNA packaging and chemical modification greatly affect gene function and access by a wide variety of regulatory molecules. These modifications can be localized (local genome topology) and also affect the whole shape of the genome (global configuration). In any given local region of the genome, it may contain looping structures, structural integration of RNA molecules, and specific nuclear matrix attachment sites. These local topological features and configurations influence gene function and are facilitated and made possible by the noncoding DNA regions of the genome. The global configuration of the genome is another key subcellular feature.

The dynamically configured overall three-dimensional structure of the genome depends on the cell type and its associated stimuli and cues.[19-21] In such a scenario, certain chromosomes and chromosomal regions are dynamically configured to occupy specific functional domains. These three-dimensional features and configurations are made possible by the noncoding DNA structural regions of the genome.

## Conclusion: Not So Junky After All

Clearly, the genome is a masterful marvel of incredibly complex engineering and design. Every new discovery shows how functional and critical every single feature is to cell function, growth, and development. Just because a scientist cannot immediately determine the function of some aspect of the genome doesn't mean that it is junk. Science has proven this over and over again.

### Notes

1. Wells, J. 2011. *The Myth of Junk DNA*. Seattle, WA: Discovery Institute Press.

2. Siepel, A. et al. 2005. Evolutionarily conserved elements in vertebrate, insect, worm, and yeast genomes. *Genome Research.* 15: 1034-1050.

3. Retelska, D. et al. 2007. Vertebrate conserved non coding DNA regions have a high persistence length and a short persistence time. *BMC Genomics.* 8: 398.

4. Elgar, G. 2009. Pan-vertebrate conserved noncoding sequences associated with developmental regulation. *Briefings in Functional Genomics and Proteomics.* 8 (4): 256-265.

5. St. Laurent, G., C. Wahlestedt, and P. Kapranov. 2015. The Landscape of Long Noncoding RNA Classification. *Trends in Genetics.* 31 (5): 239-251.

6. Morris, K. V. and J. S. Mattick. 2014. The rise of regulatory RNA. *Nature Reviews Genetics.* 15 (6): 423-437.

7. Lapidot, M. and Y. Pilpel. 2006. Genome-wide natural antisense transcription: coupling its regulation to its different regulatory mechanisms. *EMBO Reports.* 7: 1216-1222.

8. Li, K. and R. Ramachandran. 2010. Natural Antisense Transcript: A Concomitant Engagement with Protein-Coding Transcript. *Oncotarget* 1: 447-452.

9. The ENCODE Project Consortium. 2007. Identification and analysis of functional elements in 1% of the human genome by the ENCODE pilot project. *Nature.* 447 (7146):799-816.

10 Zheng, D. et al. 2007. Pseudogenes in the ENCODE regions: Consensus annotation, analysis of transcription, and evolution. *Genome Research.* 17: 839-851.

11. Pink, R.C. et al. 2011. Pseudogenes: Pseudo-functional or key regulators in health and disease? *RNA.* 17: 792-798.

12. Shapiro, J. A. and R. V. Sternberg. 2005. Why repetitive DNA is essential to genome function. *Biological Review.* 80: 1-24.

13. Hasler, J and K. Strub. 2006. Alu elements as regulators of gene expression. *Nucleic Acids Research.* 34: 5491-5497.

14. Bourque, G. 2010. Transposable elements in gene regulation and in the evolution of vertebrate genomes. *Current Opinion in Genetics and Development.* 19: 607-612.

15. Gong, C. and L. E. Maquat. 2011. lncRNAs transactivate STAU1-mediated mRNA decay by duplexing with 39 UTRs via Alu elements. *Nature.* 470 (7333): 284-290.

16. von Sternberg, R. and J.A. Shapiro. 2005. How repeated retroelements format genome function. *Cytogenetic and Genome Research.* 110: 108-116.

17. Lam, E. et al. 2009. Charting functional and physical properties of chromatin in living cells. *Genetics and Development.* 19:135-141.

18. Lieberman-Aiden, E. 2009. Comprehensive Mapping of Long-Range Interactions Reveals Folding Principles of the Human Genome. *Science.* 326 (5950): 289-293.

19. Zhao, R. et al. 2009. Nuclear neighborhoods and gene expression. *Genetics and Development.* 19: 172-179.

20. Schoenfelder, S. et al. 2009. The transcriptional interactome: gene expression in 3D. *Genetics and Development.* 20: 127-133.

21. Barash Y. et al. 2010. Deciphering the splicing code. *Nature.* 465 (7294): 53-59.

# 24

# HUMAN-CHIMP DNA MONKEY BUSINESS

Jeffrey P. Tomkins, Ph.D.

**Summary:** Evolutionists claim that humans and chimps had a common ancestor that lived three to six million years ago. Using known genetic mutation rates, modern human and chimp genomes need to be about 98 to 99% similar to have emerged from a common ancestor in that time frame.

But recent genetic research shows that the human and chimp genomes are at most only around 84% similar. This is far too much of a discrepancy to make a common evolutionary ancestor even remotely plausible. Evolution cannot explain or account for this.

The sheer magnitude of the DNA sequence discontinuity chasm utterly befuddles the mythical evolutionary presuppositions of a human-chimp common ancestor.

A key part of evolutionary dogma is the "tree of life" paradigm, the claim that all creatures are descended from an original single-cell organism. An important part of the evolutionary story is that humans and chimps shared a hypothetical common ancestor that lived three to six million years ago. Of course, no fossil evidence exists for this hypothetical ancestor. In a recent scientific journal, evolutionary scientists highlighted this embarrassing paleontological fact in a paper titled "From *Australopithecus* to *Homo*: The Transition That Wasn't," in which they stated, "Although the transition from *Australopithecus* [chimp-like ape creature] to *Homo* [human] is usually thought of as a momentous transformation, the fossil record bearing on the origin and earliest evolution of *Homo* is virtually undocumented."[1]

Three to six million years is a relatively short amount of time in the evolutionary story, so evolutionists believe the human and chimp genomes should have changed very little since humans and chimps "branched off" from this supposed common ancestor. Evolutionists claim that humans and chimps are 98 to 99% genetically identical and that this similarity is support for an evolutionary origin of man. Using theoretical models of evolution based on observed mutation rates in humans and chimps, any level of DNA similarity outside this 98 to 99% "nearly identical" paradigm would make all theoretical evolutionary speculation null and void. However, as we will show, an unbridgeable chasm of non-similarity exists between humans and chimps.

Since the beginning of the DNA sequencing era that started over 35 years ago, a variety of different chemistries and protocols have been responsible for producing individual snippets of DNA sequence called *reads*. The different technologies have produced DNA fragments ranging in length from about 75 to 1,500 DNA letters (bases) long. Considering the size of the chimp genome at about three billion bases, it has been a challenging task to stitch together the chimp DNA reads into large contiguous sections that accurately represent portions of chromosomes. The challenge is even more daunting when funding for research is low and an accurate genetic framework to stitch together the DNA snippets is lacking, as has typically been the case for chimpanzee and other great ape DNA research. Because of these issues, in combination with a strong evolutionary bias that humans evolved from a chimp-like ancestor, scientists have utilized the human genome as a framework or guide to piece together chimp DNA.[2] A good analogy is how people put together jigsaw puzzles—they use the picture on the box to assemble the individual pieces. In the case of chimp, the picture on the box was the human genome.

DNA sequencing has improved markedly throughout the past 35 years, with many of the advances occurring through a process of trial and error. Despite the rapid progress in the overall technology of the process, it only became apparent within the last 10 years that human DNA contamination from laboratory workers was affecting many DNA sequencing projects and showing up in public databases. In 2011, a shocking study was published in which scientists tested 2,749 non-primate public databases and determined that 492 were contaminated with human DNA at levels of up to 10%.[3] The polluted databases included species of bacteria, fish, and plants. Ape and monkey databases were not tested, leaving the issue open as to how much human DNA might be present in ape genomes. A study was published in 2016 revealing the occurrence of human DNA contamination to be a persisting problem. The authors of the report said, "We recommend that existing contaminated genomes should be revised to remove contaminated sequence, and that new assemblies should be thoroughly checked for presence of human DNA before submitting them to public databases."[4] The key problem in light of these contamination discoveries is the distinct possibility that human DNA could be infesting the chimpanzee DNA databases and genome constructions.

A biased method of chimpanzee genome construction using human DNA as a guide, along with the high potential of human DNA contamination, would have produced a flawed chimp genome that would appear to be evolutionarily biased and very human-like. In light of this hypothesis, I recently performed and published a research study investigating both the human contamination problem and the human-chimp DNA similarity paradigm.[5] My research evaluated over 2.5 million chimp DNA sequences sampled at random from 101 different DNA sequencing data sets compared to both the human genome and the default version of the chimp genome known as PanTro4. On average, these chimp DNA sequences were about 700 bases in length.

When comparing the chimp DNA data sets to human, my research indicated that two distinct sets of data existed. The DNA sequences produced in the initial phase of the chimp genome project from 2002 to 2004, which formed the basis of the initial version and publication of the chimp genome, were considerably more similar to human than DNA sequences produced later in the project during the years 2005 to 2011, by a difference of about 7% in overall sequence similarity. In addition, the DNA sequences from later in the chimp genome project had 6% fewer matches with the human genome. These results indicate that initial research in the chimp genome project had much higher levels of human DNA contamination during a time period in which the contamination issue in DNA sequencing wasn't well recognized. Human DNA contamination would also lead to the assembly of a chimpanzee genome that was much more human-like—falsely bolstering the claims of evolutionists.

An analysis of the apparently less-contaminated data sets during the 2005 to 2011 time frame indicated that the chimp DNA sequences are no more than 85% identical overall to human. When the chimp DNA sequences that did not have matches with the human genome were compared to the chimpanzee genome in a chimp-on-chimp test, the matched regions were very short and full of unexplainable gaps. If the chimp genome were truly an accurate representation, these chimp DNA sequences should have matched up on the chimp genome at a level of 99.9% or nearly 100%. These results clearly show that many regions of the chimp genome were errantly stitched together.

## Separate Studies Converge on Debunking Hump-Chimp Similarity

The continuously advancing field of DNA technology is steadily and reliably providing results that continue to counter the hypothetical claims of evolution. Two recent discoveries that radically debunk the human evolution paradigm were reported nearly simultaneously, one by a secular evolutionist and the other by myself. Quite remarkably, the corroborating results given in both reports are in perfect agreement with each other.

The newest version of the chimpanzee genome was published in 2018, and the results not only validated past research I published in 2016 that I discussed above, but also spectacularly confirmed new research I published in 2018. First, let's discuss the secular research paper for the newest version of the chimp genome.[6] In this report, researchers describe how they were able to utilize a new long-read DNA sequencing technology to put together the first complete version of the chimp genome based on its own merits without using the human genome as a scaffold. This new technology not only produces individual snippets of DNA 10,000 to 30,000 bases in length but also greatly reduces the problem of human DNA contamination. Significantly, this secular research report documenting the most accurate version of the chimp genome to date completely sidestepped the all-important evolutionary issue of DNA similarity with humans. In this important paper, the researchers confirmed how previous versions of the chimp genome had been biased and skewed to look human. The authors of the paper stated, "The higher-quality human genome assemblies have often been used to guide the final stages of nonhuman genome projects, including the order and orientation of sequence contigs and, perhaps more importantly, the annotation of genes. This bias has effectively 'humanized' other ape genome assemblies."[6]

Despite the controversial human-chimp DNA similarity issue being neglected in the new 2018 chimp genome publication, University of London evolutionist Richard Buggs took it upon himself to analyze the data of a comprehensive comparison of the new chimp genome with human that was posted on a public genomics database. Buggs publicly published his surprising anti-evolutionary findings on the internet, much to the shock of the academic world. He stated, "The percentage of nucleotides in the human genome that had one-to-one exact matches in the chimpanzee genome was 84.38%"[7]

What makes Buggs' assessment more amazing is the fact that my own recently published research using an alternative approach and a different algorithm gave nearly identical results.[8] In my study, I aligned 18,000 random pieces of high-quality chimp DNA that were each on average 30,544 DNA letters long onto the human genome and several different versions of the chimp genome. My analysis showed that the aligned segments of chimp DNA were on average only 84.4% identical to human, the same level of similarity reported by Buggs.

Another interesting discovery I made was that the 30,544 base chunks of chimp DNA were unable to contiguously align onto human in their entirety before the algorithm broke off the matching process due to non-similarity. On average, only about 10,508 bases of each piece of DNA (about one third) could be matched before the DNA sequence became too dissimilar. In other words, the 84% identity that I was able to achieve appears to be an upper limit for DNA similarity, and the actual amount of overall similarity between human and chimpanzee DNA is most likely much lower.

Another very important fact that I discovered is that the older version of the chimp genome known as PanTro4, which is still the default for human-chimp DNA comparisons, was deeply flawed and humanized. The 30,544 letter chunks of chimp DNA matched perfectly onto the new highly accurate version of the chimp genome at close to 100% identity for their full length, but when I aligned them onto the previous PanTro4 version of the chimp genome, the poor alignment results were almost similar to that achieved using human. Shockingly, the average identity for the matches was only 91%, and the average length of the alignments was only 10,699 letters out of 30,544 (35%). In the new PanTro6 version of the chimp genome, the researchers admitted that previous versions of the chimp genome were "humanized." My research confirmed this inconvenient truth, but sadly the PanTro4 "humanized" version of the chimp genome is still being used as the default chimp genome for research and comparison to human despite its clear evolutionary bias and deeply flawed nature.

**Putting the Research Pieces Together**

A key element of the human evolution myth is the belief that human and chimp DNA is 98.5% identical. This level of DNA similarity is an important component of the speculation that humans and chimps shared a common ancestor three to six million years ago. Based on known DNA mutation rates observed in humans and chimps, levels significantly lower than 98.5% similarity would destroy the genetic foundation of the entire paradigm.

When I first began researching the scientific literature on the subject in 2012, I soon realized there were serious discrepancies with the evolutionary concept of nearly identical human and chimp DNA. In every publication I examined, it became obvious that researchers had cherry-picked nearly identical DNA sequences that undergirded evolution and discarded or avoided data that was dissimilar.[9] Where it was possible to determine, I recalculated DNA similarities by factoring back in data that had been omitted and achieved markedly lower levels of human-chimp DNA similarity between 66% and 86%.

After a long quest of examining huge amounts of DNA sequence data myself, in 2016 I published an important comprehensive study of raw unassembled chimp DNA sequences that revealed that the overall DNA similarity between humans and chimps was no more than 85%. In a follow-up study two years later using longer and more accurate chimp DNA sequences, this number was confirmed and refined to 84% maximum similarity between the two genomes.

As things stand now, a 16% minimum difference in the overall DNA similarity between humans and chimps is a discrepancy that cannot be ignored when no greater than a 1% difference is needed to make humans evolving from an ape-like ancestor seem remotely plausible. This hard fact vindicates the scientific accuracy of the Bible that unequivocally proclaims the uniqueness of humans as stated in Genesis 1:27: "So God created man in His own image; in the image of God He created him; male and female He created them." The Bible also clearly states that all creatures reproduce "after their kind." While there is variability within kinds, discontinuity between created kinds is both a biblical and a scientific fact.

On the other hand, some people might say, "Why is there only a 16% difference? That doesn't sound like much." The fact of the matter is that humans and chimps do share many localized protein-coding regions of high to moderate DNA sequence similarity. Common code is serving a similar biochemical purpose, whether it be in humans, chimps, or even rabbits. Just as human software developers utilize similar code between software programs, the Creator has also used similar code to achieve similar function across the spectrum of life. This is a standard feature and hallmark of design and engineering. In other words, we should expect both similarity and discontinuity in the DNA of humans, apes, and various animals.

However, the main point we need to make in regard to debunking the falsehood of human evolution is the fact that overall there is extreme DNA sequence discontinuity between humans and chimps that evolution cannot explain or account for. The sheer magnitude of the DNA sequence discontinuity chasm utterly befuddles the mythical evolutionary presuppositions of a human-chimp common ancestor.

### *Notes*

1. Kimbel, W. H. and B. Villmoare. 2016. From *Australopithecus* to *Homo*: the transition that wasn't. *Philosophical Transactions of the Royal Society B.* 371 (1698): 20150248.

2. Tomkins, J. 2011. How genomes are sequenced and why it matters: implications for studies in comparative genomics of humans and chimpanzees. *Answers Research Journal.* 4: 81-88.

3. Longo, M. S. et al. 2011. Abundant human DNA contamination identified in non- primate genome databases. *PLoS ONE.* 6 (2): e16410.

4. Kryukov, K. and T. Imanishi. 2016. Human Contamination in Public Genome Assemblies. *PLoS ONE.* 11 (9): e0162424.

5. Tomkins, J. 2016. Analysis of 101 Chimpanzee Trace Read Data Sets: Assessment of Their Overall Similarity to Human and Possible Contamination With Human DNA. *Answers Research Journal.* 9: 294-298.

6. Kronenberg, Z. N. et al. 2018. High-resolution comparative analysis of great ape genomes. *Science.* 360 (6393): eaar6343.

7. Buggs, R. How similar are human and chimpanzee genomes? Posted on richardbuggs.com July 14, 2018, accessed August 9, 2018.

8. Tomkins, J. 2018. Comparison of 18,000 De Novo Assembled Chimpanzee Contigs to the Human Genome Yields Average BLASTN Alignment Identities of 84%. *Answers Research Journal.* 11: 215-219.

9. Tomkins, J. and J. Bergman. 2012. Genomic monkey business—estimates of nearly identical human-chimp DNA similarity re-evaluated using omitted data. *Journal of Creation.* 26 (1): 94-100.

# 25

# CHROMOSOME 2: FUSION OR NOT?

Jeffrey P. Tomkins, Ph.D.

**Summary:** Evolutionists struggle to explain why humans have 46 chromosomes and apes have 48 if both descended from a common ancestor. The supposed answer is the fusion of two chromosomes in the past. The alleged fusion site isn't connected to satellite DNA sequence like documented fusions are, and it's too small and muddled to be the fusion of two chromosomes.

Most importantly, the fusion site is located inside a gene and contains intricate coding functionality—soundly refuting fusion. The alleged cryptic centromere site is inside a large protein-coding gene, further refuting the fusion idea.

The overwhelming scientific conclusion is that the human chromosome 2 fusion never happened.

One of the top arguments used for humans supposedly evolving from apes is known as the chromosome fusion. The general impetus for this idea is the evolutionary problem that apes have an extra pair of chromosomes compared to humans. Humans have a complement of 46 chromosomes (one set of 23 from the mother and one from the father) while apes have 48. If humans evolved from an ape-like creature in only three to six million years—a mere blip in the grand scheme of the evolution of life on Earth that occurred over an alleged 3.8 billion years since the first cells spontaneously evolved—then why do humans and apes have different numbers of chromosomes? The evolutionary idea to solve the chromosome difference conundrum between apes and humans proposes that an end-to-end fusion of two small ape-like chromosomes (named 2A and 2B) produced human chromosome 2. For a visual illustration of the hypothetical fusion scenario, see Figure 1.

The original idea for the chromosome fusion was based on shared patterns of bands observed using light microscopy for chemically stained chromosomes.[1] This technique uses cells with highly condensed chromosomes that have been isolated during cell division (mitosis) that are then stained with dyes that bind to the DNA and produce patterns of dark and light bands. The name for this technique, which can also be used for detecting diseases associated with major chromosomal aberrations like Down syndrome, is called *karyotyping*.

When this was done with chimp cells, several small chromosomes shared a number of bands similar to human chromosome 2, and were then determined to have fused together end-to-end to form that human chromosome. Of course, there were a variety of bands not shared between the human and chimp chromosomes as well. In fact, an entire chunk of one of the chimp chromosomes is missing and not even represented in the alleged fusion. Based on a comparative analysis of the karyotypes, this created an extreme size discrepancy or unaccounted-for loss of chimp DNA of about 10%, or 24.3 million bases of chimp DNA in the purported fusion (Figure 1). This discrepancy can be calculated based on comparative karyotypes and the known highly accurate DNA sequence size for human chromosome 2.

Another important point to make regarding chromosome banding and comparing karyotypes between humans and chimps is what exactly forms the genetic basis for these banding patterns. Some people have tried to imply that the bands correspond closely to genetic information like genes and have used the false analogy of the bands being chapters in a book, with each book being a chromosome. The basis for these band patterns was not well understood in 1982 when researchers first published their comparative human-chimp karyotypes. We know now that the stained bands are related to the percentages or ratios of the DNA letters C and G to A and T, not specific genes or groups of genes.

## The So-Called Fusion Site

The alleged DNA signature of the proposed fusion event between two ape-like chromosomes is located on human chromosome 2. The particular DNA segment was first isolated and sequenced in 1991, about nine years after the whole fusion idea was first proposed based on the original analysis of comparative karyotypes.[2] Researchers discovered what they thought was the presence of a muddled head-to-head fusion of chromosome end sequences called *telomeres*. Telomeres are the six-base sequence of DNA letters TTAGG repeated over and over again at the ends of chromosomes. They act like the plastic sheaths at the ends of shoelaces called *aglets* that keep the laces from getting unraveled. The telomere fusion signature discovery was actually somewhat of a surprise to researchers because they were expecting something different based on data from known fusions in living mammals and the apparent loss of a large amount of chimp DNA that was apparent from the karyotype images (Figure 1).

If the alleged telomeric signature was evidence of a true chromosomal end-to-end fusion, then it would actually be the first such case documented in mammals that involved a telomere-to-telomere fusion. This is because all documented known mammalian chromosome fusions in living animals involve a specific type of sequence called *satellite DNA* (satDNA). This satDNA is found all over the genome, and particularly around areas inside chromosomes called *centromeres* where some chromosomes can break prior to fusing. The presence of satDNA is a DNA feature that can be involved in breakages and ends up in the subsequent fused chromosome sequence.[3-5] Although chromosome fusions in animals are very rare, in such cases the fusion junction is clearly marked by combinations of telomere-satDNA or satDNA-satDNA, and also often involves centromeres or regions near them. Chromosome fusions representing telomere-telomere DNA signatures like that found at the alleged human fusion site on chromosome 2 have never been found in nature. This absence of documented end-to-end telomere fusions in living animals is due to the fact that telomeres also contain highly specialized end caps of a protein complex that protects them from fusing.[6]

Some evolutionists have tried to counter this argument that telomeres can't fuse together by citing data from the rearranged genomes of human cancer cells. In cancer, cell division is essentially out of control, and all sorts of chromosomal anomalies can be found, including telomere-telomere fusions. But obviously, these are not healthy, normal cells, and their presence leads to serious life-threatening conditions.

In humans and other mammals, telomeres are composed of the six-base repeat TTAGGG for thousands of bases in length. Healthy human telomeres usually contain 800 to 2,500 of these TTAGGG repeats in perfect tandem.[6] So, in light of the evolutionary fusion story, the main question we must ask when investigating for a signature of telomeric fusion is does the so-called fusion signature contain the hallmarks of an end-to-end fusion of two chromosomes?

When we take a look at the fusion site in detail, it immediately becomes apparent that it is unexpectedly small, only 798 bases in length. This is surprisingly miniscule compared to what should be present if a fusion of two telomeres actually occurred. Even if two of the smallest-size human telomeres fused end-to-end, a DNA sequence of about 10,000 bases in length should exist. If two larger length telomeres fused, the fusion signature should be about 30,000 bases long.

Not only is the small size a problem for the fusion story, another major discrepancy is that the signature does not really represent a clear-cut fusion of telomeres as is often touted. Even if we assume a very generous evolutionary time frame of six million years since humans split off from a common ancestor with chimps, the muddled nature of the fusion site sequence does not cooperate. See Figure 2, which shows the DNA letters of the 798 base fusion site, with the intact telomere sequences emphasized in bold print.

One of the chief characteristics of the muddled nature of the fusion signature is that there is a marked absence of intact telomeric repeats, and the intact ones that can be found exist independently since they are not present in tandem repeats. Based on predictions for a recent evolutionary fusion, thousands of intact motifs in near-perfect tandem should exist. Within the 798-base fusion signature, only 10 intact TTAGGG telomere sequences exist and only 43 CCCTAA (reverse complement) intact reverse complement telomere sequences are present.

One of the most informative secular research papers on this subject delivered a thorough DNA analysis of the fusion site and over 600,000 bases of DNA surrounding it.[7] In this report, the researchers pointed out that the fusion signature was extremely "degenerate." In evolutionary lingo, this means that it is ambiguous and degraded, and given its supposed recent evolutionary origin, a complete surprise. In fact, compared to a fusion signature of the same length that would be composed of perfect pristine repeats, it is only 70% identical. Given the supposed evolutionary time frame, it should be about 98 to 99% identical. The researchers describing this discovery commented, "Head-to-head arrays of repeats at the fusion site have degenerated significantly (14%) from the near perfect arrays of (TTAGGG)n found at telomeres" and asked the pertinent question "If the fusion occurred within the telomeric repeat arrays less than ~6 Mya, why are the arrays at the fusion site so degenerate?"[7] It should be noted that the 14% degeneration cited by the authors refers to the corruption of just the six-base sequences themselves, not the whole 798 bases.

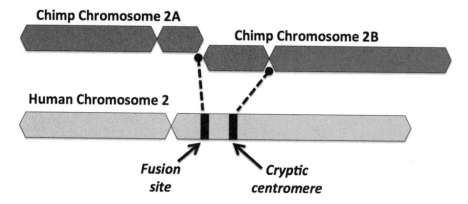

Figure 1. Hypothetical model in which chimpanzee chromosomes 2A and 2B fused end-to-end to form human chromosome 2. The chromosomes are drawn to scale according to cytogenetic images published by Yunis and Prakash.[1] Note the size discrepancy, which is about 10% or 24 million bases based on the known size of human chromosome 2.

So, why is the alleged signature of fusion so small and muddled? Is this an area of the genome with a lot of variability or mutational activity? Actually, just the opposite is the case. The variability in this area based on comparing the genomes of thousands of people around the world indicates that it is about average. In fact, secular researchers have pointed out that areas of the human genome near centromeres, like where the fusion site is located, are generally much more stable and less variable than other parts of the genome.

The fusion site itself along with the DNA immediately surrounding it are also void of another class of DNA called *transposable elements* that can alter and mutate it. Taken together, this means that any type of mutational mechanism or alteration in the general area of the fusion site is quote low, and that if it was a true hallmark of fusion it should be fairly pristine and not small and degenerate like what we actually see. In reality, the so-called fusion signature is a vague shadow of what should be present if the fusion story were true.

## The Fusion Site Inside a Gene

Despite all of the discrepancies mentioned above, the most remarkable anti-evolutionary discovery about the putative fusion site turned out to be where it was located and what it was actually doing. This discovery came about while I was reading the research paper that reported a detailed analysis of 614,000 bases of DNA sequence surrounding the alleged fusion site. I noticed in one of the report's figures that the fusion site was located inside a gene, and quite remarkably this oddity was not acknowledged or discussed in the text of the paper.[8]

You would immediately think that a finding like this would be highly noteworthy. Perhaps this significant piece of information would have been the nail in the evolutionary coffin, so the researchers refused to discuss it. Needless to say, this major anomaly inspired me to give the fusion site a much closer examination. Because this particular paper was published in 2002 and I took notice of it in 2013, I knew a huge amount of data on the structure and function of the human genome had been published since then, and there was likely much more to the story that needed to be uncovered.

When I performed further research, I did in fact verify that the fusion site is positioned inside a gene now called *DDX11L2*. Most genes in plants and animals have their coding segments in pieces called *exons* so that they can be alternatively spliced. Based on the addition or exclusion of exons, genes can produce a variety of products. The intervening regions between exons are called *introns,* which often contain a variety of regulatory signals and switches that control the function of the gene. The alleged fusion site is positioned inside the first intron of the functional RNA helicase gene *DDX11L2* (Figure 3).[9]

The DNA molecule is double-stranded with what is called a plus strand and a minus strand. It was engineered this way to maximize information density while also increasing efficiency and function. As a result, there are genes running in different directions on the opposing strands. As it turns out, the *DDX11L2* gene is encoded on the minus strand. The *DDX11L2* gene has three exons, and amazingly the so-called fusion site serves a special purpose. Because genes in humans are like Swiss army knives and can produce a variety of RNAs, in the case of the *DDX11L2* gene it produces short variants consisting of two exons and long variants with three (Figure 3).[9]

So, what might this *DDX11L2* gene be doing? My research showed it is expressed in at least 255 different cell or tissue types.[9] It is also closely co-expressed (turned on at the same time) with a variety of other genes around the genome and is connected to processes associated with cell signaling in the extracellular matrix and blood cell production. The location of the so-called fusion sequence inside a functional gene associated with the genetics of a wide variety of cellular processes strongly refutes the idea that it is the accidental byproduct of a head-to-head telomeric fusion. Genes are not formed by catastrophic chromosomal fusions!

But the data refuting fusion do not stop with the fact that it is located inside a gene. The purported fusion site is itself functional and serves an important engineered purpose. My research showed that the fusion site actually serves as a switch for controlling gene activity. In this respect, a wealth of biochemical data showed that 12 different proteins called *transcription factors* bound to this segment of the gene. One of the proteins that bind to it is none other than RNA polymerase II, the main enzyme that copies RNA molecules from DNA in a process called *transcription*. Backing up this important discovery is additional data that I uncovered showing that the actual process of transcription initiates inside the region of the so-called fusion site.

Technically speaking, we would call the activity in the alleged fusion site a *promoter region*. Promoters are the main switches at the beginning of genes that turn them on and are also where the RNA polymerase starts to create an RNA. Many genes have alternative promoters like the *DDX11L2* gene inside the gene in the first intron.

As mentioned, there are actually two areas of transcription factor binding in the *DDX11L2* gene. The first is in the promoter directly in front of the first exon, and the second is in the first intron corresponding to the fusion site sequence. This dual promoter scenario, along with the fact that the *DDX11L2* gene produces RNAs with two or three exons, indicates that the gene undergoes a process called *alternative transcription*. Not only is the gene itself complexly controlled with the alleged fusion sequence playing a role, but even the transcripts produced are very complex. My research also showed that the RNAs themselves contain a wide variety of binding and control sites for a class of small regulatory molecules called *microRNAs*.[9]

TGAGGGTGAGGG**TTAGGG**TTTGGGTTGGGTTTGGGGTTGGGGTTGGGGTAGGGGTGGGGTTGGGG

TTGGGGTTGGGG**TTAGGG**GTAGGGGTAGGGGTAGGGGTAGGGTCAGGGTCAGGGTCAGGG**TTAG**

GG**TTTTAGGG**GTTAGGATT**TTAGGGTTAGGG**TAAGGGTTAAGGGTTGGGGTTGGGG**TTAGGGTTA**

GGGG**TTAGGG**TTGGGGTTGGGGTTGGGGTTGGGGTTGGGGTTGGGG**TTAGGG**TTAGCT**AA**ACCTA

ACC**CTAACCCCTAA**CCCCAACCCCAACCCCAACCCTACCCCTACCCCTAC**CCCTAA**CCCCAACCCC

CACCCTTAACCCTTAACCCTTA**CCCTAACCCTAA**CCCAAA**CCCTAA**CCCTA**CCCTAACCCTAA**CCC

AA**CCCTAACCCTAA**CCCTA**CCCTAACCCTAA**CACCCTAAAACCGTGACCCTGACCTTGACCCTGA

CCCTTAACCCTTAA**CCCTAA**CCATAA**CCCTAAACCCTAACCCTAA**ACCCTAACCCTAAACCCTAA

**CCCTAA**CACTACCCTA**CCCTAA**CCCCAAC**CCCTAACCCCTAACCCTAA**CCCTACCCCTAACCCCA

ACCCCAGCCCCAACCCTTA**CCCTAA**CCCTA**CCCTAA**CCCTTAA**CCCTAACCCCTAACCCTAA**CCC

**CTAACCCTAA**CCCTACCCCAACCCCAAACCCAA**CCCTAA**CCCAA**CCCTAACCCCTAACCCTAA**CC

CCTA**CCCTAA**CCCCTAGCCCTAGCCCTAG**CCCTAACCCTAA**CCCTCGCCCTAACCCTCACCCTAAC

CCTCACCCTCA**CCCTAA**

Figure 2. The 798 bp core sequence surrounding the fusion site (underlined and bold). Intact forward (TTAGGG) and reverse complement (CCCTAA) telomere sequences are also in bold font. Outside of this small region, the concentration of telomere sequences totally breaks down, and they are hundreds to thousands of bases apart.

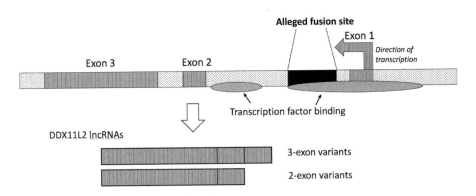

Figure 3. Simplified illustration of the alleged fusion site inside the first intron of the *DDX11L2* gene. The graphic also shows two versions of short and long transcript variants produced, along with areas of transcription factor binding. The arrow in the first exon depicts direction the of transcription.

## Functional Internal Telomere Sequences Are All Over the Genome

The presence of internally located telomere sequence repeats all over the human genome is a mystery to evolutionists and has been known since the first draft of the human genome in 2001. These seemingly out-of-place telomere repeats have been dubbed *interstitial telomeres*. Their presence is another challenge for the fusion site idea. It is a fact that very few of the telomere repeats in the fusion site occur in tandem. As noted in Figure 2, the sequence of the 798-base fusion site contains only a few instances where two repeats are actually in tandem, and there are none that have three repeats or more. However, there are many other interstitial telomere sites all over the human genome where the repeats occur in perfect tandem three to ten times or more.[10,11] Internally located clusters of telomere repeats are more common than is realized and not necessarily indicative of a fusion.

Interestingly, it now appears that interstitial telomeric repeats may serve some important function in the genome related to gene expression besides their role at the ends of chromosomes. In an extensive study, I identified interstitial telomeric repeats all over the human genome and then intersected their genomic locations with a diversity of data sets containing functional biochemical information for gene activity.[12] I discovered that literally thousands of telomeric repeats across the genome were directly associated with the hallmarks of gene expression. As it turns out, the same type of transcription factor binding and gene activity occurring at the alleged fusion site was occurring genome-wide at numerous other interstitial telomeric repeats. Clearly, these DNA features are not the accidents of evolution but purposefully and intelligently designed functional code.

## Bogus Cryptic Centromere Inside a Gene

Yet another key problem with the fusion model is the lack of viable evidence for a signature of an extra centromere region. Centromeres are key sections of chromosomes often in central locations that play key roles as an attachment site for cell machinery to pull newly replicated chromosomes apart after they have been replicated during cell division. As depicted in Figure 1, immediately following the alleged head-to-head fusion of two chromosomes there would have existed two centromere sites in the newly formed chimeric chromosome. In such a case, one of the centromeres would be functional while the other would be disabled. The presence of two active centromeres is bad news for chromosomes and would lead to chromosome dysfunction and cell destruction. The fusion event along with the silencing of one centromere would have had to occur in a cell lineage during the production of an egg or a sperm to be heritable.

Interestingly, the evidence for a cryptic centromere on human chromosome 2 is even weaker than that for a telomere-rich fusion site. Evolutionists explain the lack of a clearly distinguishable nonfunctional secondary centromere by arguing that a second centromere would be rapidly selected against. According to the evolutionary model, the disabled centromere would deteriorate over time since there were no functional restraints placed on it anymore by its doing something useful in the genome. However, the actual evidence for a second remnant centromere at any stage of sequence degeneration is problematic for the evolutionary paradigm.

Functional centromere sequences are composed of a repetitive type of DNA called *alphoid sequences*, with each alphoid repeat being about 171 bases long. There are actually different variations of alphoid sequence across the genome that can be placed into different categories. Some types of alphoid repeats are found all over the genome, while others are specific to centromeres. The structure of the alphoid sequences found at the cryptic centromere site on human chromosome 2 does not match those associated with functional human centromeres.[13] Even worse for the evolutionary overall model is that they have no highly similar counterparts in the chimp genome—they are human specific.[13]

In addition to the evolutionary problem of alphoid repeat structure and non-similarity to real centromeres, the alleged fossil centromere is exceptionally tiny compared to a real one. The size of a normal human centromere ranges in length between 250,000 and 5,000,000 bases.[14] However, the alleged cryptic centromere is only 41,608 bases long. It is also important to know that there are three different regions of it that are not even alphoid repeats.[15] Two of these are called *retroelements*, with one being a LPA3/LINE repeat 5,957 bases long and the other an SVA-E element (2,571 bases). (See Figure 4.) When we subtract the insertions of these non-alphoid sequences, it gives a length of only 33,080 bases, which is a fraction of the length of real centromere.

However, the most serious evolutionary problem with the idea of a fossil centromere is that like the alleged fusion site, it is positioned inside a gene called *ANKRD30BL* (Ankyrin Repeat Domain 30B Like).[12,15] Intriguingly, the alleged centromere sequence covers both intron and exon regions of the gene. In fact, the part of the alleged fossil centromere sequence that lands inside an exon actually codes for amino acids in the resulting gene's protein (Figure 4). This type of ankyrin-repeat protein is associated with the cell membrane and is believed to be involved in the interaction of the structural network of proteins inside the cell called the *cytoskeleton* in connection with receptor proteins imbedded in the cell membrane.[16] The fact that the so-called fossil or cryptic centromere is a functional region inside an important protein-coding gene completely refutes the idea that it is a defunct centromere.

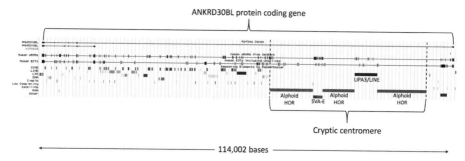

Figure 4. The 41,608-base cryptic centromere region on chromosome 2 that is positioned within the *ANK-RD30BL* protein-coding gene

## Conclusion: No Fusion

Due to the muddled signatures and small sizes of the alleged fusion and fossil centromere sites, it's highly questionable that their sequence was evolutionarily derived from an ancient chromosome fusion. Not only that, they represent functional sequence inside genes. The alleged fusion site is an important genetic switch called a promoter inside the *DDX11L2* long noncoding RNA gene, and the so-called fossil centromere contains both coding and noncoding sequence inside a large ankyrin-repeat protein-coding gene.

This is an undeniable double whammy against the whole mythical fusion idea, utterly destroying its validity. The overwhelming scientific conclusion is that the fusion never happened.

### Notes

1. Yunis, J. J. and O. Prakash. 1982. The origin of man: a chromosomal pictorial legacy. *Science*. 215 (4539): 1525-1530.

2. Ijdo, J. W. et al. 1991. Origin of human chromosome 2: An ancestral telomere-telomere fusion. *Proceedings of the National Academy of Sciences*. 88 (20): 9051 9055.

3. Chaves, R. et al. 2003. Molecular cytogenetic analysis and centromeric satellite organization of a novel 8;11 translocation in sheep: a possible intermediate in biarmed chromosome evolution. *Mammalian Genome*. 14 (10): 706-710.

4. Tsipouri, V. et al. 2008. Comparative sequence analyses reveal sites of ancestral chromosomal fusions in the Indian muntjac genome. *Genome Biology*. 9 (10): R155.

5. Adega, F., H. Guedes-Pinto, and R. Chaves. 2009. Satellite DNA in the karyotype evolution of domestic animals—clinical considerations. *Cytogenetic and Genome Research*. 126 (1-2): 12-20.

6. Tomkins, J. P. and J. Bergman. 2011. Telomeres: implications for aging and evidence for intelligent design. *Journal of Creation.* 25 (1): 86-97.

7. Fan, Y. et al. 2002. Genomic structure and evolution of the ancestral chromosome fusion site in 2q13-2q14.1 and paralogous regions on other human chromosomes. *Genome Research.* 12 (11): 1651-1662.

8. Fan, Y. et al. 2002. Gene content and function of the ancestral chromosome fusion site in human chromosome 2q13-2q14.1 and paralogous regions. *Genome Research.* 12 (11): 1663-1672.

9. Tomkins, J. P. 2013 Alleged Human Chromosome 2 "Fusion Site" Encodes an Active DNA Binding Domain Inside a Complex and Highly Expressed Gene—Negating Fusion. *Answers Research Journal.* 6: 367-375.

10. Azzalin, C. M., S. G. Nergadze, and E. Giulotto. 2001. Human intrachromosomal telomeric-like repeats: sequence organization and mechanisms of origin. *Chromosoma.* 110: 75-82.

11. Ruiz-Herrera, A. et al. 2008. Telomeric Repeats Far from the Ends: Mechanisms of Origin and Role in Evolution. *Cytogenetic and Genome Research.* 122 (3-4): 219-228.

12. Tomkins, J. P. 2018. Combinatorial genomic data refute the human chromosome 2 evolutionary fusion and build a model of functional design for interstitial telomeric repeats. In *Proceedings of the Eighth International Conference on Creationism* J. H. Whitmore, ed. Pittsburgh, PA: Creation Science Fellowship, 222-228.

13. Tomkins, J. and J. Bergman. 2011. The Chromosome 2 Fusion Model of Human Evolution—Part 2: Re-Analysis of the Genomic Data. *Journal of Creation.* 25 (2): 111-117.

14. Aldrup-Macdonald, M. E. and B. A. Sullivan. 2014. The Past, Present, and Future of Human Centromere Genomics. *Genes (Basel).* 5 (1): 33-50.

15. Tomkins, J. P. 2017. Debunking the Debunkers: A Response to Criticism and Obfuscation Regarding Refutation of the Human Chromosome 2 Fusion. *Answers Research Journal.* 10: 45-54.

16. Voronin, D. A. and E. V. Kiseleva. 2008. Functional Role of Proteins Containing Ankyrin Repeats. *Cell and Tissue Biology.* 49 (12): 989-999.

# 26

# THE MYSTERY OF LIFE'S BEGINNING

Jeffrey P. Tomkins, Ph.D.

**Summary:** Evolutionists are at an impasse when it comes to how life began. There is no fossil evidence that simple chemicals combined to form the first biomolecules, and the hurdles involved make it a scientific impossibility.

Earth's current atmosphere destroys biomolecules not protected inside living cells, and geological data indicate the past atmosphere was similar. The basic molecules would need to arise through random processes and navigate a number of impossible scenarios to form the necessary building blocks for life.

Even if they could have formed themselves into primitive proteins, that doesn't solve the problem that DNA, RNA, and proteins are wholly dependent on each other. Any one of them cannot function without the other two. And they all need the protective complex structures of a living cell's membrane to avoid being degraded. Only the special creation recorded in the Bible explains life.

"The origin of life has not been seen in Earth's rock record and poor preservation of the earth's oldest rocks suggest that it will not be."[1]

The above statement made by evolutionary researchers deeply involved in the study of life's origins makes a key point: There is no fossil record of how life began. All evolutionary "origin of life" hypotheses are speculative stories that assume from the outset that naturalistic random processes were somehow responsible. As a result, one must keep in mind that this field of science is highly speculative and subjective.

The question of how life first arose on Earth is perhaps the greatest obstacle for the evolutionary paradigm. While the whole concept of biological evolution itself is full of serious problems, the origin of the first biomolecules and the first cell (not to mention the enormous amount of information contained within the cell) is a complete impossibility from a naturalistic perspective. In fact, without a plausible explanation as to the origin of the first cell, the whole evolutionary story collapses!

The hypothetical naturalistic formation of life out of the most basic molecules is called *abiogenesis* or *biogenesis*. This concept lies at the foundation of biological evolution, but it is often ignored by most evolutionists themselves. Because of its scientific impossibility, it represents the ultimate hurdle to evolution.

### Early Earth Atmosphere Controversy

When judging the plausibility of abiogenesis models, one must consider the necessary conditions that could have allowed the formation of the first biomolecules needed for life: purines, pyrimidines, amino acids, sugars, and lipids. In living cells, these molecules are used to form large chains (polymers) and other important structures. These structures are protected within the confines of the cell from degradation by the atmosphere and solar radiation. Our current Earth atmosphere is about 21% oxygen by volume, and oxygen is destructive to biomolecules not safely enclosed inside a cell. The oxygen in the environment outside the cell rapidly degrades biomolecules through a process called *oxidation* (which is why our current atmosphere is called an *oxidizing* atmosphere).

Because oxidation rapidly degrades DNA, proteins, and membranes, some evolutionists have speculated that the early earth had an atmosphere with little or no oxygen (what is called a *reducing* atmosphere). They also believe that it must have been rich in nitrogen, hydrogen, and carbon monoxide in order to provide the basic molecules needed (amino acids, sugars, nucleotides). They believe this because our current atmosphere would have made life's origins impossible.

One big problem with this claim is that the geological data indicate that the earth's atmosphere has always been similar to what it is now (oxidizing), with significant levels of oxygen.[2,3] Geophysical research also shows that the biochemical precursors required by origin of life scenarios have never existed on Earth, or did so in levels that were far too low to allow abiogenesis to occur.[4-6]

To get around this problem, some have postulated that localized reducing environments may have been present around volcanic plumes.[7] However, the extreme temperatures and acidity in these environments would not be at all conducive to the formation of biomolecules. Evolutionists might take a little comfort in the fact that some "extremophile" microorganisms have been found to live in these environments, but these microorganisms contain highly specialized and unique cell systems that allow them to tolerate these extreme conditions. Therefore, they are not anything like the ancient simple cell prototypes that evolutionists believe existed.

Evolutionary researchers still have no plausible explanation for what sort of early Earth environment could have spawned the first hypothetical biomolecules. A highly prominent modern abiogenesis research leader, David Deamer, stated the status of this highly significant, but largely unpublicized, problem in his 2011 book *First Life*.

> But someone from the outside world would be astonished by the lack of agreement among experts on plausible sites [for abiogenesis], which range all the way from vast sheets of ice occasionally melted by giant impacts, to "warm little ponds" first suggested by Charles Darwin, to hydrothermal vents in the deep ocean, and even to a kind of hot, mineral mud deep in Earth's crust.[8]

## The First Biomolecules

Before the evolutionary process could even begin, a diverse array of basic molecules would have to be formed in some hypothetical primordial matrix or soup. These molecules would include various types of amino acids, purines, pyrimidines, sugars, and lipids. The spontaneous generation of these basic building blocks for life, in the correct forms and amounts needed, is itself a glaring impossibility. Arranging these basic molecules into larger polymer-based molecules containing coherent molecular information is also impossible! For the past 60 years, evolutionists have spent millions of dollars in research funding attempting to solve this problem, but the impossibility of evolutionary origin of life scenarios remains.

One of the first experiments claiming that naturalistic processes could synthesize the basic molecules of life was the famous 1953 experiment conducted by Stanley Miller and Harold Urey in which basic chemical gases (representative of those thought to be present in Earth's early atmosphere) were circulated through an elaborate device shown in Figure 1 and exposed to an electric discharge.[9] This early study is still held in high regard by the abiogenesis research community. In fact, archived samples of reactants from Miller's research project were rediscovered and analyzed, and the results were published in 2008 in the journal *Science*.[10]

In both Miller's original experiment and subsequent similar experiments, methane, ammonia, hydrogen, and water vapor were circulated together in a device that exposed the gases to an electrical spark. In these experiments, the

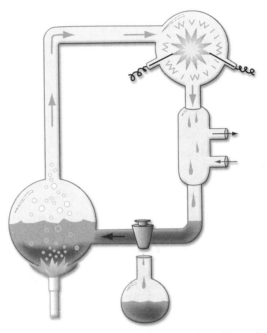

Figure 1. Apparatus used in Miller-Urey amino acid genesis experiments.

products of the reactions driven by the electrical discharge were filtered and collected in a trap before the products were cycled back through the system and destroyed by the same processes that created them (Figure 1).

The results based on Miller's general design have done very little to help the abiogenesis model of origins. In what are considered to be the most successful versions of these experiments, scientists have been able to produce six of the 20 amino acids that are used in biological proteins. Nevertheless, there are a number of very serious problems with the results of these studies that completely negate their use as an argument for the naturalistic origins of life's first biomolecules.

First, the amino acids produced in these experiments are only the most simple of the amino acids. The more complex amino acids cannot be created using these techniques. But these more complex amino acids (which are central to all biological life) contain elaborate side chains or groups of molecules that can only be synthesized through the complex biochemical pathways found in *living* cells.

Second, the *chirality problem* prevents the few simple amino acids that *were* produced from being used in real-life proteins. Amino acids can exist in both right- and left-handed versions, just like your hands are similar in structure yet are unique because they are mirror images of each other. In Miller's system, both left- and right-handed amino acids were produced, but living cells only use left-handed amino acids to make proteins. Thus, living cells only synthesize left-handed amino acids. But in a hypothetical primordial soup, one would expect equal amounts of right- and left-handed amino acids to be produced. What natural process could separate the left- and right-handed amino acids from one another?

Third, the quantities of a number of the amino acids that were produced were far too dilute to be of any significant biological use, even if only left-handed ones were produced.

Besides failing to acknowledge that only a few simple amino acids were produced using these techniques, scientists generally fail to mention that the tar-like "goo" produced in the study also contained a variety of molecules that are actually harmful to cell life, such as hydrogen cyanide and formaldehyde. Furthermore, Miller's system tended to destroy amino acids as fast as it could create them. This is why a trap was employed to filter off the products before they could be cycled back through the apparatus and destroyed.

The reason that Miller's work (and the similar work of other abiogenesis researchers) is often touted is because it represents one of the few instances where they can claim some minimal level of success—although in reality, the results have actually done very little to help the abiogenesis paradigm. In fact, these efforts do a better job of illustrating the futility of abiogenesis scenarios.

Unfortunately for evolutionists, the results of these experiments represent the *best* evidence to date. In fact, the evidence for the biogenesis of the other major basic molecules of cell life is essentially nonexistent. Evidence that the purines and pyrimidines needed for DNA and RNA could have spontaneously arisen apart from the cell's biochemistry is completely elusive. The same is true for the formation of sugar molecules like ribose or deoxyribose, which are also needed for DNA and RNA. The complex nature of cell membranes and the spontaneous origins of specific types of phospholipid molecules needed for their construction are also a complete mystery.

## The Problem of Polymerization

Another key hurdle in biogenesis is the bonding together of long chains (polymerization) of base molecules according to specific information-based sequences. In living cells, amino acids and nucleotides are linked together via chemical bonds in a process using cell-based energy and complex enzyme (protein) complexes in specific ordered sequences in which the information is specified by genes in the cell's DNA.

In 1958, Sydney Fox published a set of experiments that attempted to provide a naturalistic explanation for the biological feature of polymerization. On the surface, the results appeared to add some credence to the notion that biopolymers could form spontaneously. Using starting solutions of pure left-handed biological amino acids, Fox was able to get amino acids to bind together in short, unordered globs by heating them to high temperatures.[11] The starting solutions of pure biologically active (left-handed) amino acids bore no resemblance whatsoever to anything produced by abiogenesis experiments like Miller's. Fox essentially baked the mixtures, driving out the water molecules and linking the amino acids together in crude aggregates. He also observed the coalescing of these structures into crude spheres when they were placed in certain solutions. Fox claimed not just a primitive form of polymerization, but the beginning of early cells! Abiogenesis researchers now widely agree that this line of study was completely fruitless. However, Fox's ideas are still promoted in many educational circles as evidence for abiogenesis.

In 2004, a group of researchers investigated how carbonyl sulfide oxide, a simple chemical compound found in volcanic gases, can activate amino acids to form peptide bonds.[12] However, no more than a few molecules could be linked together, and polymers of any appreciable size could not be formed. At present, evolutionists still have no plausible explanation for how biomolecule polymerization for proteins or nucleic acids could have occurred under primitive naturalistic conditions.

## An RNA World?

Given the enormous difficulties associated with claims that amino acids could have formed themselves into the primitive functional proteins that would have served as the first enzymes, some scientists have proposed that the first biomolecules were composed of RNA. This is because some RNA molecules have exhibited catalytic properties. Because RNA can contain both genetic information and, in some cases, simple enzymatic-like properties, evolutionists have proposed that RNAs may have been the first key biomolecules in biogenesis. However, this proposition actually has even more problems than the amino acid-based origins model.

RNA and DNA molecules are composed of five nucleobases, two sugars, and a phosphate. The nucleobases contain two different purines (adenine and guanine) and three different pyrimidines (cytosine, thymine, and uracil). Therefore, before an evolutionist even considers the possibility that RNA was the first major biomolecule, he must first explain the origin of these necessary nucleobases. Second, he must explain the origin of ribose and deoxyribose, the sugars that help link nucleobases. Third, he must explain the origin of phosphate biochemistry in biological systems, a relatively uncommon molecule that plays a variety of key roles in biomolecule chemistry. Fourth, he must answer the "recurring polymerization problem": How did the complex bonds involving sugars and phosphate form a connective backbone for the polymerization of purines and pyrimidines to take place? In fact, the random generation of these molecules, along with the immensely complicated problem of their polymerization, is an even larger hurdle than that which existed for proteins.

Even if RNA molecules somehow miraculously appeared, they are inherently very unstable molecules that are quickly degraded outside the cell or outside sterile, highly controlled lab conditions. Needless to say, such conditions would not have been present on the early earth in an evolutionary scenario! In the cases where RNA has exhibited enzymatic-like catalysis, they are isolated subprocesses of much larger complex cell systems. Furthermore, their activity is based on the complex two-dimensional folding patterns that they achieve based on highly specific predetermined genetic information transferred from DNA molecules. These catalytic RNAs and the system in which they are found to function are irreducibly complex and hardly represent vestiges of evolution. And as we shall describe later, this whole scenario presents a Catch-22 for the evolutionist. If the DNA molecule encodes the information for RNA and proteins, but RNA and proteins are required for the replication and usage of information stored in DNA, which came first?

## Lipids and Cell Membranes

Because complex molecules are quickly degraded or destroyed outside the protective confines of a cell, evolutionists have argued that the biochemical reactions that supposedly led to life's origins must have taken place within some sort of protected and enclosed space. Therefore, many evolutionist researchers believe that primitive lipids self-assembled themselves into little semi-permeable, sphere-like structures that were able to capture and house the first biomolecules. This supposedly led to some sort of primitive replicating proto-cell that eventually evolved into the different forms of life that we see today.

The lipids that form real biological cells, however, are actually fairly complex structures containing different lipid chains combined with a phosphate to form unique polar structures called *phospholipids*. They are very different structures compared to the simple single-lipid chains supposedly involved in the first proto-cell. Cell membranes are also very complex assemblages that contain a wide variety of imbedded proteins and carbohydrate molecules for signaling and the import and export of a wide variety of compounds needed for cell function and metabolism. Thus, biogenesis researchers encounter many problems of required complexity for even the most primitive of cell membranes.

## Conclusion

Instead of focusing on the impossibility of life's most basic molecules arising by chance random processes, most biogenesis research has instead focused on other "downstream" aspects of the problem, although these avenues of research are fraught with insurmountable problems as well.

Neither models of amino acid synthesis nor the ideas surrounding an RNA world have produced any convincing scientific scenarios for how life began. Of course, random naturalistic DNA or RNA synthesis in a primordial soup or matrix is even more problematic. Specifically, protein, DNA, and RNA present a complex three-way version of the ancient "chicken or the egg" conundrum. DNA encodes RNA transcripts, but both RNA transcript production and DNA replication are dependent on specific proteins. And proteins are themselves encoded in genes (DNA) and produced from RNA transcripts that are copied from genes in DNA. All three of these major biomolecules need each other in the cell system, so which biomolecule evolved first? This is an irreducibly complex situation that could not have evolved by random naturalistic processes.

One evolutionary solution to this scenario is that the precursor molecules required for cell life came from extraterrestrial sources, such as some sort of planetary meteoritic bombardment, or even the intentional "seeding" of Earth by space aliens! However, even these scenarios only "push back" the problem and do not really explain the ultimate origin of these complex biomolecules. Outside of special creation as recorded in the Bible, life doesn't stand a chance.

### Notes

1. Zahnle, K., L. Schaefer, and B. Fegley. 2010. Earth's Earliest Atmospheres. *Cold Spring Harbor Perspectives in Biology.* 2 (10): a004895.

2. Davidson, C. F. 1965. Geochemical Aspects of Atmospheric Evolution. *Proceedings of the National Academy of Sciences.* 53: 1194.

3. Austin, S. 1982. Did the Early Earth Have a Reducing Atmosphere? *Acts & Facts.* 11 (7).

4. Abelson, P. H. 1966. Chemical Events on the Primitive Earth. *Proceedings of the National Academy of Sciences.* 55: 1365-1372.

5. Ferris, J. P. and D. E. Nicodem. 1972. Ammonia Photolysis and the Role of Ammonia in Chemical Evolution. *Nature.* 238:268-269.

6. Bada, J. L. and S. L. Miller. 1968. Ammonium Ion Concentration in the Primitive Ocean. *Science.* 159: 423-425.

7. Bada, J. L. and A. Lazcano. 2003. Prebiotic soup – revisiting the Miller experiment. *Science.* 300: 745-756.

8. Deamer, D. 2011. *First Life: Discovering the Connections between Stars, Cells, and How Life Began.* London: University of California Press, Ltd., 25.

9. Miller, S. L. 1953. A production of amino acids under possible primitive earth conditions. *Science.* 117: 528-29.

10. Johnson, A. P. et al. 2008. The Miller volcanic spark discharge experiment. *Science.* 322: 404-405.

11. Fox, S. W. and K. 1958. Harada Thermal Copolymerization of Amino Acids to a Product Resembling Protein. *Science.* 128: 1214.

12. Leman, L., L. Orgel, and M. R. Ghadiri. 2004. Carbonyl Sulfide-Mediated Prebiotic Formation of Peptides. *Science.* 306: 283-286.

# GEOLOGY

## RECENT CREATION OR MILLIONS OF YEARS?

# 27

# RECENT CREATION IN GEOLOGY

John D. Morris, Ph.D., and Timothy Clarey, Ph.D.

**Summary:** Geological evidence for a recent creation is found all over Earth. For example, there is not nearly enough salt in the ocean, the continents would have eroded away in less than 25 million years at current rates, and there should be more helium in the atmosphere if the earth is old.

Sedimentary structures show that Earth's sedimentary layers were deposited rapidly, not over millions of years. And experiments demonstrate that shale and limestone, which supposedly build up slowly over great periods of time, actually formed quickly through energetically moving water. In addition to that, layers of sedimentary rock are commonly stacked like pancakes, with no evidence of time or erosion between their deposition.

Modern catastrophes like the 1980 Mount St. Helens eruption provide a window into how remarkable geological change such as that caused by the Flood can take place in an extremely short amount of time. The geological data support a young earth.

As we have discussed elsewhere in this book, both good science and the Bible point to the catastrophic past of planet Earth. Geological data demand dynamic solutions to origins questions and do not allow uniformitarian ones. Both science and the Bible also teach the companion doctrine of the young age of the earth.

## Geological Evidences of a Young Earth

Numerous examples could be considered, but a few may suffice. They will not only point to recent creation but demonstrate the bankruptcy of uniformitarian thinking. Space does not allow full discussion of all of them.

**Salt in the ocean.** The oceans are salty and growing more so each year as rivers bring in more dissolved salts. Knowing the ocean's volume and average salt concentration, we can calculate how much salt is there. We can measure how fast it arrives by rivers and how fast it is removed. Evolution teaches that life evolved in a salty sea about three billion years ago. But at present uniform in-and-out rates, even in one billion years the ocean would be so choked with salt that life would be impossible. Uniformitarianism is incompatible with the ocean's salt makeup.

**Erosion of the continents.** The volume of the continents above sea level is known. The sedimentary rock on the continents is made up primarily of sediments containing marine fossils. Uniformitarianism considers them to have risen from the sea hundreds of millions of years ago.

We can measure how fast the continents are eroding. A 2011 study confirmed that outcrops (rocks visible above ground) erode at an average rate of about 40 feet every one million years.[1] At this rate, most of the continents would be gone in less than 25 million years, yet they are still here. If uniformitarianism is true, they should all be gone.

Secular geologists have had to resort to imagined rescuing devices like episodic uplift due to tectonic forces in order to explain the existence of today's continents. However, much of Canada and the eastern United States have not experienced any significant geologic uplift since the creation of the Appalachian Mountains over 250 million years ago, according to the secular timescale. Considering that much of these areas is less than 1,000 feet above sea level, it's a wonder there's any dry land at all in these regions.

As secular scientists clearly demonstrated, 1,000 feet of elevation would erode away in just 25 million years.[1] So, if the continents are extremely old, why are they still above sea level? The very existence of Earth's continents, coupled with erosion rates, testifies to the youth of our planet and the truth of God's Word.

In some places the land is rising, but at far slower rates than it is eroding elsewhere. There shouldn't be any sedimentary rock left, no fossils, no granitic core—it should all be gone. Uniformitarian thinking doesn't explain the facts, yet it dominates our universities.

**Helium in the atmosphere.** Each time an atom of uranium-238 (or thorium) undergoes alpha decay into a lead atom through a series of decay steps, it ejects eight alpha particles, which are essentially helium atoms (two protons and two neutrons = a helium nucleus, to which electrons attach). Of course, helium's light weight causes it to rise through the pores in the rocks and eventually enter the atmosphere. Through sensitive sensors, we can measure how much helium enters the atmosphere. We can also measure how much helium is in the atmosphere. If present rates have continued for the supposed previous millions of years, there should be lots more helium than is currently there. Actually, all of the current helium can be accounted for (at present rates) in only about two million years.

**Helium in the rocks.** A similar calculation can be made regarding helium content in the rocks. Select a rock of "known" uniformitarian age and measure the amount of radioactive uranium it contains. By knowing the rate of decay, we can calculate how much helium should be present. Helium atoms are quite tiny and slippery, and some will leak out through rock's pores over time faster than it is generated. If the rocks are as old as the standard view supposes, the helium should have mostly leaked out. Instead, way too much helium is still present. Helium is still building up! It looks like the rocks are not so old after all.

**Soft-sediment deformation.** Sedimentary rocks were once saturated sediments, deposited (almost always) by moving water. Sediments harden into rock rather quickly in the presence of an adequate cement binding the particles together. Later, the sediments can be deformed, either by folding or faulting. Often, the sediments give evidence of still being soft and pliable when deformed. It appears there was not enough time between deposition and deformation to harden the sediments, even though uniformitarianism often assigns dates to the two processes many millions of years apart.

**Sediments in the ocean.** As the continents erode and the sediments are carried downstream, they build up on the ocean floor. If the continents have been eroding for hundreds of millions of years at their present rate, there should be a predictable large amount there. With submarines and drill cores, we have been able to observe how much is down there, but it's not nearly as much as uniformitarianism requires. All of the sediment down there would accumulate in a time far shorter than uniformitarianism predicts.

**Human history.** Real history is human history, during which reliable eyewitnesses observed an event and recorded it for those who follow. True history began with the invention of writing, agriculture, and human society, and historians tell us that began around 5,000 years ago. Bible-believers recognize this time as about the time of the Flood. Before then, nothing survived except traditions. Any thoughts of times before 5,000 years ago are based on either biblical revelation or the concept of uniformitarianism, and that concept has proved inaccurate and based on false assumptions about the unseen past.

## Sedimentary Structures Show a Young Earth

Consider also the nature of the rocks underfoot. They were not only deposited catastrophically, but recently as well—or so it seems. Sedimentary rock, which makes up most of the surface cover of the continents, is by definition deposited by moving fluids. Normally, the sediments contain evidence of their waterborne history in what is called *sedimentary structures.* These features may be in the form of cross-bedding, paleo-current markers, graded bedding, laminations, ripple marks, etc. If the hardening conditions are met (i.e., the presence of a cementing agent and pressure to drive water from the matrix), the sediments soon harden into sedimentary rock, making the "structure" permanent. Erosion will eventually destroy even hard rock features, but rocks abound with such markings, virtually frozen in place.

While the muddy sediments are still fresh and soft, the ephemeral sedimentary structures within the deposits are in jeopardy of being obliterated by the action of plant and animal life. We know that life proliferates in every near-surface layer of soft sediment. This is true on land, and especially true underwater. Plant roots penetrate the soil. Animals such as worms, moles, clams, etc., burrow through the sediment, churning it up and turning it over through a process called *bioturbation.* This obviously destroys the sedimentary structure. But how long does it take?

A 2008 study undertook to determine just how much time was required to destroy all such structures.[2] Numerous recent storm deposits dominated by sedimentary structure were investigated in their natural setting. It was observed that within months, all sedimentary structure was destroyed, so intense is the bioturbation in soft sediments. As long as the sediments are still soft, they will be bioturbated until all is structure lost. Yet, the geologic record of Earth history abounds with such features. This comprises a good geological age indicator, and in fact points to a young earth. The total picture must be considered when considering sedimentary rocks.

Hardening of sediments into sedimentary rock itself normally takes little time if the conditions are met. Soft at the start, the sediment's internal character would necessarily be subjected to the rapid, destructive action of plant and animal life. Within a relatively short time (months or years), all sedimentary structure would disappear through their action alone. The surface of each layer would be exposed to bioturbation until the next layer covered it and until hardening was complete

The evidence suggests that each layer was laid down in a short period of time. Each soft deposit could not have been exposed for long before the next deposit covered it; they appear to have been isolated from destructive bioturbation. Thus, the length of time between the layers could not have been great. The total time involved for the entire sequence must therefore have been short.

## Shale and Limestone Are Deposited Rapidly by Moving Water

Secular science has long taught that many of Earth's sedimentary rocks were deposited slowly over vast ages. It says the slow rates of deposition for sediments like clay and lime mud are arguments for an old earth, claiming these layers form through sediments slowly settling out of stagnant water. People have been indoctrinated with the notion that enormous periods of time are necessary to explain these thick rock layers.

Yes, we do see clay settling out of stagnant water today, but the rocks we observe didn't form that way. Clay, Earth's most common sediment, doesn't slowly settle out of still water to form rocks. Clay-rich rocks like shale and mudstones often exhibit fine laminations or thin-bedded layers that only form through moving, not stagnant, water. How do we know? Empirical evidence demonstrates that laminated clays must be deposited in energetic settings by moving water.[3] Finely laminated clays rarely form today since biological activity (burrowing or bioturbation) usually destroys the thin layers.

The concept of slow-forming limestone strata has been taught as fact for generations. Such carbonate rocks comprise 20 to 25% of the total sedimentary strata on Earth's continents. The Redwall Limestone in Grand Canyon is 400 to 800 feet thick, but some carbonates can exceed 3,000 feet.[4] Uniformitarians have used the presence of these rocks to criticize the Genesis Flood account, pointing out that thick layers of "quiet water" carbonates must have taken millions of years to form.

But now, all that has changed, and another long-held uniformitarian belief has been exposed as a non-truth. Flume studies verified that carbonate mud is not deposited slowly but instead is laid down rapidly by wave and current action. Laboratory experiments demonstrate that water flowing between 10 and 20 inches per second creates ripples and laminated carbonate mud layers identical to those observed in carbonate rocks.[5] Dr. Juergen Schieber and his co-authors wrote:

> These experiments demonstrate unequivocally that carbonate muds can also accumulate in energetic settings....Observations from modern carbonate environments and from the rock record suggest that deposition of carbonate muds by currents could have been common throughout geologic history.[5]

These results match the predictions of creation geologists, who interpret mudstones, shales, and nearly all sedimentary rocks as rapid deposits from the year-long Flood.[6]

Coconino Sandstone on top of the Hermit Shale showing parallel rock layers
Image credit: John Morris

## There's a Lack of Time Between Layers

When we look at the sedimentary rocks and the various megasequences they form, we most commonly see the layers stacked like pancakes—each one paralleling the layers below and above. There's little indication within the sedimentary strata of the vast amounts of missing time claimed by secular geologists. The boundaries between strata often extend for tens and even hundreds of miles in all directions.

Secular scientists often place hundreds of thousands or millions of years between parallel sedimentary units, such as the boundary between the Hermit Shale in Grand Canyon and the overlying Coconino Sandstone.[7] But when you examine the contact between these particular layers, it's nearly perfectly planar in all directions for tens of miles. There may be small, smooth undulations of a few feet in some locations, but for the most part it's level with sharp contacts from one rock type to the next. Where are the gullies and the uneven topography that should have resulted from erosion over hundreds of thousands of years? The contact looks like brick-upon-brick with no evidence of any time delay whatsoever across the entire expanse of Grand Canyon and beyond.

Many other sedimentary units are also supposed to have vast amounts of time missing between their boundaries in Grand Canyon and elsewhere. Examples include the base of the Redwall Limestone where it rests on the Muav Limestone, supposedly missing 160 million years, and the base of the Tapeats Sandstone where it rests on the crystalline basement in western Grand Canyon, supposedly missing one billion years.[7]

The Redwall Limestone and the Tapeats Sandstone were deposited nearly perfectly flat across Grand Canyon. And recall that the Tapeats and equivalent sandstones extend over much of North America. Nearly everywhere across the expanse of North America, the base of the Tapeats Sandstone layer is a near planar surface. How could so much time for erosion to take place have left such flat surfaces? Instead, the evidence indicates rapid scouring and erosion, creating a planar surface, followed almost immediately by the deposition of new sedimentary layers as tsunami-like waves advanced across the continents.

## The Lessons from Mount St. Helens

When Mount St. Helens erupted in 1980, it was not only a major but local tectonic incident with predictable volcanic results, it spawned numerous water-related processes and products as well. Before the eruption, the mountain had been capped by a thick glacier. Sudden heating melted the glacier, and water avalanched down the mountain's northern slope. Water flowing with tsunami-like intensity savaged the forest and hillsides below, combining with ash fall and pyroclastic flows from the eruption itself. Some rock strata were quickly eroded, and sediments were instantly deposited on other areas in layers looking much the same as those to which geologists normally attach great age.

Layers of sediment up to 600 feet thick were deposited at the mountain's base, which in a few years hardened into rather solid rock. Canyons soon were gouged into these layers, producing a scale model of Grand Canyon in one afternoon. Elsewhere, wood is petrifying, coal is forming, etc.—all in the years since the 1980 eruption. The igneous rock (dacite) that should date "too young to measure" by radioisotope dating instead gives an anomalous date of 2.4 million years old when the proper isotopic dating method (potassium-argon) is used.[8] Modern local catastrophes such as the eruption of Mount St. Helens can give us a glimpse into Earth's past and geological power, even on the worldwide scale of Noah's Flood.

Thus, the Mount St. Helens catastrophe becomes a model for the great Flood. It teaches us about volcanism, erosion, deposition, solidification, fossilization, etc., all acting in a short time. A catchy slogan helps illustrate this—to form geological features, it either takes a little bit of water and a long time, or a lot of water and a short time.

Even though we didn't witness the great Flood, we do see modern catastrophes, and they rapidly accomplish things the Flood did on an even grander scale. In a short, biblically compatible timescale, such a flood can account for all the features we see on Earth's surface, features that many geologists normally misinterpret as evidence for great age.

Only biased interpretations based on unverifiable assumptions, such as the radioisotope dates that secular science relies on so heavily,[9] continue to argue for an old earth. The rocks do not show great age.

**Notes**

1. Portenga, E. W. and P. R. Bierman. 2011. Understanding Earth's eroding surface with $^{10}$Be. *GSA Today*. 21 (8): 4-10.

2. Gingras, M. K. et al. 2008. How fast do marine invertebrates burrow? *Palaeogeography, Palaeoclimatology, Palaeoecology*. 270 (3-4): 280-286.

3. Schieber, J., J. Southard, and K. Thaisen. 2007. Accretion of Mudstone Beds from Migrating Floccule Ripples. *Science*. 318 (5857): 1760-1763.

4. Boggs Jr., S. 2006. *Principles of Sedimentology and Stratigraphy*, 4th ed. Upper Saddle River, NJ: Pearson/Prentice Hall, 159-167.

5. Schieber, J. et al. 2013. Experimental Deposition of Carbonate Mud from Moving Suspensions: Importance of Flocculation and Implications For Modern and Ancient Carbonate Deposition. *Journal of Sedimentary Research.* 83 (11): 1026-1032.

6. Snelling, A. 2009. *Earth's Catastrophic Past*, vol. 2. Dallas, TX: Institute for Creation Research, 493-499.

7. Moshier, S. and C. Hill. 2016. Missing Time: Gaps in the Rock Record. In *The Grand Canyon, Monument to an Ancient Earth: Can Noah's Flood Explain the Grand Canyon?* C. Hill et al., eds. Grand Rapids, MI: Kregel Publications, 99-107.

8. Morris, J. and S. A. Austin. 2003. *Footprints in the Ash.* Green Forest, AR: Master Books, 67; Austin, S. A. 1996. Excess Argon within Mineral Concentrates from the New Dacite Lava Dome at Mount St. Helens Volcano. *Creation Ex Nihilo Technical Journal.* 10 (3): 335-343.

9. Cupps, V. R. 2019. *Rethinking Radiometric Dating: Evidence for a Young Earth from a Nuclear Physicist.* Dallas, TX: Institute for Creation Research.

# 28

# THE FLOOD IS THE KEY

John D. Morris, Ph.D.

**Summary:** Scripture records three worldwide events that impacted Earth—creation, the entry of death and corruption, and the global Flood. These events form the basics of a biblical worldview of Earth history.

The Flood has been the key to unlocking the creation-evolution question. Fossils are generally found in sedimentary rocks, which were laid down by moving water and cover vast areas. Slow natural processes could not have deposited these vast layers or the countless fossils they contain. Uniformitarianism cannot explain the past, but a biblical creationist interpretation can.

The creation-Flood reconstruction better handles the data than the secular reconstruction of history. The Flood is the key to Earth's geologic past.

According to Scripture, there have been three great worldwide events that impacted planet Earth. Every system on Earth was either formed or altered by these events. First, the Bible declares that God created the earth, "and without Him nothing was made that was made" (John 1:3). Nothing in the organic or inorganic realms arrived through purely natural causes. Everything observed would either have been directly created by God in that form or have been reshaped by subsequent events.

Second, we learn that after creation, God placed humans in charge of creation as His stewards. When they rebelled against God's authority, their entire domain came under the penalty of sin, and "the wages of sin is death" (Romans 6:23). Now all things die or wear down. Living things die biologically, but physically so do inanimate objects. The sun is burning out. The moon's orbit is decaying. Friction burns up available energy. Humanity, God's very image, also undergoes spiritual death. Only humans can sin, but Adam's sin disrupted all of creation. And today, everything is in this inward spiral of death and decay as a result of Adam's sin.

Third, the results of sin soon dominated the planet to such an extent that God had to wash it clean. He sent the Flood of Noah's day to rid the planet of its sinful and violent inhabitants, "by which the world that then existed perished, being flooded with water" (2 Peter 3:6). He used processes familiar to those we recognize (such as moving water and volcanic eruptions) to judge the earth, but in their wake everything was changed. Every location and every system was impacted. Where could you go on planet Earth and not encounter a flooded terrain?

These three great worldwide events form the basics of a biblical worldview of Earth history. All things were created in a "very good" form (Genesis 1:31) by God and maintained by His action. But then all things were cursed by God, and thus they inexorably decay or die. This was followed by a worldwide flood that restructured the entire earth.

Thankfully, the story does not stop there, for Scripture also tells us that the Creator stepped back into His completed, cursed, and flooded creation to pay its sin penalty and redeem fallen people. Furthermore, this earth will itself someday pass away and be replaced by the "new heavens and a new earth in which righteousness dwells" (2 Peter 3:13). The Creator's eternal intent for creation will then be realized. It has been delayed but not thwarted.

Both historically and currently, the great Flood of Noah's day has been the key to unlocking the creation-evolution question. Throughout the early 1900s, evolution and great age were taught with hardly a contrary voice in the schools, and even within the church. Christians were fully intimidated by the claims of secular scientists and accommodated great ages and evolutionary changes within the Bible. It was thought that science had disproved a plain-sense reading of Scripture. In particular, rocks and fossils were held to maintain the truth of evolution. They appeared to be so old and seemingly took so long to be deposited. Hardly anyone believed Genesis could be taken literally.

It wasn't until the groundbreaking book *The Genesis Flood*, co-authored by a scientist and a theologian, was published in 1961 that a serious scientific case for creation could be made.[1] For the first time, rocks and fossils could be accounted for in Scripture. The book pointed out that almost all fossils are found within sedimentary rock, by definition deposited as sediments by moving water. Furthermore, almost all fossils are of marine creatures, such as clams, coral, trilobites, and fish—things that live in water.

Secular thought is shackled by the concept of uniformitarianism, whose slogan is "the present is the key to the past." In this view, all past processes—geological, biological, etc.—that have ever occurred are possible today and have shaped our planet, life, and the entire universe. But this directly contradicts the teachings of Scripture, which claim that God created using creation processes from which He has rested. All forms of life were directly created without ancestry at a point in time. His completed creation was subsequently restructured by a dynamic flood in the days of Noah—a global flood the like of which He promised would never happen again (Genesis 9:11). Such a flood would necessarily have deposited vast amounts of sediments that have now hardened into sedimentary rock full of dead things that have become fossils. The processes involved required rates, scales, and intensities not normally seen today. Much higher energy levels are implicated.

So, uniformitarianism cannot explain the past as it relates to rocks and fossils. Major one-time events of the past were responsible. But if you ask an evolutionist "Where is the evidence for great ages?" the answer will inevitably be "In the rocks." If you ask "Where is the evidence for evolution?" the answer has traditionally been "In the fossils." But if Scripture is correct, the Flood laid down both rocks and fossils. Almost all rocks and fossils are the result of and the evidence confirming the great Flood of Noah's day.

Both sides have the same evidence, but we interpret it differently. One relies on the assumption of uniformitarianism for an understanding of the unseen past. The other view relies on the eyewitness of One who observed the past deposition of rocks and fossils, and He tells us of unimaginably dynamic processes involved. Both views can handle the data to varying degrees. Each side can even use the other's data. The two "models" can be compared to see which better interprets the data with fewer internal contradictions and fewer ad hoc explanations.

Recognizing that both sides are attempting to reconstruct history, the unseen past, what can be done? Without a doubt, one is more faithful to God's revelation about the past than the other. Scientifically, we can evaluate which historical reconstruction is more faithful to the data. Both views are entirely dependent on the assumptions held at the start. The issue becomes: Which view is more credible?

The contention of this book is that the creation-Flood reconstruction will better handle the data than the secular reconstruction of history, and will do so in a God-honoring fashion. Any attempt to reconstruct history is plagued by access only to partial information, by limited understanding and interpreter bias. Neither effort can be a strictly scientific one, dealing as it does with the unobserved past. Science and the scientific method necessarily deal with observation, and neither creation nor evolution has ever been observed in a scientific sense. We can only make predictions of the data. Each side can predict that "if my view is correct, I would expect to see certain things when I gather the data." The other side can do the same, and the one that more successfully predicts the data will be recognized as more likely correct.

As it relates to the Flood, we acknowledge that Scripture teaches that while it utilized modern processes, they were operating at rates, scales, and intensities far more dynamic than modern processes. If the Flood account of Scripture is correct, we would expect to observe deposition of rocks and fossils requiring energy levels never seen operating on local scales. Conversely, the uniformitarian would expect the majority of rocks and fossils to have been deposited at energy levels comparable to those possible today. What do the rocks say? What do the fossils tell us?

We would further expect Flood-deposited rocks to be on a grand scale. The Flood was worldwide according to Scripture, and thus we expect its products to be laterally extensive. Each episode of the Flood was not necessarily doing the same thing at all locations around the world, but we would expect that, in general, the sedimentary and tectonic evidence to at least be regional or even continental in area. The uniformitarian, relying on processes similar to today's processes, would expect to find strata of local geometry, like ocean fronts, lake beds, stream channels, deltas, etc.

Deposition due to the uniform processes of today acting on a local scale—that's what uniformitarianism predicts. Conversely, catastrophic deposition on a regional scale—that's the expected signature of the great Flood of Noah's day. These expectations of the evidence could hardly be more different. Which of these multiple working hypotheses do the data favor?

A vast amount of geologic data has now been compiled and examined across several continents.[2] The results tip the scales in favor of a global flood. Sedimentation patterns demonstrate global processes. Many stratigraphic units are found spanning vast areas across multiple continents. Furthermore, the rock data show a common high point to the floodwaters across the globe, matching the predictions of Flood geologists.

The data really do show that a global flood occurred just as Genesis describes. The Flood is the key to Earth's geologic past.

### Notes

1. Morris, H. M. and J. C. Whitcomb. 1961. *The Genesis Flood: The Biblical Record and Its Scientific Implications*. Phillipsburg, NJ: Presbyterian and Reformed Publishing Company

2. Clarey, T. 2020. *Carved in Stone: Geological Evidence of the Worldwide Flood*. Dallas, TX: Institute for Creation Research.

# 29

# THE FLOOD WAS GLOBAL ACCORDING TO SCRIPTURE

John D. Morris, Ph.D.

**Summary:** Genesis tells us the Flood covered all of Earth's highest hills, clearly indicating it was global in nature. The biblical account lists other details that demonstrate the Flood's worldwide extent. Jesus Himself mentioned the judgment of the Flood and the fact it "destroyed them all." Those who suggest Genesis describes a local flood have no scriptural support.

There's also plenty of physical evidence supporting a global flood. About 70% of Earth's surface is covered with oceans, and many areas are quite deep. There was more than enough water for the Flood. The Ark could have accommodated two of every kind of land-dwelling creature needed to repopulate the earth afterward, even the dinosaurs. Flood stories are found in cultures around the world, indicating memories handed down from those directly affected by the cataclysm.

We can rely on Scripture's record of the global Flood.

Does Scripture necessarily demand that the Flood was global in extent? The biblicist must always glean the scriptural information before attempting a historical reconstruction of unobserved events. The Bible doesn't give us all the scientific data, but it does provide the basic framework within which we must interpret scientific observations. The Author of Scripture was present when the events occurred, is capable of accurately describing what He saw and did, and cannot lie. His record is trustworthy.

On many occasions and in many ways, the Bible reveals the global nature of the Flood. To begin with, the Flood was said to cover the mountains (Genesis 7:19-20). Obviously, that implies a deep flood, but it also covered "all the high hills under the whole heaven." The term "all" can possibly be used in a limited sense, but here the all refers to everything under the whole heavens, the word for the entire atmosphere. Certainly the atmosphere is worldwide, thus the Flood was worldwide. Using military terms for the "conquering" of the land, the Flood was said to have "prevailed exceedingly." Use of the double superlative in Hebrew can only imply everything. The writer of Genesis understood the Flood as global.

The duration of the Flood also instructs us. Comparing the Flood's starting date (Genesis 7:11) with its ending date (8:13), we see that the Flood was about one year long. It rose for the first five months, prevailed over the land, and then abated. No local flood could do this, for the mountains are too high, and over time water flows downhill. There can be no such thing as a year-long, mountain-covering local flood; it must have been global. The waters are also described as coming and going (8:3), and moving water accomplishes much more work than standing water. The scriptural account can only be implying a global flood.

The listed causes for the Flood were all worldwide in scope, implying their effect was also global. At the Flood's start, it was mentioned that suddenly "all the fountains of the great deep were broken up, and the windows of heaven were opened" (Genesis 7:11). The "deep" is the oceans and the "heavens" is the atmosphere. A global cause implies a global effect.

Next, consider the fact that God instructed Noah to build the huge Ark so his family and the designated animals could escape drowning. It appears Noah had 120 years' warning the Flood was coming (Genesis 6:3). In this amount of time, he, his family, and the animals could have walked around the world several times. There was no need for the Ark if the Flood was only local. Yet, it was needed, and those not on board perished (7:23).

The Flood's primary goal was to judge sinful humans (6:5-7) and secondarily the animals (6:11-13). But animals live all around the earth, as do humans. No local, "uniform" flood could accomplish its main goal. It had to be global and energetic.

When the Flood ended, Noah made sacrifice to God, after which God promised there would never again be such a flood sent to judge the earth (9:11). But there have been many local floods since then, even regional floods that did much damage. If the great Flood was local and failed in its main mission—i.e., if it was not a global, world-restructuring cataclysm—then God lied to us. But God doesn't lie. His word is sure.

Perhaps the most important lesson comes from the testimony of Jesus Christ Himself when He was teaching His disciples about the end times and the final judgment of sinful humanity. He compared the days immediately preceding the Flood to the days right before He returns.

> "As it was in the days of Noah, so it will be also in the days of the Son of Man: They ate, they drank, they married wives, they were given in marriage, until the day that Noah entered the ark, and the flood came and destroyed them all." (Luke 17:26-27)

Note that the Flood destroyed them "all." Whether or not people lived all around the globe before the Flood, they do so today. The coming judgment will apply to all people, thus will not be local or normal. Only if the Flood of Noah's day was global and world-destroying does Christ's instruction make sense.

In a very similar fashion, Peter reminds his readers of the past time when "the world that then existed perished, being flooded with water" (2 Peter 3: 6), and bases on it his doctrine of the coming time of judgment when the entire "heavens and the earth which are now" will "pass away with a great noise, and the elements will melt with fervent heat; [and] the earth…will be burned up" (vv. 7, 10). The coming destruction and renovation of the entire planet—indeed the entire universe—producing a "new heavens and a new earth" (v. 13) is likened to the past destruction and renovation of the entire earth.

To those who advocate a lesser flood theory, we might ask:

> Will the coming re-creation of the new earth be just a local re-creation? Will it only concern the portions of Earth in which humanity sins? How does the uniformitarian flood concept not imply that only part of the earth is "reserved for fire" (v. 7)? Will some sinners escape God's coming wrath? What hope does this give the sinner?

Obviously, the local flood proposal leads to doctrinal nonsense.

## Problems Arising from a Global Flood

If the Flood was really global and tectonically destructive, several problems seem to arise. These are not new questions. They have bothered Christians for centuries. Where did all the water come from for the Flood? Where did it go? How did all the animals get on board the Ark? What about the dinosaurs? How could the animals be gathered and cared for? Do other cultures mention the Flood? These all have good answers based on the Bible and sound science. Questions regarding the geology of the Flood likewise have good answers, as we'll see in subsequent chapters.

**The Water.** An impressive volume of water still resides on Earth's surface today, contained primarily in the deep oceans. Actually, the oceans cover about 70% of the globe and they are, on average, much deeper than the continents are high. If the earth's surface were completely smoothed, with no deep oceans and no high continents, the oceans would cover the entire globe to a depth of about a mile and a half. There's plenty of water for the Flood.

Today's mountains didn't need to be covered, for they didn't even exist before the Flood. Made up primarily of Flood-deposited sediments, they were laid down at the bottom of the ocean during the Flood, then uplifted into continents and mountain chains as the Flood ended, where they hardened into rock. With the present topography, it would be hard to have a worldwide flood, but not with the previous topography. The waters drained into the modern oceans as the Flood ended and as the ocean basins sank.

**The Animals on the Ark.** To get a picture of the animals on the Ark, we must first know how many animals are involved, their average size, and the volume of the Ark. Scripture gives the size of the Ark as about 450 feet long, 75 feet wide, and 45 feet high—or about 1.5 million cubic feet of space. The animal "kinds" were commanded to come in as pairs. The definition of kind probably relates to the potential to mate. For instance, domestic dogs readily mate with coyotes and wolves, thus they would be within the same kind even though they are categorized as different species today. Only two representatives of the dog "kind" or the cat "kind" were on the Ark. Post-Flood adaptations have produced our modern varieties.

The same would apply for many other animal types. Generous estimates place the total number of animals on the Ark as less than 25,000 pairs, and probably much fewer. The average size of all animals is surprisingly small. There are only a few large animals but many small ones, with the average size on the Ark estimated as being approximately that of a rat.[1] There was plenty of room on board the Ark for 50,000 rats.

The dinosaurs present a different problem, but one that has a good answer.

All things, including dinosaurs, were created during the creation week, and there is abundant evidence that humans and dinosaurs lived at the same time after the Flood. This means they also lived in Noah's day before the Flood.

Dinosaurs were a special category of reptiles that walked differently from modern reptiles. But perhaps we can look to other large reptiles for guidance. Today, most of the larger ones live for many years and grow throughout their lives. In Scripture, we read that some humans of that time lived for almost 1,000 years. If dinosaurs were like modern reptiles, then the older ones might have been huge. It's hard to know for sure because dinosaurs are extinct and there is a lot scientists don't really know.

Obviously, there were all sizes of dinosaurs, from bird-size all the way up to massive sauropods over 100 feet long. However, the average adult dinosaur was about the size of an American bison.[2] God selected the animals to come to the Ark for their safety. Its purpose was survival and reproduction after the Flood, and He would not have chosen the oldest, largest specimens. More likely, He would have selected young, strong ones, able to reproduce each kind. The average dinosaur size on the Ark may have only been about the size of sheep. And there were only about 60 kinds of dinosaurs, so there may have been as few as 120 dinosaurs on board the Ark.[3] The Ark was immense, certainly big enough for the job, especially if the dinosaurs were represented by young adults.

Nearly all animals have an innate instinctive ability to migrate when faced with danger and go into a hibernation-like state until the danger passes. Maybe God, the Creator of animals, instilled these abilities into the chosen pairs of animals, and all of their descendants retain them.

**Flood Legends.** Human cultures also retain a "memory" of the great Flood. All people alive today descended from those eight people on the Ark. Shortly following the Flood, humans gathered at Babel in disobedience of God's command to fill the earth. God separated their languages, thus forcing migration, and as they journeyed they remembered their history of the great Flood and passed it down to later generations.

Today, almost every civilization around the world has a flood legend in its body of folklore. Each account may differ from the others in detail, but the essence of the story remains. Together, they all tell of a prior "golden age" that was destroyed by God due to humans' sin. They tell of a faithful, favored family who was warned of the coming Flood and who built a large boat and saved themselves and the family.

Even the difficult questions have satisfying answers.

### Notes

1. Woodmorappe, J. 1996. *Noah's Ark: A Feasibility Study.* Dallas, TX: Institute for Creation Research, 13.

2. Clarey, T. L. and J. P. Tomkins. 2015. Determining Average Dinosaur Size Using the Most Recent Comprehensive Body Mass Data Set. *Answers Research Journal.* 8: 85-91.

3. Clarey, T. 2015. *Dinosaurs: Marvels of God's Design.* Green Forest, AR: Master Books.

# 30

# THE FLOOD WAS GLOBAL AND CATASTROPHIC ACCORDING TO GEOLOGY

John D. Morris, Ph.D.

**Summary:** The Genesis Flood described in the Bible was both global in extent and catastrophic in nature, and left clear geological evidence around the world. Rather than a slow, relentless rising of ocean level, the Flood was a series of waves that inundated the continents and left regional and even continental strata. The Tapeats Sandstone is one such layer, as is the St. Peter Sandstone.

At least six water-deposited megasequence layers are found all over the world, with each containing sub layers. These are all evidence of water rolling over the continents in huge waves and then receding. The repetitive back-and-forth movement of the floodwaters produced the megasequences and other evidences we observe in the geologic record.

Geological processes today don't create layers like these. The biblical global Flood is the best explanation.

As we contemplate the great Flood of Noah's day and its geologic results, we need to recognize two things about it. First, it was global in extent, and second, it was catastrophic in character. Thus, geological evidence for the Flood would include strata deposited by that Flood revealing a catastrophic origin and widespread nature. The Flood, while global, was not necessarily acting the same at all points on the globe at every moment. There would be local differences, but the same overall cause. For instance, no Flood-caused tsunami could hit all portions of the globe simultaneously, nor would we expect it to. The strata would nonetheless be dominantly catastrophic and at least regional in extent. And this is what we see.

There are many examples of regional, even continental, strata. Consider the well-known Grand Canyon. The lowest layer of horizontally bedded strata is known as the Tapeats Sandstone. It is the first layer laid down in the Cambrian system and the first to contain abundant multicellular fossils. There are hardly any fossils in the layers below the Cambrian, but the "Cambrian explosion of life" contains fossils of every basic body type, even vertebrate fish. Evolutionists claim this happened 550 million years ago, but creationists insist that this layer was deposited near the beginning of the Flood. Right below the Tapeats is an erosion surface so extensive it is called the Great Unconformity. It seems the first burst of the Flood accomplished unthinkable erosion and then began to deposit large sand grains, then smaller sand grains. This sandstone can be traced throughout Grand Canyon and into Utah to the north. Using drill cores to spot it, geologists have also found it at the same stratigraphic interval across the United States and into Canada. A nearly identical layer rests in Europe and across the northern hemisphere.

The Tapeats Sandstone

Evolutionists have traditionally taught this layer was deposited by normal waves as a shoreline migrated across the continent. In recent years, many geologists have noticed evidence that the depositional agent must have been a series of massive underwater flows of sandy mud. Perhaps the time has come to consider the Flood explanation.

Another layer of great significance is the St. Peter Sandstone. Properly called a "blanket sand," it too covers much of America, hundreds of miles wide but only 50 to 300 feet thick. Comparing its width to its thickness, it becomes the equivalent of a sheet of onion-skin paper. For this thin deposit to collect on a shoreline implies an underlying extensive, extremely flat surface scoured by erosion, with no mountains or hills anywhere higher than 300 feet. No equivalent surface or depositional scenario exists today. Surely an environment quite different from those existing in the present dominated in the past. Something like a worldwide flood, perhaps?

Similar descriptions could be given of extensive limestone deposits. The majority of sedimentary deposits are extremely fine-grain, like shale, originally deposited as mud. But the tiny grains of mud only collect today on the ocean bottom in still water. The grains filter down through the water at a very slow rate, sometimes taking months to reach the bottom. No such long-term calm water location can be comprehended in our world because there are always currents and water disturbances that would keep the grains suspended. Yet, the world abounds with mudrocks. Can there be another solution?

Indeed, there is. Something must cause the grains to adhere to one another in a clump. This can happen in laboratory experiments only when the water is treated with unusual chemicals. As larger agglomerations, they fall easily through the water and can flow down a gradual slope. Such a fortuitous combination of circumstances can hardly happen in nature today and could never occur on a wide scale. But during such a flood as the great Flood, they would happen and could account for the vast deposits of shale and other mudrocks we see all around us.

Other types of rocks come into play here. Consider salt deposits, made mostly of common table salt. Of course, salt is in seawater and remains when the water boils away. Students are normally taught that when seawater gets trapped in a lagoon, the salt collects as the water evaporates. Obviously this happens on a small scale, but is it reasonable to account for the semi-continental salt beds? It must be proposed that a lagoon filled over and over again, each time evaporating and refilling. The salt left behind in a dried lagoon today is always "dirty" and contaminated. But salt beds are amazingly pure. Consider the fact that salt beds are often thousands of feet thick and cover extensive areas. Only by proposing a scenario quite unlike modern ones can large salt deposits be accounted for.

Creationists have proposed that when the "fountains of the great deep" broke open, they spewed super-saturated, hot brines into the much cooler ocean, where the chemicals crystalized and collected on the ocean bottom. There are certain places (such as local salt "volcanoes" in the Red Sea) where similar things happen today where deep vents are active, but not nearly on the same scale as happened in the past. The "fountains" idea is reasonable and sufficient to account for the deposits of salt we see.

But there's more. Oil exploration efforts have discovered the strata are bundled in sequences. These are due to oceanic transgressions onto the continents depositing strata and regressions back off the continents eroding the strata. In general, the packages of strata begin (at the bottom) with sandstone consisting of coarse sand at the base. (Lower layers came first, geologically speaking. The layers on top came later.) The successive layers are of ever-fining particles, and finish with a chemical precipitate on top (such as limestone).

Each grouping of sedimentary layers (called a *megasequence*) contains features best understood in the sense of a transgression of the ocean onto the continents, followed by a regression of the waters back into the sea and the resulting erosion, followed by a second sequence, and then another. Uniformitarians interpret each sequence as having taken many millions of years.

During transgression, the waters brought and deposited sediment (usually marine) onto the continent. During regression, the waters eroded much newly deposited and older sediments as they ran off the continents, producing a recognizable erosional boundary called an *unconformity*. The six (or more) megasequences comprise the entire fossil-bearing part of the geologic column and have been correlated with beds right across North America and even onto other continents. Since rapidly moving water can accomplish much geologic work while stationary water does little, this concept bears promise as the primary character of the great Flood of Noah's day.

The lowest megasequence is the Sauk Megasequence, with the previously mentioned Tapeats Sandstone at its base and other layers of finer-grain shale and tiny-grain limestone above, which are capped by an erosional unconformity. The overlying megasequence is called the Tippecanoe Megasequence. The pure quartz sandstone at its base is called the St. Peter Sandstone, and above that lie shale and limestone beds, also followed by erosion.

The erosion unconformity that ended the Sauk Megasequence was totally unlike anything we have ever witnessed. This erosional episode planed off the recent Sauk deposits to a nearly flat, featureless plain. On the entire continent no mountain remained, for the St. Peter Sandstone covers much of the continental area with a thin sheet of sand. Evidently, even though subsequent erosion removed the sandstone in some areas, it was essentially continuous at first, implying there were no high places on the continent that received no sediment. This could not have been accomplished by river erosion. The only adequate mechanism known is by "sheet erosion"—rapidly flowing water of equal depth that covered a wide area. That's catastrophism with a vengeance!

The standard view considers both sandstone beds mentioned to have been deposited by a transgressing shoreline, with sand accumulating on the beach and offshore over about five million years, all the while migrating across the continent.

The Genesis account of the global Flood succinctly describes stage after stage of that unique catastrophe. It even intimates successive episodes of transgression and regression. Genesis 8:3 summarizes the stage in which the floodwaters began to drain enough to allow Noah's Ark to come to rest. But while the waters were moving, they followed a remarkable rhythmic pattern of ocean-water movement—specifically, a repetitious action described in Genesis as a "to and fro" (or "back and forth") motion.

> And the waters receded continually from the earth. At the end
> of the hundred and fifty days the waters decreased. (Genesis 8:3)

The Hebrew words justify special scrutiny. The recession of the floodwaters is denoted by the verse's first verb, which means "and they returned" to where they had originated. The next two Hebrew words provide a verbal picture of the draining waters swaying in a rhythmic mega-wave movement. Although the New King James Version translates this two-word phrase with the one word "continually," the Hebrew phrase connotes the water motion as being continually "to and fro" or "back and forth"—the waters were *continually* going and returning.[1]

A repetitive back-and-forth movement of floodwaters is the rock-solid evidence we observe as megasequences in the geological record of the Flood. The sedimentary rocks and fossils left in the floodwaters' wake contain abundant evidence of the ocean-waters transgressing over the continents and then regressing back into the ocean.

The accompanying chart references the standard concept of geologic "time," with the long-ago past at the bottom and the present at the top, with the megasequences "coming and going" throughout all periods.

Of course, recognizing that old-earth scenarios are hopelessly flawed,[3,4] we would certainly disagree with the chart's long timespan of 600 million years, preferring instead to interpret the whole as the record of the great Flood of Noah's day. Moving upward, we see the bottom as the early Flood period, then the mid-Flood, the waning stages of the Flood, and the post-Flood time at the top. The Genesis 8:4 grounding of the Ark occurred during the later Zuni, when floodwaters were at their maximum and then began to wane. Within the rising and maintaining Flood portions of the chart is where geologists have seen these six (maybe subdivided into more) megasequences. During the final drainage, the waters came and went with greater frequency.

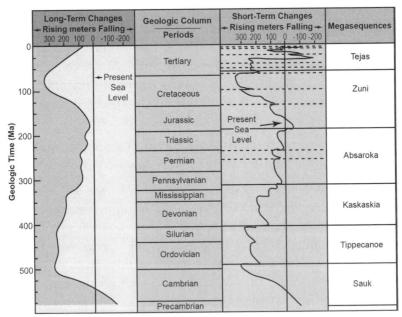

Sea level changes over geologic "time," with transgressions swinging to the left and regressions back to the right. Note that the sea level changes ignore geologic periods but define the megasequences. Modified after Sloss and Vail.[2]

Each of these sequences begins with a record of violent incursion of the ocean over the land, first depositing a basal coarse sand, then smaller grains, and then chemical precipitation as the energy levels lessened, ending with the water rushing back seaward with a mighty erosion episode. Each transgression landward followed each regression seaward in a continuous cycle of floods until all was totally destroyed. These were not separate floods but one unimaginable super-flood, with repeated pulses of terror.

Scripture doesn't give us all the details of the Flood events, but geology can "fill in the blanks." Remember, God's primary purpose for the great Flood was total annihilation of the continents and the life they held (Genesis 6:7).

The Flood involved much more than water flooding the land, standing above the mountains for a while, and then draining. Moving water contains much energy, while standing water does little work. God promised He was going to destroy the wicked, violent inhabitants of Earth along with the earth, and super-powered cleansing floodwaters—washing "back and forth" across the land—appear to be the tool God chose to accomplish it.x

### Notes

1. Young, R. 1980. *Young's Analytical Concordance to the Bible.* Peabody, MA: Hendrickson Publishers, 17, 47.

2. Sloss, L. L. 1963. Sequences in the cratonic interior of North America. *Geologic Society of America Bulletin.* 74: 93-114; Vail, P. R. and R. M. Mitchum, Jr. 1979. Global cycles of relative changes of sea level from seismic stratigraphy. *American Association of Petroleum Geologists Memoir 29,* 469-472.

3. Morris, H. M. and J. C. Whitcomb. 1961. *The Genesis Flood: The Biblical Record and Its Scientific Implications.* Phillipsburg, NJ: Presbyterian and Reformed Publishing Company; Morris, J. 2007. *The Young Earth,* revised ed. Green Forest, AR: Master Books.

4. Johnson, J. J. S. 2008. How Young Is the Earth? Applying Simple Math to Data Provided in Genesis. *Acts & Facts.* 37 (10): 4-5.

# 31

# CATASTROPHIC PLATE TECTONICS AND THE FLOOD

Jake Hebert, Ph.D., and Timothy Clarey, Ph.D.

**Summary:** Earth has a thin outer "shell" consisting of several large tectonic plates and many smaller ones. These plates constantly move against each other, with some being pulled underneath others in a phenomenon known as subduction.

During the Genesis Flood, the plates moved quickly, and this movement drastically changed the face of the earth. Subduction was very rapid, destroying the old ocean crust and creating new seafloor. The rapid plate movement explains the massive tsunami-like waves that laid down sedimentary layers all over the world and eroded the continents during the Flood year, and it also set up the conditions needed for the post-Flood Ice Age.

Accepting the Genesis Flood as literal history enables researchers to make sense of a huge array of data that cannot be explained by uniformitarian models of Earth's past.

Some Christians hesitate to embrace the notion that the earth's outer surface is moving—and moved even more dramatically during the Flood year. However, tremendous amounts of empirical data suggest significant plate movement occurred just thousands of years ago.[1] Much of these data are independent of secular deep time and the geologic timescale. In addition, the catastrophic plate tectonics (CPT) model offers a mechanism for the flooding of the continents, the subsequent lowering and draining of the floodwaters, and a cause for the post-Flood Ice Age.

The Flood also enables us to make sense of clues contained within Earth's interior. Our planet can be divided into a thin outer crust, a core at its center,

251

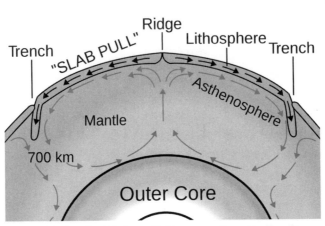

Figure 1. Diagram showing the earth's interor as well as mid-ocean ridge and two subducting slabs.
Image credit: U.S. Geological Survey.

and the mantle between them (Figure 1). The core is comprised of a solid inner core and a liquid outer core. The uppermost part of the mantle and the crust together comprise the lithosphere, about 62 miles thick. Like a cracked eggshell, the lithosphere is divided into seven or eight large plates and many smaller plates.

## Continental Drift to Plate Tectonics

Geologists derive the theory of plate tectonics from much data collected over many decades. In the early 20th century, Alfred Wegener examined how the continents seem to fit together like a puzzle and matched fossils and mountain ranges across vast oceans to suggest that the continents had split in the past. At the time, his ideas were ridiculed and ignored.

It was not until the 1960s, after immense quantities of oceanographic data were collected, including the publication of Harry Hess' hypothesis of seafloor spreading[2] and J. Tuzo Wilson's early work on plate tectonics,[3] that secular geologists slowly accepted these ideas. Nearly 50 years after Wegener first proposed the concept of continental drift, the secular community was overwhelmed with empirical data and reluctantly acknowledged plate tectonics.

## Rapid Seafloor Spreading and Runaway Subduction

If continents split, we should find evidence to support these movements under the oceans. In the 1950s and 1960s, geologists discovered that the ocean crust is very young compared to many of the rocks on the continents. In fact, the oldest ocean crust goes back to a brief episode in the Flood during the deposition of the Jurassic system. And at every ridge, the crust gets systematically older in both directions. Although secular ocean floor maps claim ages in millions of years, they do seem to be correct in a relative sense. Older age dates usually indicate older rocks. In addition, a tremendous amount of data affirms seafloor spreading independent of absolute dating methods.

Creation geophysicist John Baumgardner—described as "the world's pre-eminent expert in the design of computer models for geophysical convection"[4]—has spent many years studying the connection between plate tectonics and the Flood. Today the plates are moving very slowly, at rates of just a few centimeters per year, but Dr. Baumgardner argues that they moved much faster in the recent past.[5]

When an oceanic plate and a continental plate collide, the denser rocks of the ocean floor tend to slide under the less-dense continental rocks, a process called *subduction*. As a subducting plate moves down through the mantle, the resulting friction heats the surrounding material. This heating reduces the viscosity of the material, enabling the subducting plate to move more quickly. As long as the heat is carried away by the surrounding mantle rocks faster than it is generated by the subducting slab, subduction will be slow and gradual.

If, however, the generated heat is not carried away at a sufficient rate, the viscosity of the slab decreases still further, enabling the slab to descend even faster. This results in an effect called *runaway subduction* in which the subducting slab moves at speeds of meters per second rather than centimeters per year.[5] Fortunately, conditions for runaway subduction are not currently present in the mantle, but there are good reasons to think such conditions occurred in the past.

An imaging process called *seismic tomography* shows visible lithospheric slabs of oceanic crust going down hundreds of miles beneath ocean trenches and into subduction zones (Figure 2).[6] These are not merely faults, as some have proposed,[7] but 62-mile-thick slabs of brittle, dense rock descending into the mantle. The cooler temperatures exhibited by these subducted slabs of rock create a thermal dilemma for the secular and old-earth geologists, who must demonstrate how these slabs remained cold for millions of years. Colder, subducted slabs are best explained by runaway subduction just thousands of years ago during the great Flood.[5]

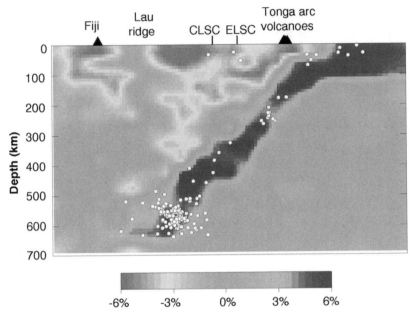

Figure 2. P-wave tomography under the Tonga Trench, Pacific Ocean. The blue shows the colder ocean lithosphere descending down into the mantle to a depth of nearly 700 km (435 miles). The white dots represent earthquake foci.
Image credit: American Association for the Advancement of Science

## Runaway Subduction: Logical Consequences

If runaway subduction did occur, then certain things logically follow. Since one expects Earth's volume to remain constant during the subduction process, rapid subduction and the destruction of the old seafloor also imply rapid creation of a new seafloor. This would occur at the mid-ocean ridges, where hot magma rises upward (Figure 1).

The lithosphere above the ridge would stretch and thin, allowing the magma to break through the crust. Dr. Baumgardner thinks the mid-ocean ridges, which encircle Earth like seams on a baseball, were the result. As this hot magma came into contact with cold seawater, the result would have been a long, linear geyser that ejected huge amounts of superheated water into the atmosphere. This may have been the source of the intense rains that fell for the first 40 days and 40 nights of the Flood (Genesis 7:12).

## CPT Explains the Sources of Water for the Flood and Where It Went

The Bible plainly states that the "fountains of the great deep were broken up, and the windows of heaven were opened" during the initiation of the Flood (Genesis 7:11). In terms of CPT, the breaking up of the fountains of the great deep may be a description of the rifting that took place at the ocean ridges and even within continents.[8] Obviously, the rainfall described as the opening of the "windows of heaven" must have contributed to the Flood.

Additionally, because newly created oceanic lithosphere is hot, less dense, and more buoyant, the CPT model provides another source for water to completely flood the continents. After its formation at the ridges, the freshly formed, lower-density oceanic lithosphere simply pushed up the top of the seafloor from below, displacing ocean water and forcing it on land. Creation geologist Dr. Andrew Snelling calculated that this elevated seafloor could have raised the global sea level by as much as 1.6 km, greatly helping flood the continents.[9]

Rapid movement of the plates during runaway subduction further supplied tsunami-like waves to wash across the land, helping deposit blanket-type sediments across continents. Recent numerical modeling by Dr. Baumgardner has found that repetitive tsunami waves, caused by rapid plate movement, could result in water accumulation more than a kilometer (0.62 miles) deep on the continents, contributing to the flooding.[10] The runaway subduction model also provides a mechanism to lower the continental crust about two miles in the proximity of the subduction zones, causing more extensive flooding of the land and creating room for thousands of feet of sediment.[5]

Subsequent cooling of the newly created ocean lithosphere later in the Flood year (after Day 150) offers an explanation for the lowering of the flood-waters. The 62-mile-thick ocean lithosphere cooled and sank, lowering the bottom of the oceans and drawing the water back off the continents and into the ocean basins.

## CPT Explains Rapid Magnetic Reversals

Molten lava, or magma, contains minerals whose magnetic domains tend to align with the direction of Earth's magnetic field. When the rock cools and hardens, this alignment is "locked" into the volcanic rock. The basaltic rocks on either side of the mid-ocean ridges depict a striped pattern consisting of alternating bands of magnetization that reverse direction as one moves away from the ridge. This striped pattern indicates that Earth's magnetic field has flipped dozens of times, with the north and south magnetic poles trading places.

If a new seafloor rapidly formed during the Genesis Flood, then the fact that these magnetic reversals are recorded in oceanic volcanic rocks (most of which were formed during the Flood) implies that the magnetic reversals must also have occurred rapidly. Uniformitarian scientists found strong evidence for rapid magnetic reversals, although such rapid reversals are very hard for them to explain.[11-13]

Creation physicist D. Russell Humphreys proposed a theory that at least qualitatively explains how such rapid reversals could occur.[14] His mechanism requires strong up-and-down motions of fluids within Earth's liquid outer core due to convection. Such convection might be initiated if a cold subducting plate were to come into contact with the outer core at the core-mantle boundary, which Dr. Baumgardner argues is exactly what happened.[15]

## CPT Explains Rapid Erosion and Deposition

As the newly formed ocean floor cooled, its density increased and it sank, allowing the floodwaters to drain off the continents. The rapidly receding waters would have eroded away an enormous amount of sediment. In places where the sediments were relatively thin, the water would have eroded all the sedimentary layers, leaving the original basement rocks exposed.

Huge volumes of fast-moving water would have planed some areas flat, resulting in so-called *planation surfaces*. Since they are not forming today, these surfaces are difficult for secular geologists to explain.[16] This extensive erosion implies that huge amounts of sediment would have rapidly been dumped into the ocean basins. The Whopper Sand in the Gulf of Mexico—a complete surprise to uniformitarian scientists—is an example of this massive, sheet-like draining of North America.[17]

## CPT Explains the Conditions for the Ice Age

Finally, CPT provides a mechanism for the Ice Age that occurred at the end of the Flood. A hot, newly formed ocean crust would have provided tremendous amounts of heat to the ocean waters above. This would have raised the overall temperature of the ocean and caused a greater amount of evaporation, resulting in staggering amounts of precipitation.[18] The increased volcanic activity from the subduction zone volcanoes within the Ring of Fire and elsewhere late in the Flood would have placed huge volumes of ash and aerosols into the atmosphere, cooling the climate most noticeably in the higher latitudes.[18]

The distinctive magmas generated by the partial melt of subducted ocean lithosphere provide the perfect recipe for explosive, ash-rich eruptions. These types of volcanoes (stratovolcanoes) are highest in silica, making them thicker and more explosive.[19] The net result of hotter oceans and tremendous silica-rich volcanic activity brought on from plate motion would be enough to start a widespread Ice Age.

As commonly observed across the bulk of the ocean basins, basalt-rich magmatic volcanoes (shield volcanoes) do not produce the necessary ash-rich explosions to generate sun-blocking aerosols.[19] Only subduction provides these ash-rich magmas. Finally, as the ocean water slowly cooled and volcanic activity diminished over the centuries after Flood, the Ice Age would have ended as abruptly as it began.[18] In contrast, the currently popular secular Ice Age theory has serious problems.[20]

## Conclusion

Accepting the Genesis Flood as literal history enables researchers to make sense of a huge array of data. Although creation scientists are still working to resolve unanswered questions, the creation-Flood model is much more robust and has much more explanatory power than secular Earth history stories. Skeptics "willingly are ignorant of" (2 Peter 3:5, KJV) the reality of the Genesis Flood—not because of a lack of evidence but because of an unwillingness to acknowledge God's Lordship.

*Notes*

1. Clarey, T. L. 2016. Empirical Data Support Seafloor Spreading and Catastrophic Plate Tectonics. *Journal of Creation*. 30 (1): 76-82.

2. Hess, H. 1962. History of Ocean Basins. In *Petrologic studies: a volume in honor of A. F. Buddington*. A. Engel, H. James, and B. Leonard, eds. Boulder, CO: Geological Society of America, 599-620.

3. Wilson, J. 1968. A Revolution in Earth Science. *Geotimes*. 13 (10): 10-16.

4. Burr, C. The Geophysics of God. *U.S. News & World Report*, June 16, 1997, 55-58.

5. Baumgardner, J. R. 1994. Runaway Subduction as the Driving Mechanism for the Genesis Flood. In *Proceedings of the Third International Conference on Creationism*. R. E. Walsh, ed. Pittsburgh, PA: Creation Science Fellowship, 63-75.

6. Schmandt, B. and Fan-Chi Lin. 2014. *P* and *S* wave tomography of the mantle beneath the United States. *Geophysical Research Letters*. 41: 6342-6349.

7. Brown Jr., W. 2008. *In the Beginning: Compelling Evidence for Creation and the Flood,* 9th ed. Phoenix, AZ: Center for Scientific Creation.

8. Reed, J. 2000. *The North American Midcontinent Rift System: An Interpretation Within the Biblical Worldview*. St. Joseph, MO: Creation Research Society Books.

9. Snelling, A. 2014. Geophysical issues: understanding the origin of the continents, their rock layers and

mountains. In *Grappling with the Chronology of the Genesis Flood*. S. Boyd and A. Snelling, eds. Green Forest, AR: Master Books, 111-143.

10. Baumgardner, J. 2016. Numerical Modeling of the Large-Scale Erosion, Sediment Transport, and Deposition Processes of the Genesis Flood. *Answers Research Journal*. 9:1-24.

11. Coe, R. S., M. Prévot, and P. Camps. 1995. New evidence for extraordinarily rapid change of the geomagnetic field during a reversal. *Nature*. 374 (6524): 687-692.

12. Bogue, S. W. and J. M. G. Glen. 2010. Very rapid geomagnetic field change recorded by the partial remagnetization of a lava flow. *Geophysical Research Letters*. 37 (21): L21308.

13. Sagnotti, L. et al. 2014. Extremely rapid directional change during Matuyama-Brunhes geomagnetic polarity reversal. *Geophysical Journal International*. 199 (2): 1110-1124.

14. Humphreys, D. R. 1990. Physical Mechanism for Reversals of the Earth's Geomagnetic Field During the Flood. In *Proceedings of the Second International Conference on Creationism*. R. E. Walsh and C. L. Brooks, eds. Pittsburgh, PA: Creation Science Fellowship, 129-142.

15. Baumgardner, J. R. 2003. Catastrophic Plate Tectonics: The Physics Behind the Genesis Flood. In *Proceedings of the Fifth International Conference on Creationism*. R. L. Ivey, Jr., ed. Pittsburgh, PA: Creation Science Fellowship, 113-126.

16. Oard, M. 2006. It's plain to see: Flat land surfaces are strong evidence for the Genesis Flood. *Creation*. 28 (2): 34-37.

17. Clarey, T. 2015. The Whopper Sand. *Acts & Facts*. 44 (3): 14.

18. Oard, M. 2004. *Frozen in Time*. Green Forest, AR: Master Books.

19. Raymond, L. 1995. *Petrology: The Study of Igneous, Sedimentary, and Metamorphic Rocks*. Dubuque, IA: William C. Brown Communications.

20. Hebert, J. 'Big Science' Celebrates Invalid Milankovitch Paper. *Creation Science Update*. Posted on ICR.org December 26, 2016, accessed May 16, 2017.

# 32

# GLOBAL STRATIGRAPHY SUPPORTS A WORLDWIDE FLOOD

Timothy Clarey, Ph.D.

**Summary:** A comprehensive study of the rocks across North and South America, Europe, and Africa documented sedimentary deposition consistent with a catastrophic global flood. All four continents contain the same six megasequences laid down by massive pulses of tsunami-like waves. Megasequences are thick sedimentary layers bounded by regional erosional surfaces. Each documents the Flood's progression as large sediment-laying initial waves were followed by smaller erosional withdrawal waves.

Since these megasequence packages are found on all four continents and demonstrate simultaneous sedimentary patterns, they are strong evidence for a violent global flood that went through phases as it rose and receded, burying and fossilizing billions of living creatures as it progressed.

Secular geologists have no satisfactory explanation for how these megasequences came into existence, but they match the biblical record. All over the globe the rocks cry out and tell the Flood story.

Geologic research confirms that the Flood recorded in Genesis was global. It also reveals the exact step-by-step account of the floodwaters' progression. Over 2,000 stratigraphic columns have been compiled from published outcrop data, oil well boreholes, cores, cross-sections, and/or seismic data tied to boreholes from across North America, South America, Africa, and Europe.

Our findings have revealed surprising results that smash entrenched uniformitarian thought. The rocks across multiple continents show similar patterns of water-based deposition, supporting the biblical account of a global flood.

## What's a Megasequence?

Sequences were defined by Laurence Sloss as discrete packages of sedimentary rock bounded top and bottom by regional erosional surfaces, and are traceable on a continent scale.[1] Because the terminology associated with sedimentary sequences has ballooned in the past decades, some have chosen to use the term *megasequence* for strata bounded by the most prominent regional unconformities.[2]

Megasequences can be thought of as massive pulses of tsunami-like waves that were pushed across the continents during the Flood year. Each major pulse was followed by a minor withdrawal. The advance and the withdrawal of each megasequence caused large-scale erosion at both the top and bottom of each cycle.

Because the megasequences are based on physical relationships demonstrated by observable erosion, they are independent of regional differences in nomenclature and even paleontological dating methods.[1] Therefore, many consider each megasequence boundary as a nearly common time surface (chronostratigraphic horizon). By not relying on the paleontological record that is so intertwined in the development of the classical geologic timescale, megasequences have become the preferred method for studying the sedimentary deposits of the great Flood.[3]

Megasequences include multiple geologic systems (Figure 1). However, they differ in that they are not based solely on changes in fossil content as are the eras, periods and epochs of the traditional geologic timescale. Although there are erosional boundaries between many megasequences, there is no evidence that millions of years have simply gone missing from the rock record. The rocks were merely stacked one on top of another, sequence by sequence, as the Flood rose higher and higher. Secular geologists can't entertain the notion of a worldwide deluge. Instead, they insist that it was all a result of isolated local floods—yet this interpretation doesn't fit the data. The stratigraphic columns found across the globe are best explained in the context of the year-long Flood.

## Megasequences Document the Progression of the Global Flood

Numerous authors have speculated on the extent of the early floodwaters and on when the Flood peaked. For example, did the Flood cover the continents early in the Flood year, recede, and then rise again? Did the waters

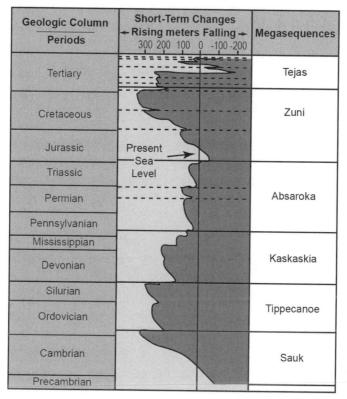

Figure 1. Chart showing the secular timescale, presumed sea level curve, and the six megasequences. Modified after Vail and Mitchum.[4]

rise once and peak around Day 150? Or was it some combination? And at what level in the geologic record did it peak? Our research is one of the first attempts to map the true extent of the sedimentary rocks across the continents and has provided some answers to these questions.[5]

A summary table of our stratigraphic data set for three continents is shown in Table 1. Notice that the area covered by the Sauk Megasequence across North America is over 12 million km². Sauk deposits are several kilometers thick along the east and west coasts of the North American continent and yet are very thin (only a few tens of meters) to nonexistent across the central part of the continental United States. They average only about 275 meters deep across the North American continent where present (Table 1).

In stark contrast to North America, the sedimentary rocks of the Sauk Megasequence across South America and Africa show much less surface cov-

| Surface Area (km²) | North America | South America | Africa | Total |
|---|---|---|---|---|
| Sauk | 12,157,200 | 1,448,100 | 8,989,300 | 22,594,600 |
| Tippecanoe | 10,250,400 | 4,270,600 | 9,167,200 | 23,688,200 |
| Kaskaskia | 11,035,000 | 4,392,600 | 7,417,500 | 22,845,100 |
| Absaroka | 11,540,300 | 6,169,000 | 17,859,900 | 35,569,200 |
| Zuni | 16,012,900 | 14,221,900 | 26,626,900 | 56,861,700 |
| Tejas | 14,827,400 | 15,815,200 | 24,375,100 | 55,017,700 |
| Volume (km³) | North America | South America | Africa | Total |
| Sauk | 3,347,690 | 1,017,910 | 6,070,490 | 10,436,090 |
| Tippecanoe | 4,273,080 | 1,834,940 | 6,114,910 | 12,222,930 |
| Kaskaskia | 5,482,040 | 3,154,390 | 3,725,900 | 12,362,330 |
| Absaroka | 6,312,620 | 6,073,710 | 21,075,040 | 33,461,370 |
| Zuni | 16,446,210 | 23,198,970 | 57,729,600 | 97,374,780 |
| Tejas | 17,758,530 | 32,908,080 | 28,855,530 | 79,522,140 |
| Average Thickness (km) | North America | South America | Africa | Total |
| Sauk | 0.275 | 0.703 | 0.675 | 0.462 |
| Tippecanoe | 0.417 | 0.430 | 0.667 | 0.516 |
| Kaskaskia | 0.497 | 0.718 | 0.502 | 0.541 |
| Absaroka | 0.547 | 0.985 | 1.180 | 0.941 |
| Zuni | 1.027 | 1.631 | 2.168 | 1.712 |
| Tejas | 1.198 | 2.081 | 1.184 | 1.445 |

Table 1. Surface area, sediment volume, and average thicknesses for North America, South America, and Africa for each of the six megasequences defined in Figure 1. Totals for the three continents are listed at the far right side for each category.

erage. The South American areal extent of the Sauk is about 1.45 million km² and across Africa is just under 9 million km². Our maps show that only the northernmost part of Africa and the west-central portion of South America exhibit any Sauk sediments. Finally, the total volume of sediment deposited during the Sauk represents one of the minimal amounts for each of the three continents compared to most later megasequences.

These rock data suggest the floodwaters rose progressively as described in Genesis 7 with only limited flooding globally during the Sauk transgression. The Sauk Megasequence was only the violent beginning of the Flood, creating the Great Unconformity at its base and encasing prolific numbers of the hard-shelled marine fossils that define the Cambrian Explosion. The peak height of the floodwaters seems to have occurred later, at Day 150 during the Zuni Megasequence, since that is when the coverage and volume of sediment also peak on most of the continents (Table 1).

## Africa Illustrates the Progression of the Flood

The evidence for a single, progressive flood is probably best illustrated by the sedimentary patterns across Africa. Here, the Sauk through Kaskaskia Megasequences show the least surface extent, followed by more and more coverage, until the Flood reached its maximum level during the Zuni, likely Day 150 of the Flood. Unsurprisingly, the Tejas shows a nearly identical amount of surface extent as the Zuni; recall, the Tejas was the receding phase that began on Day 150. The surface extent of both should be nearly identical, barring subsequent erosion.

Note in Table 1 the massive jump in sediment volume and extent in the Absaroka Megasequence across the three continents. We interpret this as about Day 40 in the Flood, when the Ark began to float (Genesis 7:17). It also coincides with the first major coal seams and the first occurrences of numerous land fossils in the rock record. Also note the even greater jump in volume and extent in the Zuni. This is when the dinosaurs were completely inundated and the water levels reached their peak around Day 150.[6]

The totals column on the far right side of Table 1 also confirms the Flood account. These data indicate a flood event that began slowly, reached a maximum in the Zuni, and then receded. This is why the Zuni has the maximum volume, thickness, and extent of sedimentary rocks globally. It was the high point of the Flood—Day 150.

## European Data Match the Global Patterns

The same stratigraphic patterns across the first three continents were also found across Europe with slight differences. The Flood across Europe began in a limited extent in the Sauk, peaked in the Absaroka, and finally receded in the Tejas, the final megasequence. This is strong evidence for a global flood. All four continents we have studied share the same general pattern and timing of limited early flooding, followed by peak flooding, and then receding.

The earliest two megasequences (Sauk and Tippecanoe) showed very limited coverage across Europe. This is the same pattern we observed across the other three continents. The totals across the four continents show the least volume and extent of sedimentary rocks in the earliest two megasequences. The later four megasequences (Kaskaskia, Absaroka, Zuni, and Tejas, respectively) show much more volume and surface extent.

Oddly, Europe has a peak volume and surface coverage extent in the Absaroka Megasequence, which encompasses the Pennsylvanian through Lower Jurassic rocks (Figure 1). Most of the other continents peak a bit later. But the four continent totals still show the maximum extent and volume occurring in the fifth megasequence, the Zuni—Middle Jurassic through Cretaceous rocks.

Figure 2 shows the four continent totals of the percentage of sediment by megasequence. These data still support that the Flood reached its peak in the Zuni. In terms of stratigraphy, this falls near the end of the Cretaceous, when most of the other continents also peak in volume and extent. This global high-water level is interpreted as Day 150 in the Flood year.

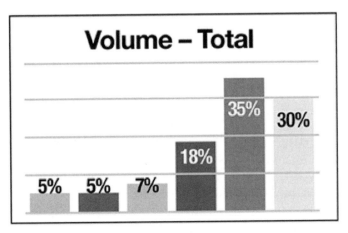

Figure 2. Worldwide sediment volume breakdown by megasequence. From left to right is the Sauk, Tippecanoe, Kaskaskia, Absaroka, Zuni, and Tejas. Note that the global peak in sediment volume is in the Zuni.

Why does Europe peak one megasequence earlier than most of the others? The answer seems to be in the pre-Flood configuration of Europe. Most of the pre-Flood European continent appears to have been lowlands and shallow seas, similar to the Dinosaur Peninsula concept for North America.[6] The floodwaters were able to inundate most of Europe earlier than the other continents, giving a peak in sedimentary volume one megasequence earlier. In contrast, Africa, South America, and North America had more extensive pre-Flood uplands. Europe apparently only had uplands across the Scandinavian Peninsula and parts of Ukraine.

## Rock Data Indicate Late Cenozoic Post-Flood Boundary

There is still debate among creation scientists about the location of the post-Flood boundary in the stratigraphic record. Some have claimed the K-Pg (formerly K-T) boundary marks the end of the Flood as well as the end of marine deposition across the continents. These scientists have insisted that the massive volumes of post-K-Pg sediments observed globally are merely the result of local post-Flood catastrophes. In contrast, other creation scientists have argued that the K-Pg wasn't the end of the Flood but that it continued through much of the Cenozoic rock record. ICR scientists agree with the latter position and interpret much of the Cenozoic strata as the receding phase of the Flood.

As we predicted, the results of the European study dramatically conflict with the K-Pg post-Flood boundary interpretation. The sedimentary rocks across much of central Europe indicate that marine depositional processes continued without interruption from the Cretaceous through the Upper Cenozoic. Many locations show continuous deposition of marine carbonate rocks across the K-Pg boundary from the Cretaceous through Miocene.

These results demonstrate that the Cenozoic rock deposited across Europe wasn't due to highly speculative and improbable localized post-Flood catastrophes but rather to the receding phase of the global Flood itself. Massive marine deposits across such vast areas of the world indicate Flood processes were still active well into the Upper Cenozoic, possibly as high as the top of the Pliocene, where a major paleontological extinction event is observed,[7] coinciding with the end of the Flood.

## New Sea Level Curve Reflects Rock and Fossil Data

After compiling and reviewing the vast stratigraphic data set, we concluded that the published secular global sea level curve is inaccurate, especially for the lowermost megasequences. Real rock data indicate that the amount of pre-Flood land inundated during Sauk and Tippecanoe deposition was extremely limited. These earliest megasequences probably represent the effects of tsumani-like waves that transported sediment across pre-Flood shallow seas only and not across pre-Flood land masses.[5,8] This could also possibly explain why so few terrestrial animals and plants are found as fossils in the first few megasequences (Sauk-Kaskaskia). The secular sea level curve (Figure 1) based on evolutionary biases is wrong.

Why don't we find dinosaur fossils in the earliest Flood sediment layers—why do we find them only in the later Flood rocks of the Absaroka and Zuni? An examination of sedimentary rock layers across the United States and Canada has provided an answer.[6]

The thickest deposition of the earliest Flood sediments (the Sauk, Tippecanoe, and Kaskaskia Megasequences) was in the eastern half of the U.S.—often more than two miles! In contrast, the early Flood sediments across much of the American West are commonly less than a few hundred yards thick, and in many places there was no deposition at all.[6]

It seems dinosaurs were able to survive through the early Flood in the West simply because they were living on pre-Flood lowland areas and elevated remnants of land—places where the earliest megasequence rock deposits are absent or aren't as deep. I call this lowland area Dinosaur Peninsula since it runs like a peninsula from the Midwest down to the Southwest and across a swath of the Rocky Mountains.[6] Due to this pre-Flood topography, dinosaurs were able to escape burial in the earliest megasequences.

The compiled stratigraphic data show that more than three miles of sediment rapidly accumulated across the American West during the subsequent Absaroka and Zuni Megasequences (Figure 1). This apparently overwhelmed and buried the dinosaurs that could no longer escape the Flood, entombing them in Triassic, Jurassic, and Cretaceous strata. As the waters rose, Dinosaur Peninsula began flooding from south to north. Supporting this interpretation, we also find the largest herds of dinosaurs, in the form of dinosaur fossil graveyards, in Cretaceous sediments across northern Wyoming, Montana, and Alberta, Canada. It's as if the dinosaurs were fleeing northward up the peninsula as the waters advanced from the south. But, by Day 150 of the Flood (Genesis 7:24), even the uplands area to the north, in present Canada, was covered by the floodwaters.[8,9]

Not surprisingly, we also found that the locations of dinosaurs across other continents fit this same pattern. Dinosaur-rich rocks are found in areas that were pre-Flood lowland and swampy areas, just like Dinosaur Peninsula in North America.[8,9] Areas matching this same dinosaur-rich ecological zone include parts of Argentina, Morocco, Egypt, East Africa, and large sections of Europe, where many dinosaur graveyards are located.

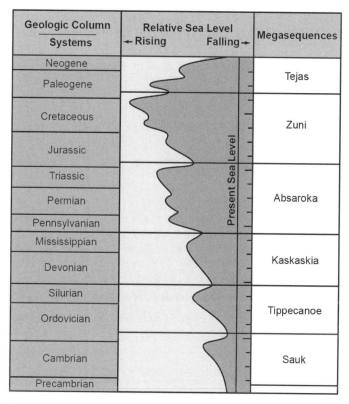

Figure 3. New data-based sea level and megasequence/geologic column chart

## Conclusion

The consistency of the rock data across four continents confirms God's Word. The columns across each continent show a clear progression of the floodwaters, just as described in Genesis 7. All of the continents begin with limited amounts of coverage early, then exhibit progressively more and more deposition until peaking at nearly the same time—and finally recede simultaneously (Figure 2).

> The waters prevailed and greatly increased on the earth, and the ark moved about on the surface of the waters. And the waters prevailed exceedingly on the earth, and all the high hills under the whole heaven were covered. (Genesis 7:18-19)

There is no other reasonable way to explain these data. Simultaneous sedimentary patterns across multiple continents are strong evidence of a global flood. All over the globe the rocks cry out and tell the Flood story. We can be thankful for God's promise in Genesis 9:15 that a global flood will never again destroy the world.

*Notes*

1. Sloss, L. L. 1963. Sequences in the Cratonic Interior of North America. *Geological Society of America Bulletin.* 74 (2): 93-114.

2. Hubbard, R. J. 1988. Age and significance of sequence boundaries on Jurassic and Early Cretaceous rifted continental margins. *American Association of Petroleum Geologists Bulletin.* 72 (1): 49-72.

3. Morris, J. D. 2012. *The Global Flood: Unlocking Earth's Geologic History.* Dallas, TX: Institute for Creation Research.

4. Vail, P. R. and R. M. Mitchum, Jr. 1979. Global Cycles of Relative Changes of Sea Level from Seismic Stratigraphy. *American Association of Petroleum Geologists Memoir.* 29: 469-472.

5. Clarey, T. L. and D. J. Werner. 2017. The Sedimentary Record Demonstrates Minimal Flooding of the Continents During Sauk Deposition. *Answers Research Journal.* 10: 271-283.

6. Clarey, T. 2015. Dinosaur Fossils in Late-Flood Rocks. *Acts & Facts.* 44 (2): 16.

7. Pimiento, C. et al. 2017. The Pliocene marine megafauna extinction and its impact on functional diversity. *Nature Ecology & Evolution.* 1: 1100-1106.

8. Clarey, T. L. and D. J. Werner. 2018. Use of sedimentary megasequences to re-create pre-Flood geography. In *Proceedings of the Eighth International Conference on Creationism.* J. H. Whitmore, ed. Pittsburgh, PA: Creation Science Fellowship, 351-372.

9. Clarey, T. 2020. *Carved in Stone: Geological Evidence of the Worldwide Flood.* Dallas, TX: Institute for Creation Research.

# 33

# FLOOD BOUNDARIES
# IN THE ROCK RECORD

Timothy Clarey, Ph.D., and Jeffrey P. Tomkins, Ph.D.

**Summary:** Genesis Flood models are based on geological bound-aries that indicate where the Flood began and ended. Creationists largely agree the Flood began near the Great Unconformity that marks a major change in the rock record.

Some creation models place the Flood's endpoint at the K-Pg boundary at the top of the Cretaceous system. But the first ap-pearance of many fossils occurs in the higher Cenozoic layers. Huge Cenozoic sand deposits and coal seams are further evidence that the Flood was still receding during this time, and it appears these layers document the ending phase of the Flood.

Rapid seafloor spreading and uninterrupted marine sedimenta-tion across the K-Pg boundary indicate the Flood was not over at this point. Powerful receding floodwaters cut features like Grand Canyon and fossilized many large animals during this runoff phase. The rocks clearly reveal that the Flood ended near the N-Q boundary at the top of the Neogene and the base of the Quater-nary.

Determining where the Flood began and ended in the rock record is of great importance in developing a Flood model. The location of the Flood/ post-Flood boundary has been debated for decades. ICR's Column Project has shed revealing insight on this topic, and we are now fairly certain in our identification of the post-Flood boundary.

## The Lower Flood Boundary

In many places the pre-Flood/Flood boundary is fairly obvious, as noted by Austin et al.[1] It resides at the Precambrian/Cambrian boundary, particularly where Cambrian system deposits are in direct contact with Archean crystalline rocks. In these instances, the boundary coincides with the Great Unconformity as observed in the bottom of Grand Canyon.

In other places, the sedimentary structures and grain size of the sediments might help determine the pre-Flood/Flood boundary, as in the Sixtymile Formation of eastern Grand Canyon. Creation scientists demonstrated in 1994 that the formation is the bottom unit of the Sauk Megasequence (the first major Flood layer) in Grand Canyon, noting that the formation contains large angular clasts (sharp-edged granules in the sediment) indicative of high-energy deposition at the start of the Flood.[2] The Sixtymile Formation is composed primarily of coarse sandstones and is approximately 200 feet at its maximum.

The secular geologic community later arrived at a similar conclusion, finding that the Sixtymile Formation was much younger than originally thought. It seems the creation scientists' predictions were correct all along. Secular geologists concluded that the Sauk Megasequence does include the Sixtymile Formation.[3] Prior to this study, the secular community insisted the formation was Precambrian and was 650 million years old. They believe, however, that this unit marks the beginning of the first of several flooding events, not the beginning of the great Flood.[3]

Even though creation and secular scientists agree that the Sixtymile Formation is part of the Sauk Megasequence, they made those interpretations from contrasting worldviews. For this reason, secular scientists struggle to explain the sudden global appearance of fully formed shelled fossils with no evolutionary precursors in Cambrian strata at the base of the Sauk Megasequence.

Where thick Precambrian sedimentary rocks exist, it can be difficult to locate an exact, universal pre-Flood boundary. For example, in the Precambrian Belt Supergroup that resides in Idaho and Montana, the location of the pre-Flood/Flood boundary has been difficult to establish. Numerous thrust faults (where older strata have slid over younger strata) have placed many of these sediments on top of one another, "thickening" the sequence considerably.

For this reason, along with the lack of fossils within the sedimentary layer and the repetitive nature of the sediments, it is difficult to know the true, original thicknesses of the Belt Supergroup. These thick sediments may be part of a massive river delta complex that formed along the pre-Flood continental margin, since there were over 1,600 years of river activity between creation and the Flood.

## Flood/Post-Flood Boundary Is in the Upper Cenozoic (Top Tejas)

For decades, creation scientists have debated the level at which the Flood ended in the rock record. Most agree that the Flood/post-Flood boundary is at one of two levels: (1) at the top of the Cretaceous system, known as the K-Pg (K-T) horizon;[1,4] or (2) at or near the top of the Neogene (Upper Cenozoic) at about the Pliocene level.[5,6]

Extensive rock data from oil wells and outcrops compiled by ICR's Column Project research team is helping to resolve this matter. First appearances and extensive fossil deposits of many forms of animal and plant life that occur in Cenozoic sediments corroborate the geology. We have therefore determined that the post-Flood boundary is in the Upper Cenozoic, at about the top of the Tejas Megasequence.[7] We call this the N-Q boundary since it occurs at the top of the Neogene and the base of the Quaternary.

## Geological Evidence for an Upper Cenozoic Post-Flood Boundary

There are five major geologic observations demonstrating that the Flood/post-Flood boundary is much higher than the K-Pg level. Some of these features are so large and/or unusual in scale that local post-Flood catastrophes could not have conceivably produced them. Others demonstrate geologic conditions that could only have existed while floodwaters were still covering large portions of the continents. Collectively, they strongly refute the claim that the Flood ended at the stratigraphic level of the K-Pg boundary.

1.  **The Whopper Sand.** Oil companies discovered the Paleocene Whopper Sand in the Gulf of Mexico by drilling wells in water depths of over 7,000 feet and over 200 miles offshore. The only reasonable explanation for this >1,000-foot-thick sand bed covering much of the floor of the deep Gulf of Mexico is a high-energy runoff of sediment-laden water from the North American continent during the final phase of the Flood—something that easily fits the Flood model. We interpret this post-K-Pg deposit as the result of a rapid shift in water direction as described for Day 150+ of the Flood year. Initial drainage rates, co-

inciding with a sudden drop in sea level at the onset of the Tejas Megasequence, provided a mechanism to transport the thick Whopper Sand into deep water. No post-Flood local catastrophe could create this deposit.[8]

2. **The tremendous amount of Tejas sediment deposited globally.** The volume of Tejas sediment is second only to the Zuni Megasequence that ended with the Cretaceous system, the presumed high-water point of the Flood. The tremendous amount of Paleogene and Neogene sediments all over the world that are part of the Tejas Megasequence cannot be easily dismissed as the product of local catastrophes. These sediments, and the fossils they contain, are better explained by the receding water phase of the Flood as mountain ranges and plateaus were being uplifted.

3. **The thickest and most extensive coal seams are found globally in Tejas sediments.** The Powder River Basin (PRB) coals in North America, which are all within Paleogene system rock layers above the K-Pg boundary, contain the largest reserves of low-sulfur subbituminous coal in the world. At least six or more coal beds in the PRB exceed 100 feet in thickness, and some individual beds have been shown to extend for over 75 miles. Some of these coal beds exceed 200 feet thick in places, such as the Big George coal layer in the PRB. These coal beds are part of the receding phase of the Flood that transported huge mats of plant and tree debris. They were derived largely from hardwood trees living at higher elevations that became rapidly buried in huge late-Flood deposits.

4. **The tremendous amount of rapid ocean crust/seafloor spreading** that continued across the K-Pg boundary and right up to the Pliocene, with no indication of a significant change in velocity. The runaway subduction model for the global Flood described by geophysicist Dr. John Baumgardner[9] caused approximately one-third of the world's ocean crust to form during the time frame of the Tejas Megasequence (Paleocene through Pliocene). The huge earthquakes and tsunamis generated by this type of plate movement would have been devastating for any type of human civilization after the Flood if the Flood/post-Flood boundary is located at the K-Pg.

5. **The identification of uninterrupted water-deposited carbonate rocks** from the Cretaceous (below the K-Pg boundary) and continuing upward through Miocene strata across much of North Africa, Europe, Turkey, and the Middle East. These locations completely surround the landing site for the Ark in eastern Turkey. The documentation of uninterrupted marine sedimentation (limestone and salt beds) across the K-Pg boundary in Syria and Iraq demonstrate that the Flood was not over at this point. If these were post-Flood deposits, it would have been impossible for humans to settle there at that time and build the Tower of Babel since the area would have still been under water.

Our research efforts have identified more geological features that further support that the Flood/post-Flood boundary is near the top of the Tejas Megasequence (encompassing the Paleogene and Neogene geological systems). One of these is the Ogallala Sandstone in North America.[10] Local post-Flood catastrophes cannot explain this continuous sand bed that covers much of the Great Plains. It must represent part of the receding phase of the Flood as well.

## Paleontological Evidence for an Upper Cenozoic Post-Flood Boundary

Many types of animals and plants make their first appearances in the fossil record in the uppermost sedimentary rock layers that are part of the Tejas Megasequence that corresponds to the Paleogene and Neogene rock units of the Cenozoic. As mentioned, hardwood trees and other temperate higher-elevation plants buried late in the Flood formed massive Cenozoic coal seams. In addition to this paleontological evidence from pre-Flood vegetation is the fact that many types of land and marine mammals make their first appearance in Cenozoic layers as well, with many now being extinct.[11-17]

It is completely unrealistic to think that the extensive burial of the huge diversity of mammals found all over the world in Cenozoic sediments is the result of numerous localized floods occurring after the global Flood, as the K-Pg boundary proponents have claimed. Perhaps the best example of this is the case of marine mammals—especially whales (Cetaceans).[17] According to K-Pg boundary proponents, rapid whale evolution occurred within the first 200 years after the Flood from walking-whale Ark ancestors.[18-19] This whole line of reasoning is based on the fact that whales make their first appearances in Cenozoic strata after the K-Pg boundary. But did whales really evolve from terrestrial Ark ancestors, which would have required numerous changes in anatomy and physiology?

Paleontology database research done on whale fossil locations mapped across the globe shows that they appear suddenly in the fossil record in the Cenozoic. In fact, whale fossils are located on the coastal margins of nearly every major landmass and are also distributed across the entire continent of Europe. This is not surprising, since the Column Project at ICR has shown that marine Cenozoic sediments cover Europe.

Not only do whales appear suddenly in the fossil record all over the world, but their pervasive global distribution debunks the ideas of creationists who claim they represent creatures buried shortly after the Flood in small localized catastrophes after supposedly evolving from walking whales that came off Noah's Ark. In fact, even secular research has shown that a massive global extinction event that involved marine mammals occurred in the Pliocene at the top of the Cenozoic.[20]

## Flood Boundary Conclusions

As mentioned earlier, the stratigraphic horizon for the beginning of the Flood is less debated and is usually quite obvious. In most places, it is marked by a layer of course sediment, such as the Tapeats Sandstone, resting on crystalline basement rocks. The boundary is the surface between the two rock types. In many cases, this boundary coincides with the Great Unconformity and the Cambrian Explosion. At other locations where there are preserved pre-Flood sediments below the Sauk Megasequence, it is not quite so clear.

As we've demonstrated, the post-Flood boundary is also quite evident. Geological and paleontological data show that much of the Paleogene and Neogene (known previously as the Tertiary) was the receding phase of the great Flood, placing the Flood/post-Flood boundary at the top of the Tejas Megasequence (Upper Cenozoic). Continuous deposition of uninterrupted marine rocks across the K-Pg boundary, surrounding the landing site of the Ark, and the massive amounts of ocean crust that formed during the Tejas together demonstrate that the Flood was not over at the K-Pg level.

Fossils of so many large mammals and the vast majority of flowering plant fossils that show up so abundantly, and for the first time, in Tejas Megasequence strata are best explained as a consequence of the receding phase of the Flood. These land animal and plant fossils were swept from the highest pre-Flood hills and buried as the floodwaters began to recede. The whale fossils appearing late in the flood sediments could be explained by two key factors. First, whales are air-breathing marine mammals that live mostly near the ocean surface and thus would have avoided much of the catastrophic tumult occurring at deeper levels. Secondly, their carcasses, being extremely large and laden with fatty tissue, would float for much longer periods of time and thus be deferred in their burial. Thus, paleontological and rock data not only confirm there was a global flood as described in the Bible, but they also help us to better understand its final stages of sedimentary deposition.

Suggestions that the Flood was completely over at the K-Pg boundary fail to explain much of these data. Nor does this allow enough time for the floodwaters to drain off the continents. Picking the wrong Flood/post-Flood boundary can also lead to other misinterpretations, such as the breach-dam explanation for Grand Canyon. In contrast, Grand Canyon is best explained as a consequence of the receding phase of the Flood.[21]

In addition, the advocates for a K-Pg Flood/post-Flood boundary consider all Cenozoic fossils to have formed in the window of time between the ending of the Flood and the beginning of the Ice Age. This only allows about 200± years for the dispersal (whatever the mechanism) and incredible diversification and subsequent burial of all Cenozoic mammals, flowering plants, and other fossils on multiple continents and in nearly the exact same stratigraphic order simultaneously. Therefore, the presumed local catastrophes used to explain these Cenozoic fossils seem to more closely resemble global catastrophes. Global catastrophes are better explained with a global flood event.

The rocks clearly reveal that the Flood ended near the N-Q boundary at the top of the Neogene and the base of the Quaternary.

### Notes

1. Austin, S. A. et al. 1994. Catastrophic Plate Tectonics: A Global Flood Model of Earth History. In *Proceedings of the Third International Conference on Creationism*. R. E. Walsh, ed. Pittsburgh, PA: Creation Science Fellowship, 609-621

2. Austin, S. A. and K. P. Wise. 1994. The Pre-Flood/Flood Boundary: As Defined in Grand Canyon, Arizona and Eastern Mojave Desert, California. In *Proceedings of the Third International Conference on Creationism*, 37-47.

3. Karlstrom, K. et al. 2018. Cambrian Sauk transgression in the Grand Canyon redefined by detrital zircons. *Nature Geoscience* 11: 438-443.

4. Whitmore, J. H., and K. P. Wise. 2008. Rapid and early post-Flood mammalian diversification evidences in the Green River Formation. In *Proceedings of the Sixth International Conference on Creationism*. A. A. Snelling, ed. Pittsburgh, PA: Creation Science Fellowship, 449-457.

5. Oard, M. J. 2013. Geology indicates the terrestrial Flood/post-Flood boundary is mostly in the Late Cenozoic. *Journal of Creation*. 27 (1): 119-127.

6. Clarey, T. L. 2016. The Ice Age as a mechanism for post-Flood dispersal. *Journal of Creation*. 30 (2): 48-53.

7. Clarey, T. L. 2017. Local Catastrophes or Receding Floodwater? Global Geologic Data that Refute a K-Pg (K-T) Flood/post-Flood Boundary. *Creation Research Society Quarterly*. 54 (2): 100-120.

8. Clarey, T. 2015. The Whopper Sand. *Acts & Facts*. 44 (3): 14.

9. Baumgardner, J. R. 1994. Runaway Subduction as the Driving Mechanism for the Genesis Flood. In *Proceedings of the Third International Conference on Creationism*. R. E. Walsh, ed. Pittsburgh, PA: Creation Science Fellowship, 63-75.

10. Clarey, T. 2018. Palo Duro Canyon Rocks Showcase Genesis Flood. *Acts & Facts* 47 (7): 10.

11. Prothero, D. R. 2017. *The Princeton Field Guide to Prehistoric Mammals*. Princeton, NJ: Princeton University Press.

12. Tomkins, J. P. and T. Clarey. 2018. Cretaceous-Paleogene Boundary Shenanigans. *Acts & Facts*. 47 (1): 14.

13. Tomkins, J. P. Monkey Fossil Reveals Diversity and Flood Boundary. *Creation Science Update*. Posted on ICR.org June 11, 2019, accessed September 30, 2019.

14. Tomkins, J. P. and T. Clarey. 2018. Darwin's Abominable Mystery and the Genesis Flood. *Acts & Facts*. 47 (6): 16.

15. Tomkins, Monkey Fossil Reveals Diversity and Flood Boundary.

16. Tomkins, J. P. Hyaenodont Fossil Highlights Diversity and Flood Boundary. *Creation Science Update*. Posted on ICR.org April 30, 2019.

17. Tomkins, J. P. and T. Clarey. 2019. Whale Fossils Confirm Post-Flood Boundary. *Acts & Facts*. 48 (12): 9.

18. Wise, K. P. 2009. Mammal kinds: how many were on the ark? In *Genesis Kinds: Creationism and the Origin of Species*. T. C. Wood and P. A. Garner, eds. Eugene, OR: Wipf & Stock 129-161.

19. Wise, K. P. 2017. Step-down saltational intrabaraminic diversification. *Journal of Creation Theology and Science Series B: Life Sciences*. 7: 8-9.

20. Pimiento, C. et al. 2017. The Pliocene marine megafauna extinction and its impact on functional diversity. *Nature Ecology & Evolution*. 1 (8): 1100-1106.

21. Clarey, T. 2018. Grand Canyon Carved by Flood Runoff. *Acts & Facts*. 47 (12): 10-13.

# 34

# THE REAL NATURE
# OF THE FOSSIL RECORD

John D. Morris, Ph.D.

**Summary:** Earth's fossil record doesn't support evolution. Instead, the fossils and the geologic column in which they are found are strong evidence for the Genesis Flood.

The lowest layers of the column reflect the earliest stages of the Flood, with an abundance of marine fossils. The next layers up mostly contain coastal and lowland life forms, and the higher layers have upland-dwelling creatures that died late in the Flood. Marine and terrestrial fossils are also found mixed together.

Basic creature types appear suddenly in the fossil record with no evolutionary transitional forms preceding them. There is no evidence of simple life evolving into more complex life forms. The fossil record displays sudden appearance and disappearance, not evolution. The real nature of that record is incompatible with evolution but remarkably consistent with the biblical record.

The fossil record leaves an inescapable impression on the honest observer. It certainly doesn't communicate the macroevolutionary picture. The record of the past written in stone contains no evidence that any particular animal ever morphed into a fundamentally different type of animal. No trend can be found of gradual Darwinian alteration through mutation and natural selection. These processes may occur, but they are not mechanisms for true evolution of basic body styles.

Nor do we see punctuated equilibrium transforming them rapidly. Without a doubt, we see sudden changes in dominant fossil shapes as we ascend the geologic column, but this is not macroevolution. The species changes touted by punctuated equilibrium that we do see are either common variation of individual offspring or adaptation of a population to differing conditions. Punctuated equilibrium doesn't even address the larger changes needed for meaningful evolution.

The array of fossils usually constitutes the main evidence for evolution. The standard geologic column presents a column of fossils with the oldest near the bottom, less ancient ones toward the middle, and recent fossils near the top—supposedly showing the progress of evolution over time, from bottom to top, from simple life to more complex life. Note that while the chart appears to be a presentation of the way fossils are found, it is really a time chart. The stack of individual periods can be considered analogous to the various geologic layers, with older ones on the bottom and newer ones on the top.

While creationists rightly reject the time component and implications of the column, it does contain good information, compiled from thousands of valid observations. The rock layers at the bottom are better understood as having been deposited at the start of the Flood, with the ones nearer the top laid down later in the Flood. The first layers document the early bursts of the "fountains of the deep" and accompanying tsunamis, which would primarily impact ocean-bottom dwellers. Episodes to follow would bury upper marine life, then coastal life, then the life on land. But rather than demonstrating evolution, does it tell us something else? We can consider it almost an ecological chart, preserving the stages of the great Flood. Once reinterpreted, it actually supports the creation-Flood concept.

In general, the animals portrayed near the chart's bottom all lived in the ocean's depths, while those in the middle lived higher in the water and on the coastlines, and those even higher on the chart lived on land. While evolutionists use the column as a statement of evolutionary dogma as documented by the fossils, we have seen that the fossils really tell a much different story.

## Sudden Appearance of Basic Types

The fossil record communicates sudden appearance of basic types, complete with all the features that characterize them. Lots of variety is on display, even at times enough to lead to a new species.

But variety is not evolution. Cats are cats and dogs are dogs and always have been so. There are similarities between them but no hint of relatedness. Both appear to have been suddenly created to live in similar environments, breathe the same air, eat the same foods, drink the same water, and survive through circulation of similar blood. We should expect similarities. But cats when they reproduce yield kittens, and reproducing dogs have puppies. They did not originate by mutations in a different type of common ancestor, nor did one come from the other. And this is what the fossils show.

## Basic Types Show Stasis

Once a basic type appeared, it demonstrated stasis. Individuals varied in appearance and whole populations varied over the generations to accommodate changing conditions as they "multiplied and filled" Earth's varied environments, but always they were fundamentally the same as the parent group.

The fossil record features stasis as a dominant trend. It does not speak of major changes. Evolution, or the descent from a common ancestor model, demands that major changes visited every population. But this is the evolutionary "story," not the conclusion drawn from the fossils.

## Complexity at the Start

Each plant or animal alive today exhibits amazing complexity. Each of its body parts is precisely designed to perform its function, and all work together for the good of the whole. Indeed, there often is no use for a particular part without the others. Some may only be used at a limited period of life or in an unusual circumstance, at which time they must be present for survival. All must be present for any to accomplish any useful purpose.

From the very first time a fossil type appears (i.e., the lowest stratigraphic interval in which it's found), it shows all the design features that make it special. Evolution necessitates the gradual accumulation of body parts through random mutation and amalgamation of previous parts with different functions into a new whole. The elegance of design, however, argues *against* a patchwork origin and *for* an intelligent cause. Mutations only mar, but do not erase, evidence of exquisite design.

## Extinction, Not Evolution

Extinction is well-documented in the fossil record, and while extinction is a necessary part of the evolutionary scenario, it is not evolution. It might better be considered as the opposite of evolution. Losing a type is not what is in question, but the gaining of new types—now, that would be interesting.

A case can be made by fossil "splitters" that new species can be found as one ascends the strata. However, speciation within basic kinds is different from the introduction of new kinds, and evolution requires a dizzying array of basic new kinds. The origination of a new form has never been documented in the modern world of scientific observation, while perhaps several species every day go extinct. The opposite of evolution occurs today, and fossils show that the opposite of evolution also occurred in the past.

## No Ancestor/Descendant Relationships

Evolution necessarily implies the concept of "descent from a common ancestor or ancestors." Yet, no ancestor/descendant relationship can be advocated with certainty based on the fossils. Indeed, the differences are obvious and make classification of types possible.

The similarities between distinct types is not a sure footing on which to base an ancestral relationship, as proved by the many mutually competing cladograms advanced by evolutionists. Whose opinion, if any, is correct? The separateness of each type is witness to their separate creations.

## Fossil Record Is Complete

The fossil record can be deemed essentially complete. Darwin was concerned about its lack of transitional forms, hypothetical creatures that demonstrate one type changing into another over time. He was hopeful they would be found one day.

But extensive exploration and fossil discovery in following years have not brought such in-between forms to light. The vast majority of taxonomic orders and families that live today are also found as fossils, yet without fossil transitions. We can be certain the record is substantially complete.

## All Phyla Present at the Start

The Cambrian Explosion constitutes a major episode in the history of life. If evolution were true, one would expect the record to start with one type of animal life, then increase to two, and so on. Yet, fossil studies have shown that essentially all phyla were present at the start, each distinct from the others and each fully equipped to function and survive. Even vertebrate fish were present in the lower Cambrian.

Some phyla have gone extinct over subsequent years, but most have continued into the present. There is no evolutionary tree found in the fossils, as Darwin and his disciples have claimed. Rather, it is more like a lawn than a tree.

## Many Fossils Found Throughout the Column

Stasis can be seen in the large, vertical, stratigraphic ranges of many fossil types. Index fossils are thought to exist only for a brief timespan. True enough, some fossils are only found in a relatively few layers. But many other fossils, such as the brachiopod *Lingula*, can be found throughout the geologic column and into the present. This animal would seemingly make a good potential ancestor for others, but it never changed into anything or arose from anything.

Various fossil types are found in many layers, with more fossil ranges being continually extended by new discoveries. Statistical treatments give reason to believe that essentially all types lived throughout a large portion of history.

## Most Fossils Are Marine Invertebrates

The vast majority of animal fossils are marine invertebrates. They are found in great variety, but all are well-designed for life in the sea. Some lived in high-energy, near-shore environments, but others lived in deeper waters, away from the pounding action of the waves.

Among the vertebrates, most fossils are fish—again mostly marine creatures. Of the terrestrial fossils, by far most are plants. Land-dwelling animals, such as mammals and dinosaurs, are poorly represented in the fossil record. The majority of animals depicted on evolutionary fossil charts in textbooks, however, are land vertebrates. It is claimed that a possible case for evolution can be made from them, but exceptions do not accurately portray the real fossil record. Where good evidence exists, no evolution can be seen.

## Fossils Found in Catastrophic Deposits

These fossilized marine creatures are typically found in catastrophic deposits. Even marine creatures that live in high-energy zones cannot live in catastrophic conditions. Many died where they were fossilized. They were either buried alive, or their remains were transported by dynamic processes to their present resting places before they could decay or be scavenged.

The processes involved must have been highly destructive yet rapidly acting. The major forces that sculpted Earth's surface were not like the processes of today.

## Indications of Violent Death

Often the fossil remains are found in a death pose. One famous *Archaeopteryx* fossil lies with its neck and tail arched back as if it were dying a horrible, drowning death. Clams are found with both halves tightly shut, "clammed up" as a living clam does for protection from danger.

Dinosaur fossils, also in death poses, are found ripped apart but often not scavenged. Fossilized animals give every indication they were violently killed and/or transported to the places we now find them.

## No Complete Ecosystems

The fossils are usually entombed in deposits with no complete ecosystems present that could have supported them in life. Often evolutionists portray a fossil's tomb as a snapshot of life and tell stories about the creature's habits.

But these plants and animals are not necessarily found where they lived or where they died. They are found where they were buried. It is not honest to presume patterns of life from transported remains of once-living things.

## Animals from Mixed Habitats

Fossil graveyards often contain numerous animals from mixed habitats. Saltwater fish are sometimes found with upland dwellers. Crocodile fossils are found with deep-sea denizens and desert and arctic mammals.

They could scarcely be lumped together in this way by the uniform processes of today. Some great cataclysm is needed.

## Fossils Found Mostly on Continents

The catastrophic deposits in which the mostly marine fossils are found are almost all on the continents. A series of marine cataclysms inundated the land, destroying nearly everything there and laying down a record plain enough for all to see. Those terrestrial fossils that were deposited primarily date from the Ice Age that followed the great Flood of Noah's day.

## Conclusion

Combining all these major concepts, we see that the fossil record is a record quite different from that presented in support of evolution. Each basic plant and animal type appeared abruptly and fully functional and then experienced stasis throughout its tenure. Each type was complex and distinct at the start, without having descended from some other ancestral type, particularly from a less complex type.

All basic types that have ever lived were present at the start, and while some have subsequently gone extinct, no new basic types have appeared since the beginning. We have reason to believe substantially all basic forms that ever lived have been found as fossils.

A general rule is that the fossils extend through a lengthy stratigraphic range with little or no change. Most of the fossils are remains of marine invertebrates, found in catastrophic deposits, often in death poses with an incomplete ecosystem present. These predominately marine fossils are almost all found on the continents, not in the ocean.

The fossil record is thus quite incompatible with evolution and uniformitarianism, but remarkably consistent with the biblical record—creation of all things in perfect form and function, the Curse on all things due to man's rebellion, and the great Flood of Noah's day that first destroyed and then renovated the entire planet.

Creation thinking predicts the evidence, while evolution must distort and flex the evidence and its position to accommodate it.

# 35

# FOSSIL FORENSICS DISPROVE DARWIN

James J. S. Johnson, J.D., Th.D.

**Summary:** In studying past events, forensic evidence is used. Courts of law use this type of evidence to investigate and decide criminal cases. Sometimes a lack of evidence—where something is missing that would not be if a witness' story were true—can conclusively prove a case.

When investigating the origin of life on Earth, there are missing transitional life forms in the fossil record that should be there if evolution were true. Instead of evidence for an evolutionary tree that traces a common descent for all life forms, we find fixed, distinct created kinds, and a great variety within kinds but no transitional forms.

The crucial missing links are still missing in the fossil record. The lack of transitional forms—the evidence of "nothing"—is a powerful proof the Bible is right and evolution is wrong.

Evaluating evidence is a key component in the search for truth, not only in science but in other areas of life. There are times, however, when nothing (i.e., the complete absence of something that should be there but isn't) counts just as strongly as "positive" evidence.

## Rules of Evidence

Over the past centuries, the search for truth in empirical (i.e., observation-based) science has been formalized into the process known as the scientific method, whereby scientific theories are developed and tested according to generally accepted standards. The ability to identify supporting facts and data is vital for proving or disproving a hypothesis about how things operate in the observable world of the present.

In the arena of forensic science (which, unlike empirical science, investigates facts and events of the unobservable past), the legal and judicial professions operate by the Rules of Evidence.[1]

Developed over hundreds of years and brought to America via English Common Law, these forensic evidence rules are relied upon to decide disputes over financial transactions, inheritances, land use and ownership, parental custody of minor children, and criminal matters, such as whether a convicted killer should be executed. Circumstantial evidence, analyzed by principles of forensic science, may involve a broken knife at the scene of a burglary or pistol discharge evidence on the clothes of a killer.[2]

For generations now, we Americans (and other countries that have adopted the British norms of forensic evidence analysis) have trusted these Evidence Rules with our lives, our liberties, and our properties. Accordingly, in legal controversies, the Rules of Evidence serve as a vital vehicle for seriously searching out and reliably reaching (it is hoped) the truth. Real truth stands up to being tested. And even the absence of evidence can operate as a "silent witness," testifying to a circumstance where there is nothing when there should be something.

But what would happen if we applied the same principles of the Evidence Rules to analyzing other types of disputes, such as scientific controversies about origins? Before answering that question, let us consider how the evidence of "nothing when there should be something" was used to sentence a medical doctor to jail time for asserting false claims.

## Circumstantial Evidence of Nothing

This Medicare fraud case involved years of federal court proceedings, with one of the appeals being decided in 2007.[3] Part of the convicting evidence was *nothing*—literally nothing when there should have been something. In the related cases of *Okoro* and *Akpan*, Victor Okoro, M.D., in concert with others, was accused of fraudulent Medicare billing practices that conflicted with his "medical missionary" trips and a bogus charity called the Sisters of Grace.

The appellate court said this about Dr. Okoro's Medicare fraud:

Although some of the patients [in Texas] received physical therapy treatments and some were examined by Okoro, each patient signed blank sign-in sheets and blank patient forms. In addition, Okoro signed most of the forms himself, yet many of the patients testified that he had never examined them....Okoro signed patient documents that stated that he had treated those patients on specific dates and at specific times on which Okoro could not possibly have rendered services. For example, many of the dates on which Okoro alleged that he provided services were dates when he was in Nigeria.[4]

Of course, the federal prosecutor had no difficulty proving that Okoro was absent from Texas due to his using airports to exit the United States. Likewise, federal records provided the dates when Dr. Okoro re-entered America, so the official federal government records were relevant (and admissible) for showing the dates of Okoro's travels in and out of the country.

Yet, just as important, from a circumstantial evidence standpoint, was the government's proof of "nothing" on other legally important dates. The federal government's trial proof included official government records with *absences* of entries on the dates in question, showing that Dr. Okoro was not recorded as having re-entered the United States in time for him to have performed the medical services for which he billed Medicare.

This illustrates the power of an argument from silence—the forensic force of such a silent witness can buttress a sentence of felony jail time. So, technically speaking, how can "nothing" become admissible circumstantial evidence at trial? Federal Evidence Rule 803(10) provides one such forensic possibility:

> **Absence of Public Record or Entry.** *To prove the absence* of a record, report, statement, or data compilation, in any form, or *the nonoccurrence or nonexistence of a matter* of which a record, report, statement, or data compilation, in any form, was regularly made and preserved by a public office or agency, evidence in the form of a certification in accordance with rule 902, if necessary, or testimony, that *diligent search failed to disclose* the record, report, statement, or data compilation, or entry. (emphasis added)

Evidence Rule 803(7) is similar, but it applies to admitting as trial evidence the fact that regularly recorded "business records" have a relevant "absence" of an entry, as well as where and when a documentary "nothing" is forensically important.[5]

## Origins, Biodiversity, Fossils, and the Evidence of Nothing

So, how does the evidence of nothing demonstrated by this particular

Medicare fraud scheme relate to the question of origins?

The comparison can be illustrated by applying the Evidence Rules that govern "nothing when there should be something" to the evolutionists' pale-ontological problem of "missing links." This evidentiary insight may be ana-lytically unusual, but it is certainly not new.[6]

Consider how "the evidence of nothing" pertains to Earth's biodiversity.[7] What explains the voluminous variety of animals on Earth today? Does it show a phylogenetic common ancestry shared by animals and humans?

The biodiversity we see today does *not* match evolutionary predictions. Evolutionary assumptions imagine a globally integrated scenario in which life forms gradually branch off from common ancestors and somehow end up as one seamless biotic community—one big family reunion—with everything and everyone (from maggots to mankind) genealogically interlinked "cousins."

But reality is different; sharp biodiversity boundary lines between created kinds exist. And the "missing links" between discrete kinds are still *missing*. If Darwin-presumed missing links ever really existed, why are they still missing?

Canines (dogs, coyotes, wolves, dingoes, and foxes) are genetically com-patible—they can all interbreed. Likewise, bears (black bears, grizzlies, and even polar bears) can interbreed. Similarly, equids (horses, donkeys, and ze-bras) can interbreed. But canines and bears cannot interbreed—there's no common ancestor "link" here! Likewise, equids can't mate with canines, and bears can't mate with horses.

There is a God-installed fixity of kinds in the animal kingdom, providing a permanent barrier to the kind of procreative progeny animals can have. Va-riety within limits is what God intended, and that is what we see all over the world. This reality not only corroborates the Bible, it also disproves Darwin's imagined "common ancestry" natural selection theory of animal origins.

If Darwin's theory of evolution were really true, as even modern-day (neo-Darwinian) evolutionists imagine, the earth should be inundated with common-ancestry transitional forms evidenced by both fossils and living life forms with no sharp biodiversity boundaries between the interbreedable kinds.

Accordingly, when examining the quixotic quest for Darwin's missing links, the real-world evidence is like *déjà vu* all over again—literally nothing when there should have been something!

To use Evidence Rule 803(10)'s logic, a diligent search for these so-called transitional form fossils over a period of 150 years has failed to disclose them. What kind of empirical data (and, when analyzed, what kind of forensic evidence) is that, applied to the origin of Earth's life forms?

Generations of diligent searching of the fossil record still indicates a glaring *absence* of molecules-to-man evolutionary phylogeny. In other words, the empirical data of Earth's fossils, if analyzed forensically, show that evolutionary phylogenetic notions are just empty imaginings refuted by the evidence of nothing.

Dr. John Morris has summarized what the global fossil record contains, and (more importantly) what it does *not* contain.

> Evolutionists often speak of missing links. They say that the bridge between man and the apes is the "missing link," the hypothetical ape-like ancestor of both. But there are supposed missing links all over the evolutionary tree. For instance, dogs and bears are thought to be evolutionary cousins, related to each other through a missing link. The same could be said for every other stop on the tree. All of the animal types are thought to have arisen by the transformation of some other animal type, and at each branching node is a missing link, and between the node and the modern form are many more. If you still don't know what a missing link is, don't worry. No one knows what a missing link is, because they are missing! We've never seen one.[8]

This argument from silence is a complete absence of evolutionary transitional forms in the evidentiary record—a "nothing where there should be something" if evolutionary theory were true. In other words, forensically speaking, when it comes to evolutionary claims about the fossil record, there is a lot of "science falsely so-called" (1 Timothy 6:20, KJV).

Some may say that the above forensic analysis is "much ado about nothing." However, now this "silent witness" is buttressed by dinosaur soft tissue evidence—collagen protein, nucleated blood vessels, osteocyte tendrils, and even DNA fragments—which is even more powerful proof that the fanciful fairytale of evolution is just a scam.[9]

## Conclusion

Forensically speaking, when it comes to the importance of missing links in the fossil record, nothing (where there should be something) is itself a powerful proof, confirming that the Bible is right and that Darwinian evolution is wrong.

### Notes

1. The Federal Rules of Evidence have been cloned, with only small modifications, by the 50 U.S. states. According to Rule 102, the Federal Rules of Evidence are supposed to be applied "to the end that the truth may be ascertained and proceedings justly determined." This article focuses mainly on Evidence Rules 803(7) and 803(10), which respectively govern the admissibility as evidence of an absence of information that could have been (but was not) entered into a regular business record or an official government record. Regarding Evidence Rule 801(d)(1)(B), applied to origins controversies, see Johnson, J. J. S. 2012. Tonsils, Forensic Science, and the Recent Fabrication Rule. *Acts & Facts*. 41 (6): 8-9.

2. See page 41 of *The Testimony of the Evangelists: The Gospels Examined by the Rules of Evidence* by Simon Greenleaf, originally published in 1874, reprinted in 1995 (Grand Rapids, MI: Kregel).

3. Trial in federal district court began in 2002. One appellate ruling was published as *United States v. Akpan*, 407 F.3d 360 (5th Cir. 2005). A later appellate decision appears at *United States v. Okoro*, 213 Fed. Appx. 348, 2007 WL 98804 (5th Cir. 2007) (non-precedent).

4. Quoting from *United States v. Akpan*, 407 F.3d at 364-365.

5. The same forensic evidence principle can be applied to critiquing historical data. See, e.g., page 146 in Dr. Bill Cooper's *After the Flood* (Chichester, UK: New Wine Press, 1995).

6. Greenleaf, *The Testimony of the Evangelists*, 41.

7. Biodiversity is the scientific word used to summarize the variety of life forms on Earth. Noah's Ark, which God used to caringly preserve the genetic potential for post-Flood biodiversity, is proof that God loves biodiversity.

8. Morris, J. 2006. What's a Missing Link? *Acts & Facts*. 35 (4).

9. Morris, J. D. and Frank J. Sherwin. 2010. *The Fossil Record: Unearthing Nature's History of Life.* Dallas, TX: Institute for Creation Research, 7-186; Snelling, A. A. 2009. *Earth's Catastrophic Past: Geology, Creation, and the Flood.* Dallas, TX: Institute for Creation Research. Regarding how dinosaur soft tissue discoveries are embarrassing evolutionists, see Tomkins, J. 2009. Dinosaur Protein Sequences and the Dino-to-Bird Model. *Acts & Facts*. 38 (10): 12-14; Johnson, J. J. S., J. Tomkins, and B. Thomas. 2009. Dinosaur DNA Research: Is the Tale Wagging the Evidence? *Acts & Facts*. 38 (10): 4-6; Thomas, B. 2009. Dinosaur Soft Tissue Is Here to Stay. *Acts & Facts*. 38 (9): 18.

# 36

# HOW DO THEY DATE
# A FOSSIL ANYWAY?

Brian Thomas, Ph.D.

**Summary:** Most scientists interpret a fossil's age in light of evolutionary time. Researchers regularly match their fossils and their rock layers to pre-determined ages given on geological charts. If igneous rocks are associated with a fossil's layer, scientists can use radiodating. But those methods often give discordant results and are regularly "adjusted" to fit assumed evolutionary dates.

One example of this was the discovery of human-like fossils in a layer that was too "old" to fit the human evolutionary story. No problem: the layer was just re-dated until it was "young" enough. And when Hell Creek Formation dinosaurs were found in an area deposited "after" they supposedly went extinct, scientists scrambled to offer explanations—but none solved the puzzle.

Secular fossil dating methods ensure that ages will match evolutionary expectations. They offer no "science" that challenges the young earth presented in God's Word.

Nothing in recent times has been more effective in robbing people of their confidence in God's Word than the supposedly scientific claim of an old earth. If the world is millions of years old, then evolution seems plausible, and God's Word—which has no hint of evolution or deep time—is placed in doubt.

However, if Earth and its fossils are only thousands of years old, that leaves no time for evolution but just the right time for biblical history. Because a fossil's date is not written on it like an ancient coin, tablet, or reliably copied document, age-dating a fossil is not straightforward, as a survey of the basic steps that workers take will reveal.

## Basic Steps in Age-Dating

Standard secular belief holds that rock layers are millions of years old. This is the filter through which "facts" must pass before they are deemed acceptable. At least one secular scientist recognized a similar self-serving circle that characterized the early 20th-century evolutionists who were having difficulty matching fossil data to Darwinian evolution.

> In other words, when the assumed evolutionary processes did not match the pattern of fossils that they were supposed to have generated, the pattern was judged to be 'wrong.' A circular argument arises. Interpret the fossil record in terms of a particular theory of evolution, inspect the interpretation, and note that it confirms the theory. Well, it would, wouldn't it?[1]

In much the same way, secularists approach all data with evolutionary time already well-ensconced in their thinking. They interpret the fossil record in those terms, then note that their interpretation confirms millions of years. This self-serving system should be severed from science.

In the next steps to age-dating a fossil or its rock layer, a paleontologist records the color, size, and chemistry of the rock, as well as any species of common, abundant, small fossils like those of clams, brachiopods, or even pollen. She then may search for other rock layers in the surrounding area that share these characteristics but also dovetail or interfinger with another geological feature—such as a volcanic rock layer—that contains minerals with radioactive elements that might be used in radiodating.

Then she matches her field observations with technical charts that separate geoscientists have worked out. These charts assign period names and date numbers to each characteristic rock layer. Or she may simply cite an age that was already published by other paleontologists, trusting that they did their age determinations accurately.

At this point, the researcher invokes a second major, but rarely questioned, assumption—that each characteristic layer represents a time or era that huge numbers of years separate from adjacent time periods.[2] Having inherited this doctrine from respected authorities, the mere idea that perhaps all the layers could have formed from successive tsunami-like pulses during a short-lived gargantuan cataclysm rarely crosses researchers' minds.

The secular researcher feels confident in the geologic chart because others in her field often refer to it. Long ago, Flood geologists made the first charts of rock layers, interpreting them as the result of catastrophes from the Flood year or from the Flood's aftereffects. But secular thinkers from Enlightenment Europe hijacked those charts and affixed ancient ages to them. Since then, scientists and those who trust them think of the layers as married to their assigned long ages.

If the paleontologist finds associated material such as igneous rock suitable for radiodating, she sends her rock samples to a radioisotope laboratory. She will usually tell them an approximate time period to expect, based on the ages published in the geologic chart that applies to that area. More samples mean more radiodates, and these often conflict, producing discordant dates. She must then decide which numbers to include in her publication and then explain away the dates she included but rejected either from among her new results or from prior studies.

Discordant radiodates are very common. Many have been published in scientific literature, but many more never even get reported. How do we know? One researcher admitted, "In the majority of cases the ages are clearly off and the data disappear in a lab datafile."[3] Another study summarized 30 radioisotope "ages" that were all older than the relevant geologic chart said was possible.[4] Another study filled 10 pages with reported discordant dates.[5] These show that radiodate results do not lead the way—they follow an expected time frame. Researchers then find excuses for discordant or unexpected radioisotope or other supposed age-informing results.

Secular scientists provide fancy terms for these excuses, like open system behavior, mixing, assimilation, or metasomatic alteration. The high volume of discordant radioisotope and other ages does not faze most researchers' confidence in evolutionary time—but it should. One geologist admitted, "There is no reliable objective way to assess the validity of given whole-rock (or mineral) isochron [radioisotope age plot] using the regressed data alone, or in combination with element concentration data." In other words, there is no objective way to calibrate or verify radiodates. He wrote that instead, one must assess the age assignment of a given rock layer or fossil "in the light of all available field, petrographic, geological, geochemical, and other geochronological evidence."[6] And the script that all that evidence must follow is the dogmatic teaching of evolutionary time. After all, it's written in black and white right there on the chart.

Two true stories illustrate how secular scientists age-date fossils by ensuring that "ages" conform to dogma.

## Example 1: Age-Dating and a Human-Like Fossil

The first story reveals changing date assignments for a layer of volcanic ash in Africa called the KBS tuff. The date of this ash layer needed to correlate with the evolutionary ages of extinct ape fossils and human tools that were found nearby and thought to indicate the beginnings of humanity. In 1970, researchers F. J. Fitch and J. A. Miller obtained an age for the tuff of 212 to 230 million years using the potassium-argon radioisotope system.[7] But this wildly conflicted with the presumed evolutionary age of the nearby ape and certain extinct pig fossils. So, they rejected the date, excusing it as having resulted from contamination.

They then sent different samples of the tuff to a radioisotope lab and this time obtained 2.61 million years. Since this age agreed with the evolutionary story for the area, they accepted the 2.61 million, as did other researchers who confirmed that age for the KBS tuff layer by using a different technique called fission track dating. But more changes soon followed.

The famous paleontologist Richard Leakey found a human-looking fossil skull *below* the KBS tuff. *National Geographic* readers in 1973 therefore learned that the newly discovered human ancestor was at least 2.7 million years old—supposedly the oldest human fossil yet found.[8] But because secular scientists already "knew" that humans had not yet evolved from ape-like ancestors—an event that supposedly occurred 2.4 million years ago—something had to change.

G. H. Curtis, a University of California at Berkeley expert in potassium-argon radioisotope dating, led a team that dated the KBS tuff *again*. This time, they obtained an age of 1.82 million years.[9] Because this agreed with the evolutionary age of the skull, and because the skull fossil represented a high-profile part in the story of evolution, they reached a new consensus that revised the once-well-accepted age assignment of 2.61 million years to this new, younger age. Additional fission track dates "confirmed" the 1.8 million-year assignment.

Radioisotope ages for this volcanic layer in Africa played second fiddle to the evolutionary scheme. This example is not isolated but characterizes the assumption-first procedure that underlies fossil age-dating.

Creation scientists recognize that the KBS tuff formed probably during the post-Flood Ice Age, when many catastrophes occurred as the earth settled from the turmoil of the great Flood. Different peoples had recently migrated to Africa from Babel, as their stone tools testify. They also lived among ape-like creatures—totally unrelated to humans—that have since gone extinct, much like wooly mammoths or any number of Ice Age animals.

## Circular Reasoning

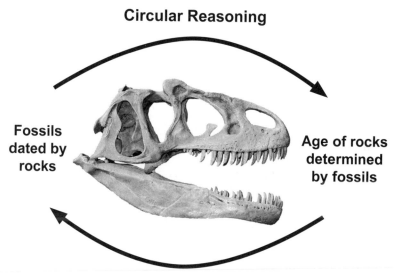

**Fossils dated by rocks**

**Age of rocks determined by fossils**

### Example 2: Age-Dating a Dinosaur Rock Layer

Some of the world's most exquisite dinosaur fossils and the sedimentary rock formation in which they lie provide a second example of how secular researchers age-date fossils by rigorously filtering data through a naturalistic narrative. Montana's Hell Creek Formation contains some nearly whole dinosaurs—some have still-flexible original proteins, arteries, bone cells, and blood cells.[10] They look fresh.

Based on differences in pollen fossils, early researchers assigned the lower majority of the Hell Creek Formation to the Cretaceous system and its upper portion to the Paleogene system. The Paleogene supposedly began 66 or so million years ago. Some marker should delineate the older Cretaceous portion from the later-formed Paleogene layers—perhaps an erosion event that deposited a different type of sediment, or an impact or volcanic event that deposited a recognizable signature. Many outcrops of the Hell Creek Formation contain a thin clay layer that paleontologists attribute to an impact event that somehow killed all the dinosaurs before the Paleogene supposedly began. (ICR scientists, along with a handful of secular scientists, reject the impact theory in part because the supposed impact did not kill the more environmentally sensitive frogs, salamanders, mammals, fish, or turtles fossilized alongside the dinosaurs.) If one could assign an age to a signature in the rock, then a process of bracketing ages above and below that signature could begin.

Secular attempts to age-date these fossils would be simpler if all the dinosaurs in Hell Creek occurred below the same thin clay layer or the change in pollen fossils that supposedly marks dinosaur extinction—but that is not the case.

Geologists reported "Dinosaurs from the Paleocene Part of the Hell Creek Formation" in 1987.[11] Having supposedly gone extinct before Paleocene "time," dinosaurs should not be there. The authors presented a number of good reasons why Paleogene dinosaur fossils from six dig sites could not have been eroded from a Cretaceous deposit and then re-deposited into younger layers a few million years later. For example, the vertebrate fossils had unbroken fine and delicate features, undamaged from some transport. Plus, there was little to no abrasion on the bone surfaces, as would have resulted from tumbling in fast-flowing water during re-deposition. A dinosaur younger than 65 million years is unacceptable, so something had to change.

Evolutionists invoke at least three "solutions" to this kind of dinosaur-dating dilemma. The first is to ignore the Paleogene dinosaur fossils. As an example, CNN interviewed a geology student named Luke Padgett at a Hell Creek dinosaur excavation in 2007. He was a student of the famous paleontologist Jack Horner. Luke said, "We know by that [thin clay layer] there was an impact at the end of the Cretaceous. At that layer we can see really easily out here with no trees. And there's an interesting pattern. There's dinosaurs below it and no dinosaurs above it."[12] Maybe Jack did not tell Luke about the 1987 report of dinosaurs above it.

A second "solution" is to counter-assert that the fossils were reworked from older sediments after all. Right on cue, in 1990 scientists listed criteria that any Paleogene (which includes Paleocene layers) dinosaur fossil claims should meet, and then conveniently found that prior dinosaur claims did not meet their criteria.[13] However, the authors did not adequately address the evidence showing that Paleocene Hell Creek dinosaur remains were buried only once.

Another "solution" raises the upper border of that which is designated Cretaceous so that it now includes the dinosaur fossils. After all, as one researcher summarized for *Discover Magazine*, "A great achievement of 19th-century science was learning to use fossils as distinctive time indicators."[14] It was really only an "achievement" in evolutionary circular reasoning, not science.

Evolutionary age assignments for Hell Creek Formation layers and their dinosaur, bird, plant, mammal, amphibian, and marine fossils are still in contention, despite confident-sounding assertions of their vast age. One intensive 2002 Geological Society of America study summarized that "the age and duration of the Hell Creek Formation are long-standing and still partially unanswered questions." Its upper boundary is in constant dispute, and "estimates of the age of the lower contact of the Hell Creek Formation are few and poorly delimited."[15] The authors had no explanation for why one report based on assumed sediment accumulation rates said that the formation formed over a span of 1.3 million years, but another report that relied on designated ages for its ammonite fossils indicated that it formed over a 4.6 million-year timespan. It can't be both. Perhaps all these age assignments are entirely wrong.

Flood geologists interpret the entire Hell Creek Formation as having been deposited in no more than months by the waters that sloshed back and forth over huge swaths of North America. Tsunami-like waves, not vast time periods, deposited sediments and their fossils, which include shark teeth and marine sea creatures.

The last step in dating a fossil is to publish the results. Secular science journals do not accept young ages for fossils, even if the data are there—ICR scientists know this because we have submitted careful research to secular journals only to have our papers summarily rejected. If scientists want to obtain funding from secular institutions for research and thereby maintain their livelihood, they must conform their results to the consensus perspective.

Thus, several checkpoints throughout the process ensure that age assignments given to rocks and fossils match the expectation of evolutionary time. The science of age-dating fossils is so bad that it leaves Genesis standing tall.

*Notes*

1. Kemp, T. S. 1985. A Fresh Look at the Fossil Record. *New Scientist*. 108: 66-67.

2. Confusingly, geologists sometimes assign multiple periods to a single layer or rock unit, and certainly assign multiple rock layers to a single period.

3. Jagoutz, E. 1994. Isotopic systematics of metamorphic rocks. *Abstracts of the eighth International Conference*

on Geochronology, Cosmochronology, and Isotope Geology. M.A. Lanphere, G.B. Dalrymple, and B.D. Turrin, eds. *US Geological Survey Circular 1107*. (157): 156.

4. Brooks, C., D. E. James, and S. R. Hart. 1976. Ancient Lithosphere: Its Role in Young Continental Volcanism. *Science*. 193: 1086-1094.

5. Woodmorappe, J. 1979. Radiometric Geochronology Reappraised. *Creation Research Society Quarterly*. 16 (2): 102-129.

6. Whitehouse, M. J. et al. 1996. Conflicting mineral and whole-rock isochron ages from the Late-Archaean Lewisian Complex of northwestern Scotland. *Geochemica et Cosmica Acta*. 60 (16): 3085-3102.

7. Fitch, F. J. and J. A. Miller. 1970. New Hominid Remains and Early Artefacts from Northern Kenya: Radioisotopic Age Determinations of Lake Rudolf Artefact Site. *Nature*. 226 (5242): 226–228.

8. Leakey, R. E. F. 1973. Skull 1470. *National Geographic*. 143: 819-829.

9. Curtis, G. H. et al. 1975. Age of KBS Tuff in Koobi Fora Formation, East Rudolf, Kenya. *Nature*. 258: 395-398.

10. As an indicator of recent age for these fossils, known protein decay rates set a maximum age limit. Secular researchers ignore this protein data when they cling to evolutionary ages. I discuss biochemistry in fossils in chapter 37. They also have to ignore dozens of carbon-14 results for comparable samples that indicate ages of only thousands of years. But the millions-of-years age assignment of some of these dinosaur fossils and their rocks has suffered enough torture even ignoring the protein and radiocarbon age implications.

11. Rigby, J. K. et al. 1987. Dinosaurs from the Paleocene Part of the Hell Creek Formation, McCone County, Montana. *Palaios*. 2 (3): 296-302.

12. Mielich, P. It's real life CSI for dinosaur detectives. CNN. Posted on edition.cnn.com March 8, 2007.

13. Lofgren, D. L., C. L. Hotton, and A. C. Runkel. Reworking of Cretaceous dinosaurs into Paleocene channel, deposits, upper Hell Creek Formation, Montana. *Geology*. 18 (9): 874-877.

14. Sasso, A. Geologists Create First New Period in 113 Years. *Discover Magazine*, January 2005.

15. Johnson, K. R., D. J. Nichols, and J. H. Hartman. 2002. Hell Creek Formation: A 2001 Synthesis. *Geological Society of America*. Special Paper 361: 503-510.

# 37

# ORIGINAL TISSUE FOSSILS CANNOT BE MILLIONS OF YEARS OLD

Brian Thomas, Ph.D.

**Summary:** Numerous soft tissues have been discovered in fossils supposedly millions of years old. Skin, retinas, and hemoglobin are some of the documented finds. Because of known chemical decay rates, these tissues shouldn't exist if the fossils are actually that old.

Secular scientists have made and thoroughly tested many of these soft tissue discoveries. Some skeptics claim the results are from contamination, but this defies the many carefully repeated studies that have published the discoveries. Other skeptics claim the alleged soft tissues were made by bacteria, but that kind of material would last an even shorter time than the original organic material.

The many soft tissues and biochemicals found in fossils are strong scientific evidence that the world is as young as the Bible says.

Many paleontologists assume that Earth's rock layers represent millions or billions of years. They haven't looked for fresh tissue inside dinosaurs and other fossils because such tissue would have completely mineralized or decayed long ago if the evolutionary timeline is true. But fresh biological material is continually being discovered, despite the biochemistry of molecular decay that clearly shows it should not exist after "all this time."

Researchers have detected molecules such as proteins, sugars, pigments, and DNA—as well as intact cells and, in some cases, skin, ligaments, retinas, bones, and blood vessels—in fossils that are supposedly many millions of years old. Below are just a few of the dozens of original tissue fossil discoveries published in the secular scientific literature.

| Animal | Supposed Age (millions of yrs) | Biochemical | Date | Reference |
|---|---|---|---|---|
| *T. rex* | 68 | Collagen | Jun. 2007 | Schweitzer, M. *Science* |
| *Psittacosaurus* | 125 | Collagen | Apr. 2008 | Linghan-Soliar, T. *Proc. RSB* |
| Hadrosaur | 80 | Elastin | Jul. 2009 | Schweitzer, M. *Science* |
| Mosasaur | 65-68 | Hemoglobin | Aug. 2010 | Lindgren, J. *PLoS ONE* |
| Lizard | 40 | Keratin | Mar. 2011 | Edwards, N. P. *Proc. RSB* |
| Mosasaur | 70 | Collagen | Apr. 2011 | San Antonio, J. D. *PLoS ONE* |
| Squid | 160 | Eumelanin | May 2012 | Glass, K. *PNAS* |
| Scorpion | 310 | Chitin + protein | Feb. 2011 | Cody, G.D. *Geology* |

A much longer list is available online at ICR.org/soft-tissue-list. The fossils in this chart likely formed during the year-long Flood of Noah's day. Local catastrophes during the post-Flood Ice Age deposited other soft tissue fossils. Paleontologists and others who insist on millions of years of Earth history have no credible explanation for these soft tissue discoveries.

Those who are skeptical of the original tissue discoveries often allege that the tissues are really contaminants, or foreign substances, that were added to the fossilized remains after they were unearthed. For example, after scientists published the specific amino acid sequence of a dinosaur's collagen protein, other scientists suggested that the sequence was accidentally taken from a nearby substance and not from the dinosaur itself. One evolutionary paleontologist even said that he believed the protein was taken from a field worker's lunch! It stretches credulity to assert that carefully repeated scientific research procedures were unable to filter out such contaminants—but it is simply irresponsible to declare that dozens of carefully repeated scientific research procedures conducted by scores of scientists working with fossil material from all over the world have all got it wrong.

Other skeptics have alleged that the proteins found in fossils were manufactured by bacteria. But the kinds of materials produced by bacteria last an even shorter time than proteins that make up vertebrates' bodies. Since the supposed source of food for the bacteria would have rotted millions of years ago, any remaining substances couldn't possibly be the result of bacterial activity. Plus, bacteria do not produce collagen protein, which scientists actually sequenced using multiple, separate labs. It is proper for scientists to be skeptical. But when the data pass all of the skeptic's tests, like original tissue fossils have, then it is time for skepticism to cease and for scientists to deal with the implications of these finds.

Weak excuses like lost lunch and bacteria do not account for the original soft tissue in fossilized remains found in so many places and in such high quality. One British researcher said that the naturally mummified skin of a hadrosaur fossil that his team excavated in North Dakota was "absolutely gob-smacking."[1] The skin still has the original dinosaur reptile scales. How could skin scales be mistaken for somebody's lunch? In any case, this scientist would not have been so surprised if he understood that the dinosaur fossil was deposited by Noah's Flood only thousands of years ago.

Many scientific reports of "soft tissue" actually describe tissue that has been partly or totally mineralized. Mineralization occurs when mineral-rich water replaces the fragile original tissue, resulting in a rock in the shape of the tissue—whether it is bone, skin, or other organs. However, other scientific reports describe, using an array of different techniques, the chemistry of what looks like still-fresh, original, unmineralized tissue. One study used six different techniques to verify original lizard leg protein chemistry in a fossil from Wyoming.[2] So, although some "soft tissues" are actually mineralized, original tissue fossils also exist.

Secular scientists have described original tissue fossils, or at least biochemistry original to the fossils, from several of the United States, Brazil, England, Germany, Belgium, Spain, Madagascar, Canada, and two Chinese provinces. Many more will probably be described in future years, perhaps from even more places. Some may sit in museum warehouses even now. This happened to a fossil mosasaur taken from a chalk formation in Kansas. Mosasaurs were marine reptiles whose fossils are found on every continent, including Antarctica. This particular one sat for over 40 years in the Natural History Museum of Los Angeles County before researchers finally tested its chemistry, finding original but partly decayed hemoglobin and still-purple retina cells.[3]

These tissues should not exist if they are millions of years old. When shown this evidence, many people ask how original tissues could possibly have lasted even as long as the thousands of years since the Flood. The answer is that laboratory measurements of protein decay rates demonstrate that they can last for thousands of years. One particular protein that can survive a very long time is collagen inside bone. Collagen is not soluble in water, a property that guards against decay and transport. Some soft tissue fossils consist of only collagen. In these cases, water removed the other rapidly decaying biomaterials. Collagen locked inside bone still spontaneously decays according to the second law of thermodynamics, which describes how overall randomness always increases. The collagen decay rate depends on the temperature. The warmer it is, the more atoms bump into one another to perform more chemistry, thereby accelerating decay.

Rigorous and repeated experiments provide the decay rate of bone collagen at a given temperature. A well-known formula called the Arrhenius equation transforms the experimental data to express the decay rates and thus the maximum time-to-dust estimates at different temperatures. For example, according to one study of collagen decay rates, "extrapolation from high temperature experimental decomposition rates using this activation energy suggest [*sic*] that at a constant 10°C (the approximate mean annual air temperature in present-day Britain) it will take between 0.2 and 0.7 Ma [million] years at 10°C for levels of collagen to fall to 1% in an optimal burial environment."[4,5]

This means that bone collagen can last no longer than 700,000 years at 50°F. So, any sample of original bone collagen tissue that is assumed to have been no warmer than 50°F since it was deposited must be younger than that. It could last as long as one million years if kept at 40°F, but some of the original tissue fossil discoveries are given an age of 70 to over 100 million years, and all of them are assigned ages of multiple millions. Clearly, the age assignments for these fossils conflict with their collagen age inferences.

On one hand, the rocks contain original cells and biochemicals from dinosaurs and other creatures. Except for having decayed somewhat, these biochemicals are real—not mineralized and not transformed into different, more resistant molecules.

On the other hand, repeatable laboratory experiments have proved that the same biochemicals discovered in fossil tissues spontaneously decay at measurable rates that limit fossil biochemistry to tens or perhaps hundreds of thousands of years maximum. They certainly could not last for a million or more years if sustained at the usual average annual temperatures of the areas where such fossils are found.

Something has to budge. Some paleontologists simply deny the measured decay rates, pretending that tissue decays much more slowly than laboratory tests show. Other researchers continue to deny that soft tissue fossils are original, ignoring the dozens of rigorous reports from the field. Both tactics struggle to accommodate millions of years. A third approach is to jettison the millions-of-years timeline, which does not come from scientific observations but from a strongly held belief system into which scientific data are force-fitted. One can accept both the measured decay rates and the well-character-ized original tissue fossils—that is, the actual sciences of biochemistry and paleontology—by removing the millions-of-years age assignments.

Original tissue fossils of dinosaurs and other creatures provide very strong scientific evidence that the world is as young as the Bible plainly describes.

### Notes

1. Mummified dinosaur skin yields up new secrets. The University of Manchester press release, July 1, 2009.

2. Edwards, N. P. et al. 2011. Infrared mapping resolves soft tissue preservation in 50 million year-old reptile skin. *Proceedings of the Royal Society B.* 278 (1722): 3209-3218.

3. Lindgren J. et al. 2010. Convergent Evolution in Aquatic Tetrapods: Insights from an Exceptional Fossil Mosasaur. *PLoS ONE.* 5 (8): e11998.

4. Buckley, M. and M. J. Collins. 2011. Collagen survival and its use for species identification in Holocene-low-ever Pleistocene bone fragments from British archaeological and paleontological sites. *Antiqua.* 1: e1.

5. The phrase "optimal burial environment" is important. Some old-world apologists claim that bone collagen can last much longer than what the measured decay rate implies because certain regions of the proteins adhere to the nearby bone mineral. They ignore the fact that the experiments used to measure the decay rate already take those effects into account. Plus, this "explanation" ignores skin, blood, and other cells and proteins found in fossils that have not been mineralized.

# 38

# DEVELOPING A SENSIBLE APPROACH TO HUMAN ORIGINS RESEARCH, PART 1: FOSSILS AND BIAS

Randy J. Guliuzza, P.E., M.D.

**Summary:** The Bible clearly teaches that the human race descended from two created human beings, Adam and Eve, and not from an ape-like ancestor. Biblical history and evolution are totally incompatible.

Paleontologists examine bone fragments and speculate about the creatures they came from. All fossils must be interpreted, and evolutionists believe evolution and fit their discoveries into that story. Similarity among creatures is a poor argument for descent from a common ancestor, and researchers ignore the bias and circular reasoning they use to reach their evolutionary conclusions.

When Christians hear that a fossil is evidence for evolution, they should ask "What is the evidence?" There is no reason to accept the evolutionary explanation for human origins.

Why not accept the evolutionary explanation for human origins? This is a fair question that is sure to come up. There is no need to jump right into a list of the many scientific problems regarding the supposed evolution of humans. It might be better to frame a discussion with a few comments on biblical authority and a reminder of how real science is performed.

**Biblical history and evolutionary stories of human origins cannot be reconciled.** If you are discussing human origins with a Christian, all believers should know that the Bible clearly teaches that humans are all descended from one human couple, Adam and Eve (Genesis 1:28; 3:20; 5:1-3; Matthew 19:4-6; Mark 10:6-9; Acts 17:26). Adam was a direct creation by God (Genesis

2:7; Luke 3:38); Eve was formed from tissue from Adam's side (Genesis 2:21-23; 1 Corinthians 11:8-9; 1 Timothy 2:13); and both were specially created in the image of God (Genesis 1:26-27; 5:2; Colossians 3:10). A real Adam disbelieved God's word, disobeyed, and brought the whole human race under God's condemnation in need of the Lord's salvation brought to mankind by the Second Adam, Jesus Christ (Romans 5:6-21; 1 Corinthians 15:45-47). Those truths should settle the issue for Christians.

Evolutionists claim that humans evolved over several million years from an ape-like ancestor. Theistic evolutionists hold to an evolutionary origin of man. A current popular teaching among some self-described evangelical Christians is that there was not a literal Adam and Eve, there was not a genuine "fall of man," and the starting population of humans was about 10,000.[1]

This position clearly clashes with biblical history and is, therefore, in error. But excellent scientific genetic studies have been published confirming biblical history.[2-4]

**Human origins research cannot be verified by observation and experiment-based science.** Evolutionary paleontological science is different from sciences that use natural, repeatable, and verifiable methods to explain phenomena. The phenomena in this case are bone fragments unearthed around the world. Evolution is fundamentally a historical narrative—a story—attempting to reconstruct unseen events.[5] Because human origins research is so subjective, one student of the researchers voices a caution applicable to all: "We have only to recall the Piltdown adventure to see how easily susceptible researchers can be manipulated into believing that they have actually found just what they had been looking for."[6]

Therefore, explanations for the history, and especially origins, of bone fragments are based on personal interpretation, which is the weakest form of evidence since it factors in a multitude of biases.

- Know that paleontology is based on historical narratives; it is not the same type of experimental science as physics or chemistry.

- Be aware that at times in human origins research, fast fame trumps facts.

**Interpretations of fossil fragments lack independent oversight.** Generally, the same researcher(s) discovers the bones, maintains initial access to the bones, publishes the first headline-grabbing description, and interprets where these fossils fit into the line of human origins—if at all—and their significance.[7] There is clearly an unavoidable bias and a predisposition to hype a discovery's significance, especially when paleontological politics and scientific credibility are big factors.[7,8] If other researchers can get access to the originals—a big "if"—their published critiques come much later with less fanfare. Thus, lacking verifiable experimental data, consensus is rare[9] and often results in personal conclusions of the fossil remains far in excess of what the data will support.[10]

- Be cautious of fossil examinations carried out in secret.

- Realize critical analysis is limited, since only a few get to study the fossils.

- Remember, history shows that nearly all fossil finds are initially over-hyped and under-investigated.[11,12]

Preconceived ideas can blind a person to alternative interpretations of data.

**Similarities are poor evidence for an ape-like ancestor to the human family tree.** Every claim about humans and apes sharing a common ancestor hangs on one type of evidence: similarities. These similarities are anatomical, physiological, social, and genetic. The huge problem is that this argument is nothing but one huge exercise in circular thinking—namely, that the evidence for common ancestry is common features, and any common features found are explained by common ancestry.

Darwin disregarded the circularity of this argument just like his followers do today. For them, this is an axiom—an obvious truth—not needing outside experimental validation. In 1859, Darwin's explanation was more like dogma: "The similar framework of bones in the hand of a man, wing of a bat, fin of the porpoise, and leg of the horse...and innumerable other such facts, at once *explain themselves* on the theory of descent with slow and slight successive modification."[13]

"Inconsistent" is the best word to describe how evolutionists compare similar features amongst organisms. This is because similar features are just that—similar—and the myriads of combinations organisms possess do not necessarily fit branching evolutionary trees. If evolutionists believe a similar feature is from a common ancestor, they say it is due to *divergent evolution*, whereas if organisms share a similar feature not due to common ancestry, it is conveniently called *convergent evolution*. Scientific-sounding lingo is substituted for data to explain why organisms with essentially no common ancestry have extraordinarily similar features, such as the camera-like eye shared by squids and humans.[14]

- Circular arguments are naturally self-certifying.
- Explanations for the presence or absence of similar features are totally arbitrary.
- Evolutionists pick and choose which similar traits, especially human-chimp genetic comparisons,[15] to showcase...or to make excuses for inconsistencies (anatomical, molecular, or anatomical-to-molecular) of the data.

## Bias and More Bias

So, what do the fossilized bones say for themselves? Nothing. They must always be interpreted. Interpretations of fossil fragments are constrained by personal bias. Often these interpretations are eventually determined to be in error. Nevertheless, one source of evolutionary bias is unalterable: The fossils will *always* be interpreted within the total evolutionary context. Though this is just another example of circular thinking, for evolutionists it would be inconceivable not to interpret these fossils as evidence for evolution.

Donald Johanson, co-discoverer of the famous fossil Lucy, summed up this self-evident fact: "Unique Lucy may be, but she is incomprehensible outside the context of other fossils. She becomes meaningless unless she is fitted into a scheme of hominid evolution." This interpretation is fitted into a bigger context of descent from a common ancestor: "That story could not even begin to be told, of course, until Charles Darwin suggested in 1857 [*sic*] that we were descended from apes and not divinely created in 4004 BC as the Church insisted."[16]

- Ask "what is the evidence" and "does it make sense" regardless of what "the experts" say.

- Recognize that human evolutionary theory is "plastic"...easily absorbing any observation or finding.

### Notes

1. Hagerty, B. B. Evangelicals Question the Existence Of Adam And Eve. NPR *Morning Edition.* Posted on npr.org August 9, 2011.

2. Carter, R. W. The Non-Mythical Adam and Eve!: Refuting errors by Francis Collins and BioLogos. Creation Ministries International. Posted on creation.com August 20, 2011.

3. Carter, R. W. Does Genetics Point to a Single Primal Couple?: A response to claims to the contrary from BioLogos. Creation Ministries International. Posted on creation.com April 30, 2011.

4. Thomas, B. Christian Professor Claims Genetics Disproves Historical Adam. *Creation Science Update.* Posted on ICR.org August 26, 2011.

5. Mayr, E. Darwin's Influence on Modern Thought. *Scientific American*, July 2000, 80. Later, Ernst Mayr (Harvard University's leading evolutionary theorist) reiterated the role of historical narrative in paleontological sciences when he said, "The earliest fossils of *Homo, Homo rudolfensis* and *Homo erectus*, are separated from *Australopithicus* by a large, unbridged gap. How can we explain this seeming saltation? Not having any fossils that can serve as missing links, we have to fall back on the time-honored method of historical science, the construction of a historical narrative." Mayr, E. 2004. *What Makes Biology Unique?* New York: Cambridge University Press, 198.

6. Maienschein, J. 1997. The One and the Many: Epistemological Reflections on the Modern Human Origins Debates. In *Conceptual Issues in Modern Human Origins Research.* G. Clark and C. Willermet, eds. Hawthorne, NY; Aldine de Gruyter, 413

7. Johanson, D. and B. Edgar. 1996. *From Lucy to Language.* New York: Simon & Schuster, 32.

8. Holden, C. 1981. The Politics of Paleoanthropology. *Science* 213 (4509): 737-740.

9. Keim, B. Bone Crunching Debunks 'First Monkey' Ida Fossil Hype. *Wired Science.* Posted on wired.com October 21, 2009.

10. Gee, H. 2001. Return to the planet of the apes. *Nature.* 412 (6843): 131.

11. Thomas, B. and F. Sherwin. Ida: Separating the Science from the Media Campaign *Creation Science Update.* Posted on ICR.org May 22, 2009. See also Thomas, B. 2009. The Ida Fossil: A Clever Campaign for a Lackluster "Link." *Acts & Facts.* 38 (7): 17.

12. Thomas, B. New Fossil Hype Fits Old Pattern. *Creation Science Update.* Posted on ICR.org May 27, 2009.

13. Darwin, C. 1872. *The Origin of Species By Means of Natural Selection*, 6th ed. London: John Murray, 420. Emphasis added.

14. Guliuzza, R. 2009. *Clearly Seen: Constructing Solid Arguments for Design*. Dallas, TX: Institute for Creation Research.

15. Tomkins, J. and J. Bergman. 2012. Genomic monkey business—estimates of nearly identical human-chimp DNA similarity re-evaluated using omitted data. *Journal of Creation*. 26 (1): 94-100.

16. Johanson, D. and M. Edey. 1981. *Lucy: The Beginnings of Humankind*. New York. Touchstone, 24.

# 39

# DEVELOPING A SENSIBLE APPROACH TO HUMAN ORIGINS RESEARCH, PART 2: UNDERSTANDING THE FOSSILS

Randy J. Guliuzza, P.E., M.D.

**Summary:** Hominid fossils consist mostly of bone fragments, which makes it hard to reconstruct appearance. Many illustrators use artistic license that reflects evolutionary expectations rather than hard data. The fossils themselves don't support these depictions.

Hominid fossils fall into two distinct categories: human and ape. Both groups show up suddenly and fully formed in the fossil record, without transitional forms. So far, no fossil fits human evolution. This matches Genesis history, in which God created each creature kind instantly.

Even Neanderthals were not "subhuman" but were culturally similar to modern humans. Be wary of "scientific conclusions" that don't accurately reflect the evidence.

## Artistic License Fills Great Gaps in Fossil Evidence

Researchers use a great deal of artistic license in interpreting what fossils look like. The problem is that there is rarely enough bony material to provide reliable information to put flesh on the bones.

Thus, when it comes to reconstructing a fossil considered to be "hominid" (the category into which evolutionists lump both apes and humans), the researcher's and artist's preconceived bias will determine facial and other anatomical features as expressed in type of skin, amount and color of hair, posture, and if it will have distinctively unique human features such as the white portions of the eyes, and, in females, a wide pelvis and permanently enlarged breasts. Conversely, fossils with distinctly human features such as *Homo erectus* often have artistic renditions emphasizing ape-like characteristics.

Though these artistic features may have nothing to do with reality—since no one can verify if they are right or wrong—they can greatly skew any conclusions about the fossil evidence, which is more akin to propaganda. A famous evolutionary artist reverently commented on his reconstruction of the fossil called Lucy: "I wanted to get a human soul into this ape-like face, to indicate something about where she was headed."[1]

- Be cautious of "scientific conclusions" with signs of strong emotional or spiritual bias.

- Note that evolutionary artists regularly "ape-ify" humans and humanize apes.

- Never underestimate the power of reconstruction.

## Hominid Fossils Fall into Basically Two Discontinuous Categories: Apes and Humans

Though interpretations of such fossils are confined by bias, there are several telling facts about these bones that make evolutionary interpretations difficult. First, they are generally fragments. One leading evolutionist said these "fragments of jaws" and "scraps of skulls" serve as the "basis for endless speculation."[2] Second, there are not very many of them…especially to build a strong case for human evolution.[3]

Third, major fossils for supposed human ancestry fall into distinct types that are "seemingly separated by discontinuities from their nearest ancestors and descendants. This is particularly true for the break between *Australopithicus* and *Homo*."[4] (In general, the fossils called *Australopithicines* show predominantly ape-like traits and those labeled *Homo* show human-like traits.) Fourth, human-like fossils demonstrate a sudden increase in brain capacity and essentially appear suddenly in the fossil record.[5]

Distinct types of "hominid" fossils fall into ape-like fossil or human-like fossil categories—they are not transitional. One fossil called Ardi (*Ardipithecus ramidus*) received much media attention in 2009 as possibly leading to an ancestor of the australopithecines. The significance of Ardi in that regard may have been overblown,[6] but by all accounts Ardi is clearly ape-like.[7] The australopithecines, which include Lucy, are also plainly ape-like,[8] with questionable evidence that they were upright bipedal walkers,[9] and, as noted earlier, are discontinuous with *Homo*. The 2011 report of *A. sediba*, the supposed youngest australopithecine, describes a creature with principally ape-like features.[10]

Fossils of the group called *Homo*, principally *H. erectus*, *H. neanderthalensis*, and *H. sapiens*, demonstrate features most similar to living humans (notable exceptions are *H. habilis* and *H. rudolfensis*, which are now in the Rudolfensis group due to more ape-like features). Fossil skeletons of both *H. erectus* and *H. neanderthalensis* are within the range of living humans, and all evidence suggests that both of these are so similar they probably could have reproduced with *H. sapiens* (humans living today).[11,12]

Some fossils take time to discern. Healthy human heads can take more different shapes and sizes than most other creatures God made. Some ancient human skulls look a bit like apes, but no more so than some folks alive today.

When *Australopithecus sediba* hit the headlines, popular news outlets labeled it as an evolutionary link between apes and humans. Its promoter initially described it as a mosaic, having both humans and ape features. However, other evolutionary experts examined the two *A. sediba* skeletons during the decade that followed. They found that each bone came either from an extinct ape or from a human. Turns out the bones never belonged together! What a mess.

*Homo floresiensis* (nicknamed "Hobbit") from Indonesia and *Homo naledi* from South Africa look strange, having tiny heads but human jaws and other parts. Initial reports declared them each a possible ancestor, but later work showed good matches between Hobbit (and possibly *H. naledi*) and tiny people today with developmental diseases that cause microcephaly, or tiny heads.[13,14] Diseased humans don't show evolution, just sin's curse on creation.

So far, no fossil fits human evolution. Whether an extinct ape, an imaginary mix of bones, or a diseased or healthy human, fossils confirm created kinds and humans in our not-so-distant past.

Not surprisingly, therefore, four general depictions of fossils of these creatures are the same as for fossils in general. (1) They appear abruptly in the fossil record; (2) they remain essentially unchanged throughout their history; (3) a fossil and its living counterpart show no or only minor differences; and (4) there are discontinuities between kinds.

The Neanderthals and *H. erectus* were not "subhumans" who lived before Adam but were people who lived after the Flood. They were not dimwitted, clumsy brutes, as characterized in much of evolutionary literature or rendered as "cavemen" by evolutionary artists. At least for Neanderthals, they could be characterized as culturally similar to other humans living contemporaneously.[15]

Many post-Flood humans certainly did live in caves after dispersal at the Tower of Babel. The patriarch Job, who lived only a few centuries after the Flood, describes this condition: "They were driven out from among men, they shouted at them as at a thief. They had to live in the clefts of the valleys, in caves of the earth and the rocks" (Job 30:5-6). In absolute contrast to evolutionary stories, the Bible teaches that humans were created fully functional, fully human, and fully in the image of God (Genesis 1:26-28).[16]

- Fossils of both ape-like and human-like creatures are scarce.

- Be ready for the usual overblown fanfare trumpeting all new "ancestors to humans."

- Know that both ape-like fossil and human-like fossils appear suddenly in the fossil record.

- Be aware that major discontinuities exist between ape-like fossil and human-like fossils.

- Focusing on fossils or similar features sidetracks discussion from the main question evolutionists have failed to answer: How did the complex information and molecular construction machinery needed to make any feature on any creature originate?

*Notes*

1. Johanson, D. 1996. The Dawn of Humans: Face-to-Face with Lucy's Family. *National Geographic.* 189 (3): 96-117.

2. Gould, S. 1980. *The Panda's Thumb: More Reflections in Natural History.* New York: Simon & Schuster, 22.

3. Holden, C. 1981. The Politics of Paleoanthropology. *Science.* 213 (4509): 737-740.

4. Mayr, E. 2001. *What Evolution Is.* New York: Basic Books, 238. In a later publication, Mayr wrote on the same topic: "The earliest fossils of *Homo, Homo rudolfensis* and *Homo erectus*, are separated from *Australopithicus* by a large, unbridged gap. How can we explain this seeming saltation? Not having any fossils that can serve as missing links, we have to fall back on the time-honored method of historical science, the construction of a historical narrative." Mayr, E. 2004. *What Makes Biology Unique?* New York: Cambridge University Press, 198.

5. Mayr, *What Evolution Is,* 246.

6. Thomas, B. Scientists Back Off of Ardi Claims. *Creation Science Update*. Posted on ICR.org December 4, 2009.

7. Wood, B. and T. Harrison. 2011. The evolutionary context of the first hominins. *Nature*. 470 (7334): 347-352; Thomas, B. 2009. Did Humans Evolve from "Ardi"? *Acts & Facts*. 38 (11): 8-9; Thomas, B. Evolutionist Tosses out 'Ardi' as Human Ancestor. *Creation Science Update*. Posted on ICR.org June 8, 2010, accessed July 31, 2012.

8. Morris, J. 2010. *The Fossil Record: Unearthing Nature's History of Life*. Dallas, TX: Institute for Creation Research, 107.

9. Spoor, F., B. Wood, and F. Zonneveld. 1994. Implications of early hominid labyrinthine morphology for evolution of human bipedal locomotion. *Nature*. 369 (6482): 645-648; Lubenow, M. Lucy's child, "Selam," from Ethiopia. Answers in Genesis. Posted on answersingenesis.org November 1, 2006.

10. Dewitt, D. It's an Ape...It's a Human...It's...It's...a Missing Link! Answers in Genesis. Posted on answersingenesis.org September 13, 2011.

11. Johanson, D. and M. Edey. 1981. *Lucy: The Beginnings of Humankind*. New York: Touchstone, 144.

12. Dalton, R. Neanderthals may have interbred with humans. *Nature News*. Posted on nature.com April 20, 2010.

13. Hershkovitz, I., L. Kornreich, and Z. Laron. 2007. Comparative Skeletal Features Between *Homo floresiensis* and Patients With Primary Growth Hormone Insensitivity (Laron Syndrome). *American Journal of Physical Anthropology*. 134 (2): 198-208.

14. Martin, R. D. et al. 2006. Flores Hominid: New Species or Microcephalic Dwarf? *The Anatomical Record Part A*. 288A (11): 1123-1145.

15. Thomas, B. Humans Used Fire Earlier than Believed. *Creation Science Update*. Posted on ICR.org May 21, 2012; Sherwin, F. Humans Are Humans, After All. *Creation Science Update*. Posted on ICR.org April 5, 2008.

16. Guliuzza, R. J. 2009. *Made in His Image: Examining the complexities of the human body*. Dallas, TX: Institute for Creation Research.

# 40

# DO RADIOISOTOPE DATING METHODS PROVE AN OLD EARTH?

Jake Hebert, Ph.D.

**Summary:** Radioisotope dating is often used to argue for an old earth. The various dating methods yield ages of millions or billions of years. But can those ages be trusted?

The dating is based on elements that decay over time. If we know an element's decay rate and how much of the parent and daughter elements are in a sample, we could hypothetically calculate the number of years since the rock formed. But this calculation employs a number of assumptions that call the results into question.

Another problem is that radioisotope dating gives wrong dates for rocks of known age, as well as contradictory dates for the same sample. These and other problems highlight the uncertainties and unreliability of these methods and the ages they produce.

Christians don't need to be intimidated by the claims of radiometric dating.

Without a doubt, radioisotope (or radiometric) dating methods are one of *the* main arguments for an old earth. Volcanic and metamorphic rocks are "dated" by these methods to be millions or even billions of years old. Likewise, the carbon-14 dating method sometimes yields ages of multiple tens of thousands of years for carbon-containing materials (generally from formerly living organic matter). Do these methods present an unanswerable challenge to the Bible's 6,000-year timescale?

No, they do not. But before explaining why, it is necessary to briefly describe the theory behind the method. Some atoms are unstable, which means that they spontaneously change into other atoms through a decay process. For instance, uranium-238 ($^{238}$U) changes into lead-206 ($^{206}$Pb)[1] through a multi-step process that involves the emission of, among other things, alpha particles (helium nuclei consisting of two protons and two neutrons) from the nucleus. The rate at which $^{238}$U decays into $^{206}$Pb has been accurately measured, and this decay rate may be expressed in terms of a half-life, the amount of time required for half a sample of $^{238}$U to be converted into $^{206}$Pb.[2] Uranium-238 is called the *parent* element, while lead-206 is the *daughter* element. Since the rate of decay is known, it is thought that measuring the amount of daughter material compared to the amount of parent material can reveal the age of a sample. But scientists cannot directly measure the age of rocks or organic remains. In order to "convert" these element quantities into an age, some assumptions must be made.

An analogy illustrates these assumptions.[3] Suppose we enter a lecture hall. At the front of the hall is a table on which sits a basket of potatoes, some of which have been peeled and some of which have not. We notice that once every minute, a man standing by the table grabs a potato, peels it, and then places it back into the basket. After 10 minutes of observation, we wonder how long the man has been peeling potatoes.

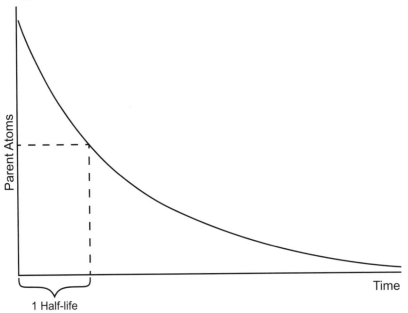

One half-life is the time needed for half an arbitrary number of parent atoms to undergo radioactive decay.

If the basket contains 35 peeled potatoes, we might conclude that the man has been peeling potatoes for 35 minutes. This seems reasonable, but we implicitly made some assumptions in order to reach this conclusion, and our conclusion will only be correct if those assumptions are accurate. What are the assumptions?

First, we assumed that none of the potatoes had already been peeled beforehand. But it's possible that some of them *had* already been peeled at the time the man began the peeling process.

Second, we assumed that no peeled potatoes were added to or removed from the basket before we began observing. What if the man got hungry and ate some of the peeled potatoes before we arrived?

Third, we assumed that the man has been peeling potatoes at a constant rate, even for the time we did not observe him. Perhaps he was peeling faster in the past but simply tired and slowed down to our observed rate of one potato per minute. Although it may seem reasonable to assume that his rate of peeling was constant in the unobserved past, we simply don't know that this is really the case.

Despite the sometimes complicated math involved, radioisotope dating uses very similar assumptions to estimate the age of a given rock. As noted earlier, a scientist can't measure the age of a rock directly—rather, he measures the number of daughter atoms within a rock compared to the number of parent atoms. In the analogy, the peeled potatoes are analogous to the daughter atoms, while the unpeeled potatoes are analogous to the parent atoms.

---

### Fundamental Assumptions of Radioactive Dating Techniques

1. Known initial conditions of the sample
2. The amount of parent or daughter elements altered only by radioactive decay
3. Constant decay rate (or half-life)

---

Radioisotope dating is based on certain assumptions.

So, are radiometric dating assumptions correct? There is a simple way to find out. If radiometric techniques yield nonsensical or inconsistent results,

319

this is a clear indication that one or more of these assumptions is wrong. There are indeed many examples of nonsensical radiometric dating results:

- **Incorrect estimated dates for rocks of known age.** Theoretically, a rock's radioisotope "clocks" should be reset whenever it melts. This implies that newly formed volcanic rocks should have radiometric ages of essentially zero. Yet, radioisotope ages for "young" rocks of known age are often very old. For instance, volcanic rocks from New Zealand's Mount Ngauruhoe were radiodated by a respected laboratory. Despite the fact that the rocks were *known* to have been formed during eruptions less than 50 years earlier, potassium-argon dating yielded ages for the rocks ranging from less than 270,000 years to 3.5 million years.[4] Of course, one could claim that the lower value is the correct one—a 50-year-old rock *is* less than 270,000 years old—but this is only because the true ages of the rocks are known. Without that knowledge, one easily could have reached the erroneous conclusion that the rocks were millions of years old. Many similar examples could be cited.[5,6]

- **Dates that contradict each other.** Different radioisotope "clocks," and even the same clock applied to different parts of the same geological formation, often yield dramatically different ages.[7,8]

- **Detectable amounts of carbon-14 ($^{14}$C) in specimens that are supposedly hundreds of millions of years old or more.** Because $^{14}$C decays quickly into nitrogen-14 ($^{14}$N), it has a relatively short half-life of 5,730 years. Therefore, you would not expect $^{14}$C to be present in specimens that are millions of years old.[9,10] Yet, measurable amounts of $^{14}$C have consistently been found in carbon-containing specimens that are supposedly tens and even hundreds of millions of years old, at levels far above the detection limits of the measuring apparatus.[11] Measurable $^{14}$C has even been found in diamonds, which are supposedly more than a *billion* years old![12] Because diamond is extremely hard, and because laboratories take great pains to avoid contaminating samples, it is very difficult for uniformitarians to blame these results on contamination.

- **Helium in zircon crystals found within hot "Precambrian" granitic rock.** These zircon crystals contain uranium that has partially decayed into lead. The amount of decayed uranium suggests an apparent radioisotope age of 1.5 billion years for the zircons. The helium atoms that are formed as a result of alpha emission during the decay process "leak" (or diffuse) out of the zircons so quickly that very little helium should still remain in the zircons if they are really that old, yet the zircons still contain *large* amounts of helium.[13]

These results indicate problems with all three radiometric dating assumptions. If we are not present when lava cools to form a volcanic rock and are unable to observe it throughout its entire history, we simply cannot confirm the validity of the first and second assumptions. Uniformitarians have devised techniques such as the isochron method in an attempt to overcome some of the uncertainties in radioisotope dating, but even the isochron method makes assumptions and often yields contradictory results.[14-16]

Most important, these results show the error of the third assumption. The high amounts of helium in zircon crystals within "old" granitic rock can be explained if nuclear decay rates have *not* been constant throughout time: 1.5 billion years of nuclear decay—based on today's rates—*did* occur (along with the accompanying alpha emission), but did so quite rapidly during an episode or episodes of accelerated decay within the last 6,000 years. This is why the helium has not yet had time to leak out of the zircon crystals. Likewise, the presence of detectable $^{14}C$ in supposedly very ancient specimens is another indication that nuclear decay rates have changed in the past. These specimens are said to be hundreds of millions of years old in large part because of radiometric dating's assumption of constant decay rates, yet this very assumption leads to a contradiction: Detectable $^{14}C$, with its relatively short half-life, simply should not be present in such specimens if they are really that old—and yet it is!

In short, although this is an area of ongoing research, no Bible-believing Christian should be intimidated by the claims of radiometric dating.

### Notes

1. The 238 in $^{238}U$ refers to the *mass number* of uranium, the sum of the number of protons and the number of neutrons within the nucleus of this variety (isotope) of uranium. Likewise, the 206 in $^{206}Pb$ means that this particular variety of lead has a combined total of 206 protons and neutrons within its nucleus.

2. Today's measured half-life for $^{238}U$ is about 4.5 billion years.

3. Morris, J. D. 1994. *The Young Earth.* Colorado Springs, CO: Master Books, 45-47.

4. Snelling, A. 1999. Radioactive 'dating' failure. *Journal of Creation.* 22 (1): 18-21.

5. Swenson, K. 2001. Radio-dating in Rubble, *Journal of Creation.* 23 (3): 23-25.

6. Morris, *The Young Earth,* 54-56.

7. Snelling, A. 2000. Conflicting "Ages" of Tertiary Basalt and Contained Fossilized Wood, Crinum, Central Queensland, Australia. *Journal of Creation.* 14 (2): 99-122.

8. Snelling, A. 2005. Radioisotope dating of rocks in the Grand Canyon. *Journal of Creation.* 27 (3): 44-49.

9. Many are surprised to learn that even if one started with a "lump" of $^{14}$C with the same mass as the earth itself, the decay of $^{14}$C occurs so quickly that *all* the $^{14}$C would be gone in less than a million years! See footnote 3 in reference 12 for the details of this calculation.

10. Baumgardner, J. R. et al. 2003. Measurable $^{14}$C in Fossilized Organic Materials: Confirming the Young Earth Creation-Flood Model. In *Proceedings of the Fifth International Conference on Creationism.* Pittsburgh, PA: Creation Science Fellowship, 127-142.

11. Ibid.

12. Sarfati, J. 2006. Diamonds: a creationist's best friend. *Journal of Creation.* 28 (4): 26-27.

13. Humphreys, D. R. 2008. Helium evidence for a young world continues to confound critics. Creation Ministries International. Posted on creation.com November 29, 2008.

14. Austin, S. A. 1994. *Are Grand Canyon Rocks One Billion Years Old? Grand Canyon: Monument to Catastrophe.* Santee, CA: Institute for Creation Research, 119.

15. Snelling, A. 1994. U-Th-Pb "Dating": An Example of False "Isochrons." In *Proceedings of the Third International Conference on Creationism.* Pittsburgh, PA: Creation Science Fellowship, 497-504.

16. Austin, S. A. 1998. Discordant Potassium-Argon Model and Isochron "Ages" for Cardenas Basalt (Middle Proterozoic) and Associated Diabase of Eastern Grand Canyon, Arizona. In *Proceedings of Fourth International Conference on Creationism.* Pittsburgh, PA: Creation Science Fellowship, 35-51.

# 41

# THE BASICS OF RADIOISOTOPE DATING

Vernon R. Cupps, Ph.D.

**Summary:** Radioisotopes are unstable atoms that omit energy and matter. Since this radioactive decay process occurs at certain rates under certain conditions, it is used as a clock for dating fossils and rocks.

Several assumptions are essential for this approach: the amount of initial parent (undecayed) isotope must be known, the rate of decay must be known and remain constant over time, the amount of initial daughter (decayed) isotope must be known, and no substantial change could have happened to the specimen being dated since it solidified.

One problem with radioisotope dating is that it does not correctly date rocks of known ages. Another issue is that different versions of this type of dating produce discordant results. The assumptions on which radioisotope dating is based do not hold true, and multiple radioisotope dating methods have proved to be invalid.

We can have confidence in the eyewitness report about creation recorded in Genesis.

Radioactive dating has played a key role in estimating the age of the earth without reference to Scripture. Many secular scientists use it to dismantle the faith of Christians. Too many Bible believers accept uniformitarian assumptions that underlie the use of radioisotopes to make age estimates. Uniformitarian philosophy demands the absence of miracles in the past. It allows only natural, everyday processes. In addition to its scientific error, it demands a figurative and distorted interpretation of the history in Genesis.

It turns out that time is a model-dependent variable in any radioisotope

## Radioactivity

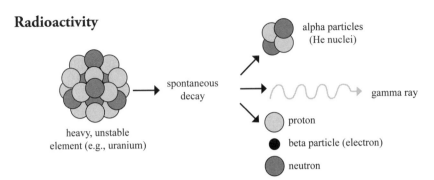

dating method. Radioisotopes refer to unstable versions of an element that eject matter and energy over time until they stabilize. Time, therefore, depends on the assumptions that go into that dating model. Knowledge of such a widespread dating method is essential for Christians in order for them to address opposing arguments and critics. Is radioactive dating valid?

French physicist Henri Becquerel discovered natural radioactivity in 1896. A decade later, American chemist Bertram Boltwood suggested that lead was a disintegration product of uranium and could be used as an internal clock for dating rocks. By the mid-1940s, Willard Libby realized that the decay of $^{14}C$ might provide a method of dating organic matter. He proposed that the carbon in living matter might include $^{14}C$ as well as non-radioactive carbon. Libby received the Nobel Prize for Chemistry in 1960 for his $^{14}C$ research. Whether by long-lived isotopes such as uranium or the much shorter-lived isotopes such as radiocarbon, the age of radioactive dating began.

### What Is a Radionuclide?

Before we delve into radioactive decay and its use in dating rocks, let's review some essential physics. Each atom is made up of protons and neutrons concentrated in the atom's center—its nucleus—around which electrons orbit. The protons and neutrons form the nucleus of an atom, with approximate diameters ranging from 1.75 fm for the hydrogen atom to 15 fm for the uranium atom.[1] This nucleus contains approximately 99.94% of the atom's total mass. The smallest electron orbitals range from approximately 1.06 Å for the hydrogen atom to 3.5 Å for the uranium atom.[2] Thus, the closest electrons orbit approximately 100,000 times farther from the center of the nucleus than the outermost nucleons.[3] This means that the atom is mostly empty space, as Ernest Rutherford aptly demonstrated with his alpha particle-gold foil scattering experiment in 1911.[4]

The number of protons each element contains in its nucleus specifies the number of corresponding electrons that orbit it. Electron configurations give each element its unique chemical properties. However, elements larger than hydrogen's single proton have varying numbers of neutrons. Neutrons do not necessarily equal the amount of protons in the nucleus. This feature of nuclear construction produces *elemental families*—groups of elements with the same number of protons but differing numbers of neutrons. Because these families have the same number of protons in the nucleus, they also have the same number of electrons orbiting the nucleus and thus exhibit the same chemical behavior.

The differing number of neutrons gives rise to stable and unstable isotopes (radioisotopes) within a given elemental family. As it turns out, nearly every element from hydrogen (Z=1) to bismuth (Z=83) has at least one stable isotope, with technetium (Z=43) and promethium (Z=61) as the exceptions. All elements heavier than bismuth in the periodic table are unstable; i.e., they are in a constant state of releasing energy or matter, i.e., *decaying*.

## Sidebar A

Standard nomenclature for common forms of radioactive decay follows

| | |
|---|---|
| Alpha decay: | $^A_Z P \rightarrow\ ^{A-4}_{Z-2}D +\ ^4_2\alpha + energy$ |
| Beta decay: | $^A_Z P \rightarrow\ ^A_{Z+1}D +\ ^0_{-1}\beta + energy + \bar{v}$ |
| Positron decay: | $^A_Z P \rightarrow\ ^A_{Z-1}D +\ ^0_{+1}\beta + energy + v$ |
| Electron capture: | $^A_Z P +\ ^0_{-1}e \rightarrow\ ^A_{Z-1}D + energy + v$ |
| Gamma decay: | $^A_Z P^* \rightarrow\ ^A_Z P + \gamma$ |

where: P ≝ the parent nucleus of the elemental family P, e.g., H, C, K, Rb, Sm, Re, or U
     D ≝ the daughter nucleus of the elemental family D, e.g., N, Ar, Sr, Nd, Os, or Pb
     A ≝ the total number of nucleons[3]
     Z ≝ the number of protons that defines the elemental family.
     β ≝ an electron or positron originating from a neutron or proton respectively in the parent nucleus
     P* ≝ An excited or energetic state of the parent nucleus

Note that all the decays exhibit *exothermic* behavior, i.e., they release energy. In fact, only the decay modes for which energy is released are possible in nature.

Alpha decay generally occurs only in the heavier radioactive nuclides, i.e., radionuclides, with atomic masses greater than 146 (A ≧ 146). This decay can be thought of as a process that stabilizes the nuclear charge to mass ratio.[5,6]

For alpha emission, the decay energy is manifest as the kinetic energy of the ejected alpha particle ($\alpha$).

In the processes of beta and positron decay, the released energy is shared between the emitted beta or positron particles and an antineutrino or neutrino respectively. As a result, the decay energy is not manifest solely as the kinetic energy of the beta or positron particle but is instead shared with the accompanying antineutrino or neutrino respectively. This makes energy spectroscopy for these decays more challenging than for alpha or gamma decays. If the parent nucleus decays to an excited state of the daughter nucleus for any of the above decays, then gamma rays can also accompany the emitted particles and energy spectroscopy becomes easier.

Less common modes of decay are direct emission of a neutron or proton, double-beta decay, and spontaneous fission. As with alpha decay, the heavier radionuclides show these modes, with a few exceptions such as $^{53}$Co (proton emission), $^{13}$Be, and $^{5}$He (neutron emission).

Soon after its discovery, scientists recognized radioactive decay as a potential clock for dating various types of materials such as rocks, crystals, and fossils. It essentially evolved into settled science or fact for many in the scientific community who had embraced naturalism as a part of their worldview (basic belief system).

Science requires that repeatable observations constitute the only facts. Is this the case for radioisotope dating? Can the proponents of such dating as fact go back in time and actually observe the process of radioactive decay? Clearly these are rhetorical questions, and according to the scientific method, dates obtained through measurement of the isotopic ratios of parent and daughter nuclei should never be considered fact or settled science.

## An Analog to Radioisotope Dating

The process of radioactive decay can be envisioned as an hourglass implanted in an igneous rock. Igneous rocks arise from melt, whereas cemented particles form the other major category of rock called *sedimentary*. Sand in the upper chamber of the hourglass represents the parent radioisotope. Sand in the lower chamber resembles the daughter radioisotope. The narrowness of the hourglass neck regulates the throughput rate. A wide neck would illustrate radioisotopes that decay fast, for example.

## Sidebar B

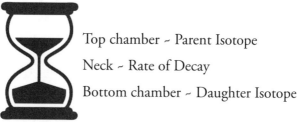

Top chamber ~ Parent Isotope

Neck ~ Rate of Decay

Bottom chamber ~ Daughter Isotope

Figure 1

For this hourglass illustration, the rate at which the sand accumulates in the bottom chamber is generally linear and can be expressed mathematically as:

$$-\frac{dN}{dt} = \alpha_o$$

where:  N $\overset{\text{def}}{=}$ number of sand grains in the top chamber at a time t
$\alpha_o$ $\overset{\text{def}}{=}$ the rate at which the sand grains accumulate in the bottom chamber
$N_0$ $\overset{\text{def}}{=}$ the initial number of sand grains in the top chamber at the start time $t_0$

An integration yields the linear equation for N at time t as:

$$N = N_0 - \alpha_0 t$$

If one knows $N_0$ and $\alpha_0$ and measures N, then the hourglass time (t) can be calculated.

## Sidebar C

A similar equation describes the radioactive decay of one isotope into another. Experimentation established that the rate of decay of a given parent isotope is proportional to the number of atoms of that isotope present in a given material, i.e.:

$$-\frac{dN}{dt} = \lambda N$$

Note that this functional dependence of the rate at which the parent isotope decays to the daughter isotope is different than that which described the movement of sand grains through the hourglass. For radioisotopes, the rate depends on the number of parent atoms present. More parent atoms increase the rate. The formula also assumes that the rate of decay is always characterized by the same constant multiplied by the number of parent nuclei present. This assumption is part of a uniformitarian worldview—i.e., the processes of the past are accurately described by the present processes. Integration yields an equation describing the time progression of the decaying parent isotope:

$$N(t_p) = N_0\, e^{-\lambda(t_p - t_0)}$$

*(continued)*

327

where: $N_0 \stackrel{\text{def}}{=}$ initial number of parent nuclei at time of formation
 $N(t_p) \stackrel{\text{def}}{=}$ number of parent nuclei at present time
 $\lambda \stackrel{\text{def}}{=}$ rate at which the parent nucleus decays into the daughter nucleus
 $t_p \stackrel{\text{def}}{=}$ present time
 $t_0 \stackrel{\text{def}}{=}$ time at which material containing the parent isotope formed. By convention, this
 time is usually set equal to 0.

If $N_0$ and $\lambda$ are known and $N(t_p)$ can be accurately measured, then the apparent age ($t_a = t_p - t_0$) of a material containing the parent nucleus can be determined from the equation:

$$\frac{1}{\lambda} \ln \frac{N_0}{N_{t_p}} = t_a$$

This is the basic equation for determining the age of a material matrix using radioisotope decay as the "clock." All other methods are variants of this fundamental equation (relationship). Also note that this equation guarantees extremely long ages for any radioisotope with a large decay constant, which all the commonly used radioisotopes have.

The primary variant method casts the above equation into the number of radiogenic daughter nuclei produced by the decaying parent. That is, $D^* = N_0 - N_{t_p} \equiv$ [defined as] number of radiogenic daughter nuclei generated during time $t_a$ by the original parent nuclei, $N_0$. Now redefine $N_{t_p}$ as just N and $t_a$ as t. This is how they appear in most textbooks. Then:

$$D^* = N_0 - N$$

Substituting $N_0 = N\, e^{\lambda t}$: $\qquad D^* = Ne^{\lambda t} - N$

Generally, the total number of daughter isotopes in a given sample should be given by :

$$D = D_0 + D^*$$

where $D_0$ is the number of daughter isotopes present when the parent starts to decay. Substituting for $D^*$ we then have the basic equation in most textbooks that is used as a starting point for age determinations of rocks and minerals, i.e.,

$$D = D_0 + N(e^{\lambda t} - 1)$$

This equation is now in the general form of a linear equation but with the additional variable of time (t).

$$y = y_0 + mx$$

where y is the current amount of the daughter nucleus in the sample being tested (D), $y_0$ is the original amount of the daughter nucleus in the test sample ($D_0$), m is the slope a line described by the linear relationship between D and N, and N is the current amount of the parent nucleus in the test sample. The age of the sample is then estimated by the equation:

$$t = \frac{1}{\lambda} \times [ln(m + 1)]$$

Note that this equation assumes that all the daughter isotopes from the decay of the parent isotope have remained in the mineral/rock. This assumption fails for natural decay chains like $^{40}K$ and $^{238}U$ because each chain includes the noble gases argon and radon, respectively. These gases are notorious for slipping right out of rocks.

The uranium 238, uranium 235, and thorium 234 decay chains also produce the highly reactive radium, polonium, bismuth, and thallium isotopes. Thus, there is plenty of opportunity for migration away from the site of the parent isotope for any of these four decay chains. Thus, age is a quantity derived from a specific model and not an actually measured quantity.

The most common isotope dating models in use today are the potassium-argon ($^{40}K$-$^{40}Ar$) model, the rubidium-strontium ($^{87}Rb$-$^{87}Sr$) model, the samarium-neodymium ($^{147}Sm$-$^{143}Nd$) model, the uranium-lead ($^{238}U$-$^{206}Pb$) or ($^{235}U$-$^{207}Pb$) models, and the lead-lead ($^{206}Pb$-$^{207}Pb$) model.

---

All radioisotope dating methods involve five basic assumptions. These are:

- The radioactive decay constant for a given parent nucleus must remain constant for all time

- Enough time has passed for measureable concentrations of the radioactively generated daughter nucleus to be present in the material being dated

- The initial concentrations of the parent or daughter nuclides can be deduced from the model used to date a given material

- The material containing the parent and daughter nuclides has been a closed system during the time calculated as its age

- There has not been extensive fractionation, hydrothermal movement, or diffusion within the material being dated

---

References 7 and 8 detail the assumptions unique to each of the dating models.

## What Does the Evidence Imply?

For any dating model, the first question science would pose is does it reproduce known ages of objects? A 10-year-old dacite lava rock sample from the post-eruption Mount St. Helens crater dome[9] was submitted to a reputable analysis laboratory for K-Ar dating. The commercial lab measured isotope ratios and used formulas like those given above to convert these ratios into isotope "ages." Table 1 gives the results from the various minerals in the dacite rock. Clearly the radiometric dating model has not produced the correct age of the rock components. Reference 10 provides a sampling of volcanoes dated by the K-Ar or the Ar-Ar method. None come even close to reproducing the known ages. They all show much older isotope ages than actual recorded ages. According to the scientific method, these results invalidate the dating model used.

| | Sample Type | Age/Millions of Years |
|---|---|---|
| 1 | Whole rock | $0.35 \pm 0.05$ |
| 2 | Feldspar, etc. | $0.33 \pm 0.06$ |
| 3 | Amphibole, etc. | $0.9 \pm 0.2$ |
| 4 | Pyroxene, etc. | $1.7 \pm 0.3$ |
| 5 | Pyroxene | $2.8 \pm 0.6$ |

Table 1. Potassium-argon ages for whole rock and mineral concentrate samples from the lava dome at Mount St. Helens, from reference 9

Do the various dating models agree with each other? Geologist Steve Austin analyzed dating results for samples from the Grand Canyon's Beartooth andesitic amphibolite and the Bass Rapids diabase sill.[11] The Rb-Sr dating method gave very different results from the Sm-Nd dating and the Pb-Pb dating methods for the same rock! Potassium-argon (K-Ar) dating was more than 200 million years discordant with the Rb-Sr dating results.

It is also interesting to note that the results for different minerals seemed to congregate around $^{87}Sr/^{86}Sr$ and $^{87}Rb/^{86}Sr$ concentration ratios corresponding to each particular mineral along the isochron line. Similar discordances were noted for the andesitic amphibolite samples. Geologist Andrew Snelling selected a larger number of case studies to further explore possible isochron discordances.[12] His results drew conclusions similar to Steve Austin's concerning the discordances of the various isochron dating models when applied to igneous rocks from Australia and New Zealand. A survey of the secular technical literature reveals dozens of similar discoveries of discordant isotope "ages" for the same rock samples. Together, these show that the methods fail.

Do the results of radioisotope dating models match results of other time-based measurements in rock crystals? In 1990, physicist Larry Vardiman noted a perplexing absence of radiogenic $^4He$ in the earth's atmosphere.[13] In particular, he found far less $^4He$ in the atmosphere than billions of years of nuclear decay would have produced. A simple calculation in the secular literature estimated that the atmosphere contains less than 0.01% of the $^4He$ evolutionists would expect after five billion years of radioactive decay.[14] In order to further investigate this apparent enigma, physicist Russell Humpheys began a systematic study of zircon crystals extracted from the GT-2 bore hole at Fenton Hill just west of the volcanic Valles Caldera in the Jemez Mountains near Los Alamos, New Mexico.[15,16] The zircon samples were extracted from the hot granitic Precambrian basement rock at the site. He found that the zircon crystals exhibited $^4He$ retention best described by a diffusion model using 6,000 years for the age of the zircon crystals.

In response, the secular community suggested that this investigation was somehow flawed. It had to be flawed because it refuted the deep time–evolutionary paradigm in which they had vested their reputations. Dr. Humphreys has refuted their objections with understanding and grace.[17-9]

Humphreys also found[20] that if he extended Gentry's diffusion calculation[21] for Pb to the deepest and hottest (313°C) Jemez zircons, the Pb should diffuse out of the zircon crystals in only a few hundred thousand years in theory. Yet, the deepest and hottest zircon samples still retained essentially all their Pb. A recent paper by R. B. Hayes provides further evidence that the effects of solid state diffusion, fractionation, mixing, and hydrothermal transport do not seem to be taken into account by deep-time advocates.[22] Reasonable diffusion rates for radiogenic isotopes clash with deep time.

Finally, no definitive way to distinguish an isochron from an isotope mixing line currently exists.

## Conclusion

The deep time–evolutionary paradigm has done great damage to science.

It has repressed valid scientific investigations under the pretense of being the only real science. Therefore, any observational evidence that contradicts its tenets are simply to be ignored as perplexing but irrelevant to reality.

The public schools of Western culture nowhere mention the discordant results, unprovable assumptions, and falsified samples that scientist have found. They have consistently taught deep time as "settled science" throughout the latter part of the 20th century. During this time, radioisotope dating has been the fallback support for secular scientists to elevate the deep time–evolutionary paradigm to the status of scientific fact.

Ironically, declaring a hypothesis like the deep time–evolutionary paradigm as "settled science" contradicts the basic tenets of the scientific method. No one can go back in time to verify the assumptions that go into the radioisotope dating models. Therefore, they should never be declared a scientific fact. So, we can have confidence in the eyewitness report concerning creation contained in the Genesis record.

### Notes

1. A fermi (fm) is a unit of measure equal to $10^{-15}$ meters. It is usually used to express internuclear distances.

2. An angstrom (Å) is a unit of measure equal to $10^{-10}$ meters. It is usually used to express interatomic distances.

3. Nucleon is a term used to collectively identify the two major constituents of the nucleus, i.e., the protons (Z) and neutrons (N). The number of nucleons in a given nucleus is designated by the letter A (= Z + N).

4. In 1911, Ernest Rutherford performed an experiment to test the Plum Pudding Model of the atom. He fired energetic α [He$^{2+}$] particles at a sheet of gold foil and measured the deflection of the particles as they came out the other side. From this, he deduced that the atom was mostly empty space because very few α particles experienced any measurable deflection from their initial path.

5. A radionuclide is any nucleus of a given elemental family that is radioactively unstable.

6. The charge to mass ratio $\left(\frac{Q}{m}\right)$ for any nucleus is the ratio of the number of protons (Z), which define the elemental family of that nucleus, to the number of protons plus the number of neutrons resident in that nucleus (A). Mathematically: $\frac{Q}{m} = \frac{Z}{A}$.

7. Cupps, V. R. 2019. *Rethinking Radiometric Dating: Evidence for a Young Earth from a Nuclear Physicist.* Dallas, TX: Institute for Creation Research.

8. Faure, G. 1986. *Principles of Isotope Geology,* 2nd ed. New York: John Wiley & Sons.

9. Austin, S. A. 1996. Excess argon within Mineral Concentrates from the New Dacite Lava Dome at Mount St. Helens Volcano. *Creation Ex Nihilo Technical Journal.* 10 (3): 335-343.

10. Morris, J. 2011. *The Young Earth.* Green Forest, AR: Master Books, 52.

11. Austin, S. A. 2005. Do Radioisotope Clocks Need Repair? Testing the Assumption of Isochron Dating Using K-Ar, Rb-Sr, Sm-Nd, and Pb-Pb Isotopes. In *Radioisotopes and the Age of the Earth: Results of a Young-Earth Creationist Research Initiative.* L. Vardiman, A. Snelling, and E. Chaffin, eds. El Cajon, CA: Institute for Creation Research and Chino Valley, AZ: Creation Research Society, 325-392.

12. Snelling, A. A., Isochron Discordances and the Role of Inheritance and Mixing of Radioisotopes in the Mantle and Crust, *Radioisotopes and the Age of the Earth: Results of a Young-Earth Creationist Research Initiative*, 393-524.

13. Vardiman, L. 1990. *The Age of the Earth's Atmosphere*. El Cajon, CA: Institute for Creation Research.

14. Cook, M. A. 1957. Where is the earth's radiogenic helium? *Nature*. 179: 213.

15. Humphreys, D. R., Young helium diffusion age supports accelerated nuclear decay, *Radioisotopes and the Age of the Earth: Results of a Young-Earth Creationist Research*, 25-100.

16. Humphreys, D. R. et al. 2004. Helium diffusion age of 6,000 years supports accelerated nuclear decay. *Creation Research Society Quarterly*. 41 (1): 1-16.

17. Humphreys, D. R. 2010. Critics of helium evidence for a young world now seem silent. *Journal of Creation*. 24 (1): 14-16.

18. Humphreys, D. R. 2010. Critics of helium evidence for a young world now seem silent. *Journal of Creation*. 24 (3): 34-39.

19. Humphreys, D. R. 2018. Answer to a persistent critic of RATE helium research. *Journal of Creation*. 32 (3): 49-57.

20. Humphreys, D. R. 2000. Accelerated Nuclear Decay: A Viable Hypothesis? In *Radioisotopes and the Age of the Earth: A Young-Earth Creationist Research Initiative*. L. Vardiman, A. A. Snelling, and E. F. Chaffin, eds. El Cajon, CA: Institute for Creation Research, and Chino Valley, AZ: Creation Research Society, 350.

21. Gentry, R. V. et al. 1982. Differential lead retention in zircons: implications for nuclear waste management. *Science*. 216: 296-298.

22. Hayes, R. B. 2017. Some Mathematical and Geophysical Considerations in Radioisotope Dating Applications. *Nuclear Technology*. 197 (2): 209-218.

# 42

# RADIOCARBON CLOCKS

Vernon R. Cupps, Ph.D., and Brian Thomas, Ph.D.

**Summary:** Radiocarbon is a radioactive carbon isotope. Tiny amounts of $^{14}C$ from Earth's atmosphere end up in living things. When they die, the $^{14}C$ slowly decays to $^{14}N$ from that time forward. Testing done on organic remains shows that radiocarbon dating appears to be accurate for more recent specimens. But many factors can affect dating results, especially for older materials.

The best equipment cannot detect radiocarbon in specimens older than 57,000 years because the $^{14}C$ would have decayed to an unmeasurable level. But dozens of documented discoveries show measurable amounts of $^{14}C$ in specimens supposedly millions of years old, including dinosaur fossils.

This refutes the deep-time version of Earth history but is perfectly consistent with the biblical record.

News headlines regularly cite carbon dates that run to tens of thousands of years. They treat these "ages" as facts. But Scripture only allows six or so thousand years for the history of the whole world. This dilemma forces many to distrust God's Word. Who is right, scientists or the Bible? To answer this, it helps to know some carbon dating basics.

In the 1940s, a chemist named Willard Libby began to develop a method to date organic material using $^{14}C$, a radioactive isotope (radioisotope) of carbon. He based the method partly on the belief that Earth's atmosphere has constantly generated $^{14}C$ for millions of years. Tiny amounts of this $^{14}C$, along with $^{12}C$ and $^{13}C$, form $CO_2$ that moves to the lower atmosphere. Organisms take it up through photosynthesis and eating. Yes, you are very slightly radioactive! Carbon 14 decays[1] back to $^{14}N$. As in other radioisotope systems, the parent isotope (radiocarbon) decays into a daughter (nitrogen). The decay throws off beta particles (e⁻) that detectors can count. The number of beta counts gets converted into a concentration of $^{14}C$.

The basic equation used to convert most radioisotope systems into an age isn't enough for $^{14}C$. The daughter nucleus $^{14}N$ moves fast, reacts easily, and occurs everywhere. So, the use of $^{14}C$ as a clock requires a more complicated equation. If we can measure the current amount of $^{14}C$ (i.e., the $^{14}C/^{12}C$ ratio) in a given sample *and* we can accurately guess the amount of $^{14}C$ that was in the sample originally, then we can estimate a carbon age for the sample using the formula shown to the side.

Sensitive instruments can accurately measure the amount of $^{14}C$ currently in any given sample (. However, problems emerge with estimates of the original amounts ($N_{t_p}$). The amount of $^{14}C$ in any organism at death depends not only on time but also on surroundings. For example, the Industrial Revolution (~1764 AD) began diluting the concentration of $^{14}C$ in the atmosphere. This lowered the prior normal $^{14}C/^{12}C$ balance. Nuclear testing beginning in 1945 put extra $^{14}C$ into the air.

Reservoir effects also alter isotope ratios and any "date" they yield. This happens where organisms get their carbon from a source other than the atmosphere, like the deep sea. Because of this, land animals that eat lots of seafood tend to produce older "ages." Last, volcanoes release $CO_2$ with less radiocarbon into the atmosphere, and ash falls indicate they exploded more often during the Ice Age. These and other unknown factors muddy assumptions about past carbon isotope ratios.

## How It Works

So, how can one possibly estimate original amounts of radiocarbon? Carbon dating practice uses a standard of known $^{14}C$ content corrected for fractionation of $^{14}C$. This happens when cellular processes like protein production take up one isotope more often than another, effectively skewing the atmospheric radiocarbon ratio. This absolute radiocarbon standard was chosen to correspond to the $^{14}C$ content of wood from the "no fossil fuel" atmosphere of 1890.

By convention, 1950 represents "present" in the "before present" (BP) expression. The absolute radiocarbon standard now gets $^{14}C$ decay-corrected to 1950. The first standard used in $^{14}C$ dating was oxalic acid from a 1955 crop of sugar beets. Later, oxalic acid from a 1977 French beet molasses crop took its place. Workers use math to correct these $^{14}C/^{12}C$ ratios to match that of 1950. The third formula[2] in the side bar shows how the mean lifetime of $^{14}C$ (which is the measured half-life divided by ln 2), helps calculate a conventional radiocarbon age for a given sample.

Today, accelerator mass spectrometers (AMS) precisely measure radiocarbon in a sample. AMS labs can give results in the form of *carbon years* or as *percent modern carbon* (pMC),[2] which refers to the fraction of the radiocarbon from 1950 found in a given sample. Workers can convert between these and other expressions using standard formulas. A smaller pMC equates to more carbon years. Importantly, the amount of $^{14}C$ in the sample ($N_{tp}$) and the sample blank used to determine its value in the AMS instrument cease to be direct measurements after labs apply a fractionation correction to both values. These operations leave more room for error at this stage.

AMS instruments measure mass ratios (i.e., $^{14}C$, $^{13}C$, and $^{12}C$), not ages! Carbon years depend on the model used to calculate it from the ratios. Standard models assume an old earth. They assume that Noah's Flood never happened. These practices can produce carbon ages, especially for very old samples, much older than their actual ages.

# Some $^{14}C$ calculations

Atmospheric generation of radiocarbon knockout nuclear reaction: $^{14}N(n,p)^{14}C$

Radiocarbon beta decay reaction: $^{14}C \rightarrow {}^{14}N + e^- + \bar{\nu}_e$

Formula for age of sample based on $^{14}C$ content:

$$\frac{1}{\lambda} \ln \frac{N_0}{N_{t_p}} = t_a$$

where $\lambda$ is the decay constant for $^{14}C$, $N_{t_p}$ is the current amount of $^{14}C$ ($N \equiv$ nuclei) in the sample, and $N_0$ is the amount of $^{14}C$ originally in the sample. $N_0$ is assumed as equal to the $^{14}C$ measured in an international radiocarbon standard corrected for fractionation.

Formula for conventional radiocarbon age from Stuiver and Polach (1977)[2]:

$$t_a = -\frac{5568}{\ln 2} \ln \left(\frac{N_{t_p}}{N_0}\right)$$
$$= -8033 \ln \left(\frac{N_{t_p}}{N_0}\right)$$

Many labs use the older Libby half-life of 8,033 years to keep convention rather than the more current and accurate half-life of 8,267 yrs.

An accelerator mass spectrometer (AMS)[3] can typically detect one radiocarbon atom per quadrillion ($10^{15}$) carbon atoms.[4] Thus, most AMS devices cannot detect radiocarbon in something older than 57,000 theoretical years. After that long, the $^{14}C$ will have decayed to unmeasurable levels. This restricts radiocarbon dating to the more recent remains of archaeology from the secular point of view. This short shelf-life also means that no rock formations, minerals, or organic material older than 57,000 theoretical years should contain detectable $^{14}C$.

The reliability of carbon dates decreases with increasing age. Even secular experts prefer to bolster carbon ages with outside sources like historical records or archaeological artifacts for objects more than several thousand years old.[5]

Does carbon dating work? Generally yes on more recent material, yet not on older samples with age assignments that ignore key ways that Noah's Flood and the Ice Age would have altered isotope ratios. But radiocarbon offers more than ages in carbon years. We can use it to test the concept of millions of years.

## Contamination? How?

Since the mid-20th century, evidence has been mounting that $^{14}C$ exists in measurable amounts in carbon-bearing rocks and organic matter that secular scientists believe to be tens to hundreds of millions of years old.[6-13] These detections devastate deep time. Secular and Bible-believing scientists both have found $^{14}C$ in dozens of fossils from different continents, using different preparations and laboratories. And radiocarbon in coal has long mystified experts.

More recently, ICR predicted that since diamonds formed thousands, not billions, of years ago, they might still have $^{14}C$. Tests on diamonds from different places confirmed this prediction. Later, a secular team verified those results with their own diamonds. They attributed the short-lived radiocarbon in supposedly billion-year-old diamonds to contamination from within the AMS instrument. Did they offer scientific evidence for or against that assertion? No, they simply assumed contamination. Logically, they had to. The only other option is to get rid of belief in deep time, and that would spell the end of respect from their peers and maybe the end of their careers.

In 2016, a Christian biologist who teaches an old earth despite the scientific and biblical evidence against it wrote about another possible source of contamination. He needed to explain $^{14}C$ in coal, fossil teeth, sea shell fossils, collagen and bones, plus diamonds, natural gas, and marble, all published in technical journals. We summarize 60 such results in the figure below. He suggested that the decay of uranium in the earth recently generated new $^{14}$C that became part of the coal and fossils.[14] Is this reasonable?

It's laughable, and here's why. Some kind of Earth material would need to have very recently supplied neutrons with high enough energy to induce the proton-to-neutron reaction that converts $^{14}$N to $^{14}$C. (See the formula sidebar.) In theory, this reaction would produce $^{14}$C in buried organic or inorganic matter and would lead to artificially young age estimates. The neutrons necessary for this reaction can originate either from above (cosmogenic) or from below (subsurface).

Since neutrons do not penetrate deep into the ground, neutrons from above lose their energy right at Earth's surface. Consider a 30-cm-diameter by 30-cm-long bone section sitting exposed on the ground and being bombarded by a typical cosmic neutron flux (approximately $6.4 \times 10^{-3}$ neutrons/cm$^2$–second, under current conditions). This would generate $1.52 \times 10^{10}$ $^{14}$C atoms in 124,000 theoretical years. This also accounts for decay of $^{14}$C in the bone sample. At that point, the $^{14}$C/$^{12}$C ratio will be reduced by approximately a factor of $10^4$ —one order of magnitude below the detection limits of an AMS. It would register no results and no carbon years. Yet, dozens of samples register plenty of measurable carbon years' worth of $^{14}$C atoms! Clearly, contamination from above has no chance of producing the quantities of ra-

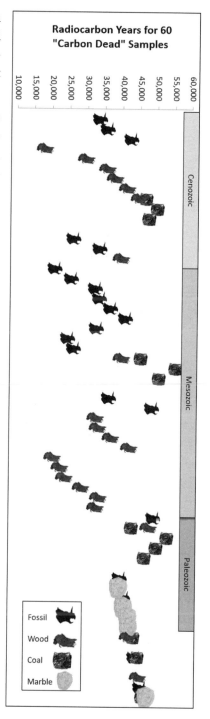

Radiocarbon Years for 60 "Carbon Dead" Samples

diocarbon measured in so many deeply buried samples.

What about radiation underground? Secondary nuclear reactions of alpha particles that impact O, Si, Al, Fe, Ca, or Na[15] are the only way to get underground neutrons. These reactions occur very rarely. And the neutrons they release have too little energy to make $^{14}C$ out of $^{14}N$ underground. Geophysicist John Baumgardner demonstrated this back in 2005.[16] Whoever would claim that underground nuclear reactions contaminate buried materials earns a poor score in nuclear physics and in basic homework skills.

## Mistaken Backgrounds?

Secular experts assert that background levels of $^{14}C$ during AMS analyses create the low levels that very old $^{14}C$ samples have. Why do they say this? Possibly they thought beta-counting devices were not sensitive enough to distinguish between cosmic ray background beta particles and $^{14}C$ decay beta particles at very low concentrations of $^{14}C$. However, today we use the highly sensitive AMS.[2] No material older than about 57,000 years should contain detectable $^{14}C$. Thus, we can use the AMS to test evolutionary time simply by detecting radiocarbon in carbonaceous materials deemed to be tens to hundreds of million years old. The table shown here clearly shows dozens of such detections. Each one debunks deep time.

Secularists recently objected to these kinds of measurements. They claimed that they resulted from misunderstanding the use of background blanks in standard lab procedures.[17] Reference 13 shows the statistical analysis that refutes this claim, which boils down to arguing in a circle. Because coal and diamonds are millions and billions of years old, they cannot possibly have radiocarbon and thus must be "carbon dead." Therefore, any radiocarbon found in these samples must come from contamination. Such circular reasoning is a poor substitute for measurement science. Science keeps providing results that refute this circular reasoning and deep-time philosophy.

## But 50,000 Years Aren't in the Bible

Looking at the chart of 60 samples, readers will notice more carbon years than the approximately 6,000 calendar years from scriptural data. How can this be? Carbon years and calendar years do not always match. The two diverge in a pattern. Carbon years veer further and further from the actual years with age of the sample. Clearly, the ancient earth had less $^{14}C$ than today.

Noah's Flood would have done this in at least three ways. The much greener pre-Flood world had more carbon at Earth's surface. This would dilute $^{14}$C. The earth's magnetic field was stronger. The field before the Flood would have reduced $^{14}$C production in the upper atmosphere. Finally, $^{14}$C production would not have been going on for millions of years. The isotope ratio may not have leveled off. It may be still climbing since creation, when the atmosphere may have had zero radiocarbons.

## Conclusion

Over 100 published samples have enough radiocarbon in them to refute their millions-of-years age assignments. Carbon-14 exists in measurable amounts even in some of the lowest rock formations. An earth no more than 50,000 years old—for example, the earth according to the Bible—accounts for all these results.

### Notes

1. Although it is impossible to predict when a particular radiocarbon atom will transform into nitrogen, the behavior of a large number of radiocarbon atoms is very predictable. The half-life, the amount of time required for half of any starting amount of radiocarbon to change into nitrogen, is about 5,730 years. This means that 50% of the starting number of $^{14}$C atoms will remain after 5,730 years, 25% will remain after 11,460 years, etc. In 57,300 years, 10 half-lives, the amount of remaining $^{14}$C in any specimen is reduced by a factor of $2^{10}$, a reduction in concentration of more than a thousand.

2. Stuiver, M. and H. A. Polach. 1977. Discussion Reporting of $^{14}$C Data. *Radiocarbon.* 19 (3): 355-363.

3. Radiocarbon Dating. "Accelerator Mass Spectrometry (AMS) technology…gives the most advanced precision and accuracy for carbon-14 measurements." Beta Analytic fact sheet. Posted on radiocarbon.com, accessed January 31, 2020.

4. The Center for Accelerator Mass Spectrometry claims that the precision of AMS for detecting $^{14}$C in organic material is between 0.5 and 1.0%. Holloway, C. A New World of Biomedical Research: The Center for Accelerator Mass Spectrometry. *Science & Technology Review.* November 1997: 4, 7.

5. Morris, J. D. 2007. *The Young Earth.* Green Forest, AR: Master Books, 64.

6. Baumgardner, J. R. 2005. $^{14}$C Evidence for a Recent Global Flood and a Young Earth. In *Radioisotopes and the Age of the Earth: Results of a Young-Earth Creationist Research Initiative.* L. Vardiman, A. A. Snelling, and E. F. Chaffin, eds. El Cajon, CA: Institute for Creation Research, and Chino Valley, AZ: Creation Research Society, 587-630.

7. Hebert, J. 2013. Rethinking Carbon-14 Dating: What Does It Really Tell Us about the Age of the Earth? *Acts & Facts.* 42 (4): 12-14.

8. Snelling, A. A. 2008. Radiocarbon in "Ancient" Fossil Wood. *Acts & Facts.* 37 (1): 10-13.

9. Snelling, A. A. 2008. Radiocarbon Ages for Fossil Ammonites and Wood in Cretaceous Strata near Redding, California. *Answers Research Journal.* 1: 123-144.

10. Morris, *The Young Earth,* 63-70.

11. Giem, P. 2001. Carbon-14 Content of Fossil Carbon. *Origins.* 51: 6-30.

12. Thomas, B. and V. Nelson. 2015. Radiocarbon in Dinosaur and other Fossils. *Creation Research Society Quaterly.* 51 (4): 299-311.

13. Cupps, V. and B. Thomas. 2019. Deep Time Philosophy Impacts Radiocarbon Measurements. *Creation Research Society Quarterly*. 55: 212-222.

14. Rana, F. 2016. *Dinosaur Blood and the Age of the Earth*. Covina, CA: RTB Press, 49.

15. The necessary reaction for generation of subsurface neutrons is the $(\alpha, n)$ reaction on the most abundant isotopes in the earth's crust, such as $^{16}O$, $^{28}Si$, $^{27}Al$, and $^{23}Na$. Approximate threshold energies for this reaction to occur on these elements are 12.43 MeV, 8.39 MeV, 2.94 MeV, and 6.03 MeV respectively. This means that the alpha particles emitted in the uranium and thorium decay chains would need at least the listed kinetic energy to initiate the $(\alpha, n)$ nuclear reaction, but they do not. Note that the uranium decay chain alphas do not provide the requisite energy to initiate the $(\alpha, n)$ reaction on the two most common elements in the earth's crust since the highest energy alpha in the uranium decay chain is 7.83 MeV.

16. Baumgardner, $^{14}C$ Evidence for a Recent Global Flood and a Young Earth, 614-616.

17. Taylor, R. E., J. R. Southon, and G. M. Santos. 2018. Misunderstandings Concerning the Significance of AMS Background 14C Measurements. *Radiocarbon*. 60 (3): 727-749.

# 43

# WAS THERE AN ICE AGE?

Jake Hebert, Ph.D.

**Summary:** There is abundant evidence that glaciers once covered vast areas of Earth. Even though secular scientists claim there were dozens of Ice Ages, they can't explain them because it takes many years of significant snowfall and cold summers for them to develop.

The Genesis Flood provided the conditions needed for an Ice Age. The volcanism that occurred before and after the Flood provided aerosols that blocked sunlight, cooled the summers, and allowed ice sheets to grow. Volcanism and tectonic plate movement heated the oceans, putting large amounts of moisture into the atmosphere and causing increased precipitation. This post-Flood Ice Age would've lasted for several hundred years.

The Ice Age isn't a mystery for creation scientists—there was only one and the Genesis Flood caused it.

There is abundant geological evidence that Northern Hemisphere glaciers (large bodies of ice resulting from the accumulation of snow) once extended to lower latitudes than they do today. For instance, unconsolidated dirt and rock debris (moraines) similar to those associated with modern-day glaciers are found at these lower latitudes and elevations. Likewise, scratches or grooves on surface rocks are believed to have been formed by rocks embedded within these large, slow-moving bodies of ice.[1]

A period characterized by the expansion and advance of high-latitude ice sheets and mountain glaciers is called an Ice Age.[2] Evolutionists currently believe more than 50 Ice Ages have occurred within the last few million years.[3] Supposedly, for the last million years Ice Age cycles each lasted about 100,000 years. The glacial phase of each one is thought to have lasted about 90,000 years, with an interglacial phase of about 10,000 years.[4]

Although evolutionists routinely mention these supposed multiple Ice Ages, they have great difficulty explaining even a single Ice Age. In fact, a popular magazine listed this as one of the great remaining mysteries in science.[5]

One might think that colder winters are the key to producing an Ice Age, but there's more to it than that. Extremely cold temperatures generally result in less, not more, snowfall due to the lower moisture content of extremely cold air.[6] Also, some places on Earth today are very cold in the winter, but warm summers melt the winter snow before glaciers can form.[7]

An Ice Age requires cold summers and much more snowfall, and the conditions must persist over many years. In that way, snow and ice can build up year after year.

It is difficult to meet both of these conditions for any extended period of time in today's world. For instance, realistic computer simulations have shown that even a dramatic 12°C summer temperature decrease in northeastern Canada would result in only a modest advance in permanent snow cover. The snow cover would not even extend past the southern tip of Canada's Hudson Bay.[8] Yet, geological evidence indicates that glaciers once extended well into the northern United States. Conditions in the past must have been radically different in order to produce an Ice Age.

The Genesis Flood provides these conditions. Extensive, dramatic volcanism would have occurred during the Flood as a consequence of the breaking up of the "fountains of the great deep" (Genesis 7:11) and the resulting tectonic activity. Abundant evidence for such catastrophic volcanism on a continental scale appears in the geological record, although evolutionary scientists incorrectly assign ages of millions of years to these formations.

Basaltic lava flows during the Flood were hundreds—and even thousands—of cubic kilometers in volume.[9,10] During the Flood, the heat released by the rapid formation of new seafloor (see chapter 31) greatly warmed the world's oceans, causing the water during and after the Flood to have been considerably warmer than today, perhaps by tens of degrees Celsius.[11,12] Flood currents and Earth movements would have mixed the water so that after the Flood the oceans would have been very uniform in temperature, which is unlike today's varied ocean temperatures. More evaporation would have occurred, particularly at the mid and high latitudes, as a result of a higher average ocean surface temperature. This would have provided the additional atmospheric moisture needed for greater snowfall.

The Flood would also have made possible the cooler summers needed to keep the winter snow from melting, due to the extensive volcanism that occurred more frequently during the Flood and less frequently afterward. Explosive volcanic eruptions would have ejected large amounts of aerosols (tiny particles) into the stratosphere. Even today, aerosols from explosive volcanic eruptions remain suspended in the atmosphere for a number of years, so the same would have been true after the Flood. These aerosols would have reflected a great deal of sunlight back to space, resulting in the cooler summers needed for snow to accumulate.

Modern-day volcanic events have shown that volcanic aerosols can cause such cooling, as they did in the 1783 Laki basaltic eruption in Iceland and the 1991 eruption of Pinatubo in the Philippines.[13] Yet, these eruptions were miniscule in comparison with the volcanic activity that occurred during the Flood.

As the earth slowly returned to equilibrium after the Flood, residual volcanism would have continued to sporadically eject aerosols into the stratosphere for many years, ensuring that summers remained cool enough to prevent the ice from melting. Also, because water has a high heat capacity, it relinquishes heat slowly. It would therefore have taken a significant amount of time for the oceans to cool to their present average surface temperature. As the oceans gradually cooled, evaporation would have decreased, resulting in less snowfall. Decreasing volcanic activity would have meant a gradual reduction in the amount of stratospheric aerosols, enabling more sunlight to reach Earth's surface. That would have enabled the glaciers to begin melting.

Meteorologist Michael Oard used "heat budget" equations to estimate the amount of time for the oceans to cool to their present average temperature. Although there are considerable uncertainties in the calculation, he estimated that the post-Flood Ice Age lasted for about 700 years—500 years for the glaciers to reach their maximum extent and another 200 years for the glaciers to recede.[14] Since the Flood occurred around 2300 BC,[15] this would mean that the post-Flood Ice Age could have possibly lasted until about 1600 BC.

It may not be a coincidence that the book of Job, believed by conservative scholars to have been written around 2000 BC, has more references to snow and ice than any other book of the Bible. And harsher conditions as the Ice Age ended likely resulted in the extinction of many animals, including the wooly mammoths.[16,17]

As noted earlier, evolutionists claim many Ice Ages have occurred throughout history, even in the (supposed) distant past. For instance, they claim that nearly the entire earth was frozen at least twice between 750 and 580 million years ago (the "Snowball Earth" hypothesis).[18]

The argument for these ancient Ice Ages is based largely upon the existence of diamictite, or lithified rubble, in sedimentary layers that is interpreted to be glacial in origin. However, almost all the diamictite properties cited in support of this view can be duplicated by other mass-flow processes,[19] especially underwater debris flows and "turbidity currents."[20] Moreover, many of their properties are more consistent with underwater debris flows.[21,22] Within the creation model, one would expect many catastrophic underwater mass flows to have occurred during the Genesis Flood.

So, not only is the Ice Age not a problem for the creation model, the creation model does a far better job of explaining the data than the evolution model does.

*Notes*

1. Oard, M. 2006. Where Does the Ice Age Fit? In *The New Answers Book 1*. K. Ham, ed. Green Forest, AR: Master Books, 207-219.

2. Ibid, 208.

3. Walker, M. and J. Lowe. 2007. Quaternary science 2007: a 50-year retrospective. *Journal of the Geological Society.* 164 (6): 1073-1092.

4. Oard, Where Does the Ice Age Fit?, 210-211.

5. Watson, T. 1997. What causes Ice Ages? *U.S. News & World Report.* 123 (7): 58-60.

6. Lutgens, F. K. and E. J. Tarbuck. 2010. *The Atmosphere: An Introduction to Meteorology,* 11th ed. New York: Prentice Hall, 145-146.

7. Warm summers in Siberia prevent glaciation despite very cold winter temperatures.

8. Williams, L. D. 1979. An Energy Balance Model of Potential Glacierization of Northern Canada. *Arctic and Alpine Research.* 11 (4): 443-456.

9. Woodmorappe, J. and M. Oard. 2002. Field studies in the Columbia River basalt, Northwest USA. *Journal of Creation.* 16 (1): 103-110.

10. Silvestru, E. 2001. The Permian extinction: *National Geographic* comes close to the truth. *Journal of Creation.* 15 (1): 6-8.

11. Clarey, T. 2016. Embracing Catastrophic Plate Tectonics. *Acts & Facts* 45 (5): 8-11.

12. Vardiman, L. 1998. Numerical Simulation of Precipitation Induced by Hot Mid-Ocean Ridges. In *Proceedings of the Fourth International Conference on Creationism*. R. E. Walsh, ed. Pittsburgh, PA: Creation Science Fellowship, 595-605.

13. de Castella, T. 2010. The eruption that changed Iceland forever. *BBC News Magazine.* Posted on news.bbc.co.uk April 16, 2010.

14. Oard, M. 1990. *An Ice Age Caused by the Genesis Flood.* San Diego, CA: Institute for Creation Research, 93-117.

15. Osgood, J. 1981. The Date of Noah's Flood. *Journal of Creation.* 4 (1): 10-13.

16. Oard, M. 2000. The extinction of the woolly mammoth: was it a quick freeze? *Journal of Creation.* 14 (3): 24-34.

17. Oard, M. 2004. *Frozen in Time.* Green Forest, AR: Master Books.

18. Cronin, T. M. 2010. *Paleoclimates: Understanding Climate Change Past and Present.* New York: Columbia University Press, 59-64.

19. Oard, M. 1994. Submarine Mass Flow Deposition of Pre-Pleistocene "Ice Age" Deposits. In *Proceedings of the Third International Conference on Creationism.* R. E. Walsh, ed. Pittsburgh, PA: Creation Science Fellowship, 407-418.

20. A turbidity current is a sediment-laden, rapidly moving current of water that flows through a larger body of water.

21. Molén, M. 1990. Diamictites: Ice-Ages or Gravity Flows? In *Proceedings of the Second International Conference on Creationism.* R. E. Walsh & C. L. Brooks, eds. Pittsburgh, PA: Creation Science Fellowship, 177-190.

22. Oard, M. 1997. *Ancient Ice Ages or Gigantic Submarine Landslides?* Chino Valley, AZ: Creation Research Society Books.

# 44

# DO SEAFLOOR SEDIMENT AND ICE CORE DATA PROVE LONG AGES?

Jake Hebert, Ph.D.

**Summary:** Scientists have drilled seafloor cores and claim the depths of the sediment layers are proof of millions of years because seafloor sediments accumulate very slowly today. They also assign very old ages to high-latitude ice sheet cores.

But the methods the researchers use to reach these ages are flawed. They match isotope ratios within the seafloor cores to supposed climate variations in Earth's past, but the theory they base this on is invalid. Deep layers in the ice cores are difficult to determine, so dates from the seafloor cores are used to determine the timescales for them—which is circular reasoning, not science.

The Genesis Flood provides a better explanation. Sedimentation rates were much higher during this event, and increased precipitation and cooler summers in the Ice Age following the Flood resulted in the thick ice sheets.

Seafloor sediment and ice core data fit the biblical timeline of only thousands of years.

Sediments today are deposited very slowly on the seafloors. At current rates, it can take a thousand years to lay down just a few centimeters of sediment.[1,2] Scientists have drilled and extracted cylindrical cores from these sedimentary layers that can have combined lengths of hundreds of meters. Given these slow deposition rates, uniformitarians argue that the layers were deposited over many millions of years.

Likewise, very old ages are assigned to layers within the high-latitude ice sheets. For instance, ice in the Greenland GISP2 ice core from a depth of

2,800 meters was supposedly deposited about 110,000 years ago.[3] Clearly, these old ages are incompatible with the Bible's timescale of about 6,000 years. Do ice core and seafloor sediment data really require long ages?

The fact that sedimentation and precipitation rates would have been much higher shortly after the Genesis Flood (not to mention during the Flood itself) enables the seafloor sediment layers and high-latitude ice sheets to easily form within the biblical time frame. However, uniformitarians might counter that their denial of recent creation and the Flood is justified. They would claim that ice core and seafloor sediment data both tell consistent "stories" about how climate has varied in the distant past.

If completely independent data sets really tell similar and consistent stories of climate variation over hundreds of thousands of years, this would indeed be a strong argument for an old earth. But is this really the case? In order to answer this question, it is necessary to briefly explain a quantity called $\delta^{18}O$ and what is known as the astronomical theory.

### $\delta^{18}O$ Variations within Seafloor Sediment Cores

The $\delta^{18}O$ ratio is a comparison of the amount of a "heavy" variety (or isotope) of oxygen (oxygen-18, or $^{18}O$) compared to a "lighter" variety (oxygen-16, or $^{16}O$). Values of $\delta^{18}O$ in the calcium carbonate ($CaCO_3$) shells of marine organisms called *foraminifera* can be measured.

Past researchers used a relationship between the $\delta^{18}O$ ratio in the calcium carbonate and that of the seawater associated with the $CaCO_3$'s formation to estimate the $^{18}O/^{16}O$ ratio of seawater at the time the $CaCO_3$ was deposited. Because the $^{18}O/^{16}O$ ratio of seawater is temperature-dependent, it was used as a means of inferring seawater temperatures.[4]

Researchers currently believe that the $\delta^{18}O$ ratio is strongly dependent upon the volume of the high-latitude ice sheets, so now they interpret it more as an indicator of the amount of glaciation than of temperature per se.[5] Since these values are thought to be indicators of the amount of ice cover on Earth, $\delta^{18}O$ within a seafloor sediment core can be used, in theory, to construct a chronology of climate variations in Earth's past.

### The Astronomical (Milankovitch) Theory

The amount of sunlight reaching Earth varies with latitude and season. Moreover, Earth undergoes slow changes in its orbit over time. These orbital changes cause variations in the latitudinal and seasonal distribution of the sunlight reaching Earth. Because uniformitarians believe the solar system is very old, they extrapolate these slow changes back into the distant past. They think that the variations in $\delta^{18}O$ found in the seafloor sediments indicate changes in climate that were caused by these orbital variations. The "match" between $\delta^{18}O$ variations and supposed past changes in climate expected from these orbital variations is said to be an argument for an old earth.

However, this "astronomical theory" has serious problems. One such problem is that glacial-interglacial climate cycles supposedly occurred at 100,000-year intervals for about the last million years. This is thought to match a 100,000-year period of variation in the "eccentricity" (elongation) of Earth's orbit around the sun, but variations in eccentricity would result in only *tiny* changes in the sunlight reaching Earth.

Many other serious difficulties with the theory could be cited.[6,7] In fact, it was the results of a well-known 1976 scientific paper that convinced many secular scientists that the astronomical theory is correct, even though those results were obtained using an age assignment that they themselves no longer consider valid![8]

If the astronomical theory has such serious difficulties, why then is there apparently good agreement between its predictions and the variations in $\delta^{18}O$ found in seafloor sediments? Despite its difficulties, uniformitarians are so certain the astronomical theory is correct that they use it to "tune" their seafloor sediment age-depth models.[9] In some cases, dates based upon radioactive dating have been adjusted based on "orbital tuning" considerations.[10] Not surprisingly, such tuning results in good agreement between predictions of the theory and what is found in the sedimentary record. Even some uniformitarians have acknowledged that this approach could be criticized as circular reasoning.[11]

## Determining Annual Layers in Ice Cores

Because snow and ice generally do not melt in the polar latitudes, they accumulate over time. Thus, a previous layer of snow is covered by a succeeding layer, and that layer is covered by another layer, and so on. As layers of snow accumulate and the vertical thickness of the ice increases over time, the snow is transformed into ice as the air is squeezed out.

This accumulated ice contains "layers" that can theoretically be used to construct a chronology. Summer and winter snow layers are distinct from one another. For instance, winter snow tends to be more homogeneous than summer snow.[12] Likewise, because nitric acid ($HNO_3$) production in the stratosphere is higher in the spring/summer, variations in the acidity of the ice (determined by measurements of the ice's electrical conductivity) could also conceivably be used in the construction of a chronology.[13]

As in the case of seafloor sediments, scientists drill and extract cores from the ice in the hopes of using layers within the cores to date events in Earth's past.

## Difficulties in Determining Annual Layers

Earth scientists would like to be able to determine the elapsed time since a layer within an ice core was deposited by visually inspecting and counting the annual layers within the ice. In actual practice, however, there are complicating factors.

Layering becomes more indistinct at greater depths within the core. This means that one cannot simply visually inspect and count these deeper layers if one wants to extend the chronology into the more distant past. Nor can one simply "guess" the locations of these deeper layers based on corresponding layer thicknesses higher in the core. The weight of the overlying snow and ice causes the layers to be forced downward, with a corresponding thinning of the layers that increases at greater core depths (Figure 1).

Therefore, a theoretical flow model is needed to convert a measured distance down the length of the core into a time. These flow models implicitly assume that the ice sheets have been in existence for vast amounts of time.[14] Not surprisingly, they yield enormous ages for the ice sheets. Based on the target age from flow models and particular events recorded in the ice sheets, annual layer counting is matched to these flow models.[15,16] Moreover, the dates from the seafloor sediment cores are used to determine the timescales for the glacier flow models![17]

The "reinforcement syndrome" is another factor contributing to the supposed match between the seafloor sediment and ice core data and the predictions of the astronomical theory. Researchers have a tendency to see in the data what they expect. This is not necessarily intentional dishonesty but a subtle, usually unconscious form of bias.

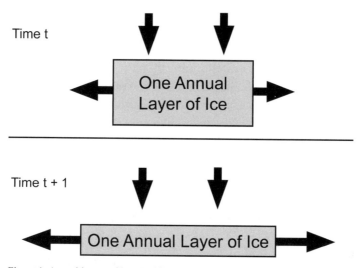

Figure 1. Annual layers of ice are thinned vertically due to pressure from the ice above. Horizontal lengthening compensates for the vertical shortening.[18]

Examples of the reinforcement syndrome abound in the historical sciences. Geologists used to believe that four Ice Ages had occurred within the last few million years, and this model was supposedly confirmed by virtually all the data for about 60 years.[19] Earlier this century, some museum displays still taught this older model of Earth history.[20] Yet, this older model has now been abandoned in favor of the modern astronomical theory, with its much higher number of Ice Ages. Why, then, did so many evolutionists "see" evidence for a view of Earth history that even they now admit is wrong?[21]

So, the "matches" between the predictions of the astronomical theory and what is found in ice and seafloor sediment cores are not independent arguments for an old earth.

**Creation Models**

Creation scientists Michael Oard and Larry Vardiman have constructed qualitative and simple quantitative age models for seafloor sediments and glacial ice.[22,23] These models quite reasonably assume higher deposition rates shortly after the Flood. For instance, during the latter stages of the Flood, one would expect sediments to be deposited into the oceans at much higher rates than those of today. Likewise, shortly after the Flood high-latitude precipitation rates would have been much higher than they are today. This, combined with cooler summers in the years after the Flood, would have enabled the high-latitude ice sheets to be formed in just hundreds of years (see chapter 43).

These creation models result in greatly reduced ages for the ice sheets and seafloor sediments, ages that are compatible with the biblical timescale. Moreover, these models can explain aspects of the data that puzzle evolutionists.[24,25] As is often the case in the creation-evolution controversy, the "facts" are not neutral. The conclusions one draws from the data are dramatically affected by one's starting assumptions.

### Notes

1. Cronin, T. M. 2010. *Paleoclimates: Understanding Climate Change Past and Present.* New York: Columbia University Press, 28.

2. Vardiman, L. 1996. *Sea-Floor Sediment and the Age of the Earth.* El Cajon, CA: Institute for Creation Research, 10.

3. Meese, D. A. et al. 1997. The Greenland Ice Sheet Project 2 depth-age scale: Methods and results. *Journal of Geophysical Research.* 102 (C12): 26,411–26,423.

4. Vardiman, *Sea-Floor Sediment and the Age of the Earth*, 49.

5. Walker, M. and J. Lowe. 2007. Quaternary science 2007: a 50-year retrospective. *Journal of the Geological Society.* 164 (6): 1073-1092.

6. Cronin, *Paleoclimates*, 130-139.

7. Oard, M. 2007. Astronomical troubles for the astronomical hypothesis of ice ages. *Journal of Creation.* 21 (3): 19-23.

8. Hebert, J. 2018. More Problems with Iconic Milankovitch Paper. *Creation Science Update.* Posted July 13, 2018 on ICR.org, accessed January 28, 2020.

9. Herbert, T. D. 2009. Paleoceanography: Orbitally Tuned Timescales. In *Climates and Oceans.* J. H. Steele, ed. Amsterdam, NL: Academic Press, 370-377.

10. Ibid, 374.

11. Ibid.

12. Alley, R. B. et al. 1997. Visual-stratigraphic dating of the GISP2 ice core: Basis, reproducibility, and application. *Journal of Geophysical Research.* 102 (C12): 26,367–26,381.

13. Meese, The Greenland Ice Sheet Project, 26,412.

14. Dansgaard, W. and S. J. Johnsen. 1969. A flow model and a time scale for the ice core from Camp Century, Greenland. *Journal of Glaciology.* 8 (53) :215-223.

15. Oard, M. 2005. *The Frozen Record.* Santee, CA: Institute for Creation Research, 74-75.

16. Meese, The Greenland Ice Sheet Project, 26,417–26,419.

17. Waelbroeck, C. et al. 1995. A comparison of the Vostok ice deuterium record and series from Southern Ocean core MD 88-770 over the last two glacial-interglacial cycles. *Climate Dynamics.* 12: 113-123.

18. Oard, *The Frozen Record*, Figure 3.13, 45.

19. Ibid, 122.

20. Ham, K., ed. 2006. *The New Answers Book.* Green Forest, AR: Master Books, 211.

21. Other examples of the reinforcement syndrome in the creation-evolution controversy could be cited. See Lubenow, M. 1995. The pigs took it all. *Creation.* 17 (3): 36-38.

22. Vardiman, L. 2001. *Climates Before and After the Genesis Flood.* El Cajon, CA: Institute for Creation Research, 41-80.

23. Oard, *The Frozen Record,* 35-50.

24. Ibid, 133-135.

25. Patrick, K. 2010. Manganese nodules and the age of the ocean floor. *Journal of Creation.* 24 (3): 82-86.

# DINOSAURS
# AND HUMANS

## WALKED TOGETHER OR
## RULED APART?

# 45

# DINOSAURS AND THE BIBLE

Frank Sherwin, M.A.

**Summary:** Creationists and evolutionists have very different understandings of dinosaur history. Like other past events, dinosaur origins can't be proved by laboratory science. Christians can rely on God's written record that He created them on Day 6, while evolutionists must speculate based on their naturalistic worldview.

Rather than dinosaurs dying off millions of years before the arrival of humans, ancient eyewitness accounts from all over the world depict people seeing dragon-like creatures that resemble dinosaurs. Living dinosaur-like animals are also described in Job and other Old Testament passages.

As land-dwelling, air-breathing creatures, dinosaurs were taken aboard the Ark and then dispersed after the Flood. Historical accounts and archaeological and geological evidence all point to the Bible's account of dinosaur creation just 6,000 years ago.

In the war of the worldviews, creationists and evolutionists have very different understandings regarding the origin and demise of dinosaurs. Christians have the written record of One who was there "In the beginning," while the evolutionist has no such record and must speculate within a naturalistic framework.

## Dinosaur Origin

When discussing dinosaurs, one must know where true scientific research (experimental or empirical) leaves off and where non-scientific interpretation begins. For example, a biologist conducts research on plants and animals in the laboratory or in the field by observing, testing, and repeating a biological process. Conversely, a historian collects reliable past material and eyewitness accounts in order to verify a certain historical event, be it a war, election, or assassination. The historian does not test or repeat as the scientist does.

This should be remembered when discussing the *origin* of plants, animals, people, or planets. Simply put, the origin of dinosaurs (or any other creature) cannot be "proved" by laboratory science techniques. It is a past event that cannot be presently tested. We must consult eyewitness accounts instead. A judge will tell you that when reconstructing the past—either ancient or recent—the testimony of reliable eyewitnesses routinely takes precedence over other forms of evidence.

Whatever their zoological classification (see below), God tells us clearly that He created dinosaurs on Day 6 of the creation week just 6,000 years ago. Evolutionists maintain dinosaurs evolved from non-dinosaur ancestors around 235 million years ago. However, it is interesting that when dinosaurs are unearthed, they are 100% dinosaurs—as predicted by creationists.

In Genesis 1:24, we read of the formation of cattle (referring to domestic animals), creeping things (small creatures), and beasts of the earth (the large, non-domestic animals). There were perhaps about 50 different basic "kinds" of dinosaurs, and their fossils show that they had well-proportioned bodies that were well-designed for the life each led. Some dinosaurs, like *Compsognathus* or *Mussaurus*, were small "creeping things." But others, like *Tyrannosaurus* or *Ultrasaurus*, were large "beasts of the earth" made alongside man on Day 6, according to the testimony of the only One who was actually there.

So, we see the first and most important eyewitness when it comes to dinosaur origin was the Creator Himself. He wrote in Genesis 1:25:

> And God made the beast of the earth according to its kind, cattle according to its kind, and everything that creeps on the earth according to its kind.

Evolutionists claim that dinosaurs were wiped off the earth millions of years before the arrival of humans. But Genesis makes clear that dinosaurs did not become extinct (if indeed they are) before humans because they were given dominion over all types of animals (Genesis 1:28).

Evolutionists, of course, routinely dismiss the eyewitness biblical record. In 2001, a husband/wife team wrote, "Likewise, humans did not directly observe the evolution of the dinosaurs, but their evolution is nonetheless considered to be scientific fact."[1] But the authors simply *assume* that real or vertical evolution occurred—in a book dedicated to defending vertical evolution.

Meanwhile, a 2011 *Science* magazine article stated:

> The demise of *T. rex* and most other dinosaurs some 65 million years ago may grab all the headlines. But paleontologists are equally concerned with puzzling out how these mighty beasts got their start. Who were their ancestors?[2]

Dinosaurs called titanosaurs "were one of the most widespread and successful species of sauropod dinosaurs, [but] their origin and dispersion are not completely understood."[3]

## Dragons and Dinosaurs

Ancient cultures worldwide, as well as having flood legends, also have dragon legends. One of the more fascinating recent discoveries is a fossil called *Dracorex hogwartsia* unearthed in North America. It had spiky horns and a long muzzle that surprised paleontologists. In a press release from Stanford University, an evolutionist stated, "The skull looks strangely familiar to anyone who has studied dragons! *Dracorex* has a remarkable resemblance to the dragons of ancient China and medieval Europe."[4] Creationists maintain that many different cultures in the past (e.g., ancient Welsh, Babylonian, Chinese, Australian aboriginal, and Egyptian) have similar dragon legends that they could not have gotten from just viewing dinosaur fossils. It is probable that ancestors of various people groups actually saw these dragons (dinosaurs) and passed the sightings on to the next generation.

Many are familiar with England's St. George and the dragon with which he had to contend. Alexander the Great's army encountered a dragon, as did Marco Polo. Flavius Philostratus provided this account in the third century AD:

> The whole of India is girt with dragons of enormous size; for not only the marshes are full of them, but the mountains as well, and there is not a single ridge without one. Now the marsh kind are sluggish in their habits and are thirty cubits long, and they have no crest standing up on their heads.[5]

Pliny the Elder also referenced large dragons in India in his *Natural History.*

What exactly is a dinosaur? Answering this question is not as easy as it first seems. Until the advent of dinosaur soft tissue discovery, paleontologists only had mineralized remains—fossils—of these creatures. Because we have just the fossils, it is difficult, though not impossible, to say how many different kinds of dinosaurs there were.

Additionally, were dinosaurs warm-blooded or cold-blooded? How do zoologists classify them—as mammals, reptiles, or just uniquely dinosaurs? Answers to these scientific questions require more research.

## Dinosaurs in Scripture

One cannot find "dinosaur" in the King James Bible (1611) because the word did not exist when it was translated. Dinosaurs were rediscovered as fossils in 1822 (remember, Adam and his progeny saw living dinosaurs first!), and the word "dinosaur" was coined in 1841 by Sir Richard Owen, first super-intendent of the prestigious British Museum.

The book of Job offers eyewitness testimony, providing the reader with a good answer to the question regarding dinosaurs and the Bible. In addition, James, Ezekiel, and Paul refer to the book of Job, authenticating its historical reliably.

In chapter 40 beginning at verse 15, God compares Job to the power of a large creature called behemoth, a term that may be defined as a "huge beast." We read, "Look now at the behemoth, which I made along with you…he moves his tail like a cedar." Unfortunately, many Bible commentators inexplicably think the creature Job describes is a hippopotamus or elephant, despite their both having a tail that is nothing like a cedar. It would seem that these modern commentators are influenced by corrupt evolutionary thinking, supposing that dinosaurs were long-extinct by Job's day.

Further in Job 40, we read the phrase "first of the ways of God." This phrase indicates this was the largest land animal God created, and the elephant and hippo were certainly not the largest land animals.

Jeremiah 9:11 and 10:22 (KJV) speak of "den of dragons," using the Hebrew word *tannim*, meaning "monsters." There's no reason to think Jeremiah was not referring to dinosaurs that survived for centuries in isolated areas after the Flood.

## Dinosaurs, the Flood, and the Ark

At least two of each land-dwelling, air-breathing kind, including dinosaurs, went aboard the Ark. Genesis 7:8-9 states, "Of clean animals, of animals that are unclean, of birds, and of everything that creeps on the earth, two by two they went into the ark to Noah, male and female, as God had commanded Noah." The three sons of Noah were firsthand eyewitnesses to these events and co-authored this section of Scripture, which ends with their "signatures" in Genesis 10:1.

Those who claim that dinosaurs could not have fit on the Ark might recall that the average dinosaur size was on the order of a large dog. Even the massive dinosaurs started out from football-size eggs, and juveniles of these groups could have easily been selected to board the lifesaving vessel. All air-breathing, land-dwelling animals—including the dinosaurs—found outside the Ark perished in the worldwide deluge described in Genesis 6–8. The massive sedimentary (water-deposited) rock units containing billions of fossils of dinosaurs (and other animals and plants) on the continents are testimony to the Flood. Most dinosaur fossil deposits are composed of solid-rock fossils formed during and soon after the Flood. But dinosaur soft tissue has been discovered (and discoveries continue to be made) that is described as "still squishy" and containing recognizable blood cells. Science continues to demonstrate that dinosaurs did not predate humans and that dinosaur kinds did not go extinct (*if* they all have) until after the Flood. Indeed, a mummified (*not* fossilized) hadrosaur (dubbed "Leonardo") was studied in a Discovery Channel special in September 2008. The whole body was still intact, making it "unquestionably one of the most unexpected and important dinosaur discoveries of all time."[6]

## Post-Flood Dinosaurs

After the Flood some 4,300 years ago, dinosaurs migrated throughout Europe, China, and the rest of the post-Flood world. Certainly after the Flood, when the Ark rested on Mount Ararat, there was a period of dramatic radiation of all animals—including the dinosaurs.

Despite evolutionary stories of dinosaurs living and dying countless millions of years ago, the evidence of archaeology, history, and geology all point to the accuracy of the Bible's depiction of the unique creation of dinosaurs at the same time as man just 6,000 years ago.

**Notes**

1. Alters, B. J. and S. M. Alters. 2001. *Defending Evolution in the Classroom: A Guide to the Creation/Evolution Controversy*. Sudbury, MA: Jones and Bartlett Publishers, Inc., 119.

2. Balter, M. 2011. Pint-Sized Predator Rattles the Dinosaur Family Tree. *Science*. 331 (6014): 134.

3. Plant-eating dinosaur discovered in Antarctica. Posted on phys.org December 19, 2011.

4. Dinosaurs and Dragons, Oh My! Stanford Fossil Historian Links Dinosaur Bones to Mythological Creatures. Stanford University Humanities press release, October 2008.

5. Flavius Philostratus (c170-c247 AD). 1912. *The Life of Apollonius of Tyana*, volume I, book III. F. C. Conybeare, trans. New York: Macmillan Co., 243-247.

6. Unveil the "Holy Grail" of Paleontology in Secrets of the Dinosaur Mummy. Discovery Channel. Posted on discovery.com.

# 46

# DID FEATHERED DINOSAURS EXIST?

Brian Thomas, Ph.D.

**Summary:** Some evolutionists believe that birds evolved from a theropod dinosaur. "Feathered dinosaurs" are artistically displayed in literature and media, but a true feathered dinosaur has yet to be discovered.

In the 1990s, filaments on dinosaur fossils were labeled "proto-feathers" and assumed to be evolutionary precursors to feathers. But birds and dinosaurs are separate kinds of creatures with distinct anatomies. And researchers disagree over which purported feathered dinosaurs were actual dinosaurs or had genuine feathers.

The dinosaur filaments resemble fragments of decayed skin rather than intricate feather structures, dinosaur skin did not have the follicles needed for feathers, bird and dinosaur fossils are found together, and any transition between a bird and a dinosaur would have rendered the resulting creature unable to either fly or walk.

Rather than showing proof of dino-to-bird evolution, the fossils in question fit well with the Genesis concept of created kinds.

The concept of "feathered dinosaurs" prevails in scientific literature and popular media. Textbooks and museums that have dinosaur displays include artistic renderings of dinosaurs sporting colorful feathers. For example, the Rocky Mountain Dinosaur Resource Center in Colorado Springs has a placard that states, "Fossil feather impressions are far more rare, but have been found at several localities in Asia. These wonderful fossils prove that some dinosaurs, particularly the small theropods, had an integument [skin] closer to a bird."

But a closer look at these fossils shows that they offer no such proof. Instead, they fit well with the Genesis concept of created kinds.

Those anxious to support evolution believe that an as-yet-unidentified theropod dinosaur evolved into the first bird, which then evolved into all other bird kinds.[1] After all, if dinosaurs evolved into birds, they must have developed feathers at some point. Unfortunately for this story, no fossil so far found meets the defining standards.

What makes a dinosaur? All dinosaurs have an open acetabulum—the hole in the hip into which the femur bone fits. In contrast, modern birds, reptiles, and mammals have a cup-shaped acetabulum or a partially closed one. What makes a bird? Well, classically it was feathers. Logically, we should demand a fossil creature with feathers and an open acetabulum before we agree to feathered dinosaurs. We still await such a discovery.

Evolutionary researchers disagree over which purported "feathered dinosaurs" were actual dinosaurs or had genuine feathers. Some such fossils show bird, not dinosaur, anatomies. Other scientists object to their colleagues' claims by pointing out a mismatch between fossil fibers and actual feather structure.

Overall, we find more reasons to doubt the feathered dinosaur idea than there are reasons to affirm it. Just like the well-illustrated but totally faked "feathered dinosaur" *Archaeoraptor* that adorned the November 1999 issue of *National Geographic*,[2] the entire feathered dinosaur enterprise may soon be viewed as one of paleontology's big mistakes. Chinese workers built that "fossil" using bone bits and artists' tools. Do modern paleontologists build the "feathered dinosaur" concept using rhetorical tools in place of fossil evidence?

The idea of feathered dinosaurs became popular after researchers found uniquely well-preserved dinosaur remains in fossil assemblages in China. Published descriptions of dark filaments associated with dinosaur remains began in the 1990s. Evolutionary proselytizers soon attributed the mysterious filaments to not-yet-evolved feathers they called *protofeathers*. But the veneer of feathered-dinosaur factuality presented in textbooks and museums hides hotly debated arguments in the scientific literature over the identity of these filaments.

Thus, the author of the *Archaeoraptor* article in *National Geographic* reached far beyond the scientific reality when he wrote, "We can now say that birds are theropods just as confidently as we say that humans are mammals."[2] But as argued below from anatomy, we can now say that the only way to affirm birds as theropods is to change the definition of "theropod" or "dinosaur" to include birds.

Since 1999, evidence has accumulated to show that scientists may have pinned the name protofeather to fossil fibers merely because of a desperate need to backfill fossil expectations for bird evolution. But this evolutionary idea relies far more on fiction than on fossils. One authoritative book on the subject, *The Feathered Dinosaurs: The Origin of Birds*, contains artists' illustrations of how certain feathered dinosaurs may have looked, but no images of any real fossils.[3]

Similarly, in 2011 ICR zoologist Frank Sherwin, a contributing author of this book, and I scrutinized the displays at the temporary "Chinasaurs" exhibit at the Museum of Nature and Science in Dallas, looking for real fossil evidence of feathers.[4] We saw feathers on birds and fibers on dinosaurs.

As an example, consider a dinosaur fossil discovered in China named *Yutyrannus huali*. The name means "beautiful feathered tyrant," even though it was most likely not covered with beautiful feathers. It made headlines as the largest of the now-famous Chinese "feathered dinosaurs." The authors describing it titled their article "A gigantic feathered dinosaur from the Lower Cretaceous of China." But the detailed description below the title does not support that claim, since it admits that the fibers are merely "filamentous integumentary [skin] structures."[5] It also ignores any alternate explanation for them.

Real bird feathers are complicated, with semi-hollow cores and branching barbs. The fossil's filaments did not have these features. If the word "feather" just means "filament," then could any filament—like a hair or plant fiber—not also be called a "feather"?

Answering this correctly is important. Why would God have placed feathers on dinosaurs when, today at least, only birds have feathers? God could have done so, but we should feel no obligation to believe that He did without anatomical evidence for feathered dinosaur. Meanwhile, "the idea of protofeathers has strengthened

George Sternberg discovered a duck-billed dinosaur mummy in 1908 in Montana's Hell Creek Formation. In 1912 Henry Osborn photographed and described its skin, which clearly shows scales, or thickened bumps of skin, just like that which appears on many living reptiles.

the resolve of many palaeontologists that birds are direct descendents [*sic*] of theropod dinosaurs."[6] Their resolve did not waver even after these same kinds of simple fiber "feathers" were discovered on non-theropod dinosaurs, too.

Facsimile fossil of *Caudipteryx* at the "Chinasaurs" museum exhibit. Dark smudges along its spine were not very feather-like. Credit: Brian Thomas

Other observations fail to fit the dinosaur feather hypothesis. First, neither dinosaur skin impressions nor original dinosaur skin have large follicles like those that produce feathers in bird skin.[7] Second, actual bird fossils are found mixed among dinosaur remains. Museums do not show birds and dinosaurs side by side as they should since the technical scientific literature lists fossils from ducks, loons, albatross, parrot, and other water birds, as well as extinct bird kinds that had clawed wings. How could dinosaurs be evolving pre-feathers if real feathers were already on the scene? Those who insist that dinosaurs evolved into birds have to willfully ignore the fossil bird bones and footprints found in rock layers containing some of the "earliest" dinosaurs—the supposed ancestors of birds![8,9] Feathered dinosaurs just don't fit the fossil evidence.

None of the supposed "feathered dinosaur" fossils have actual feathers except fossil birds that researchers conveniently call dinosaurs. Instead, the dark "protofeathers" along the spine of such dinosaurs are probably just partly decayed skin, just like the dark smudges inside its body cavity are partly decayed or carbonized tissues. Credit: Sam / Olai Ose / Skjaervoy from Zhangjiagang, China

So, what were these fibers? They look like fossilized fragments of partly decayed skin. Studies on modern carcasses show that soluble fleshy parts slough off first. The thickly woven collagen fibers are not water soluble and last longer. Apparently, the mud or wet sand encompassing the carcass quickly turned to dry rock, discouraged collagen-eating microbes, and preserved some Chinese dinosaur carcasses at that stage of decomposition.

A 2005 report showed an excellent match between partially decayed skin from a variety of animal carcasses and "feathered dinosaur" fibers.[10] The authors even contended that calling dinosaur fibers "feathers" was "misleading" people into believing that theropods evolved into birds. It turns out that protofeathers are just protein fibers that once supported dinosaur skin.

These study authors also admitted that theropods have "exactly the wrong anatomy for flight." A bird's center of gravity is balanced between its wings in the front of its body, and a dinosaur's center of gravity was balanced over its thighs near the back of its body.[10] The authors instead choose to believe that some unknown reptile other than a theropod dinosaur evolved into birds.

Even if science will someday discover genuine feathers on a dinosaur fossil, we can be confident that dinosaurs never evolved into birds because of their either-or anatomies. Transmutating a dinosaur skeleton into a bird skeleton would have rendered the transitional creatures unfit, being unable to either fly or walk properly. Bird breathing depends on a rigid connection between their hip and thigh bones. This structure supports air sacs that connect to their one-way, flow-through lungs. As a result, birds run by bending their legs at the knees.

In contrast, theropod and other dinosaurs walked or ran by bending their legs mostly at the hip joint, the same as modern reptiles and mammals. One study demonstrated that if a bird's legs or ribs were removed or significantly altered as evolution would have required, the poor resulting creature would suffocate.[11] Basic bird anatomy makes bird evolution from any reptile impossible. This all-or-nothing anatomy explains why each proposed transitional form lacks consensus on its supposedly transitional status.

*Confuciusornis*, a fossil bird from China. It had fully formed feathers and came from rock layers below some "feathered dinosaur" fossils. Image credit: Brian Thomas

The famous bird fossil from Germany named *Archaeopteryx* still holds status as an icon of evolution. It supposedly has a mixture of bird and reptile parts. Unlike dinosaurs, *Archaeopteryx* had a large braincase for the increased motor control and sensory input that were required for flight. It had a robust furcula (wishbone) like other birds and unlike theropod forelimbs. Even claw measurements of *Archaeopteryx* fall within the range of true perching birds. Of course, it had flight feathers. It was a bird without a single transitional feature.

But don't take my word for it. Bird fossil expert and evolutionist Alan Feduccia, in the process of refuting the feathered dinosaur status of another fossil called *Anchiornis,* had this to say about *Archaeopteryx*: "*Anchiornis,* considered to have been a troodontid dinosaur, is best interpreted as an archaeopterygid bird, as originally thought, closely allied with the urvogel [first bird] *Archaeopteryx.*"[12] It was just a bird.

Scientists scanned the iconic *Archaeopteryx* bird fossil to find signs of original feather and bone proteins. It had the same chemistry that comprises today's feathers.[13] Proteins don't last a million years, yet this fossil is supposedly 150 million years old. This apparently recent fossilization leaves no time for bird evolution.

A separate study found that the supposed "feather" filaments in another Chinese dinosaur comprised original biochemicals.[14] After a million or so years, these would have spontaneously degraded to dust. So, instead of protofeathers that show bird evolution, these dino-filaments look more like original protein fibers that show recent creation!

Consider the last line of this concluding statement from a study of mites trapped in Cretaceous amber with branching feathers:

> In summary, the new findings provide the earliest known evidence about the origin of ectoparasitic insects feeding on feathers, which strongly support that the integument-feeding behaviors of insects appeared during or before the mid-Cretaceous along with the radiations of feathered dinosaurs including birds.[15]

Clearly, these researchers regard "birds" as "feathered dinosaurs." How convenient for evolution. By calling birds dinosaurs, they insulate themselves from the burden of waiting to discover an actual dinosaur (open acetabulum) with actual feathers (not filaments).

A feathered dinosaur may someday be discovered. Even then, feathers on a dinosaur would not solve evolution's biophysical impasse of converting a reptile skeleton into that of a bird. Overall, fossils show that dinosaurs and birds have always been separate creatures.[16] And this is exactly what one would expect if dinosaurs and birds were created separately, each to reproduce "after their kind," as Genesis 1 describes.

**Notes**

1. Theropod dinosaurs had three toes, had lizard-like hip bone structure, and include *T. rex*.

2. Sloan, C. P. 1999. Feathers for *T. rex*? New birdlike fossils are missing links in dinosaur evolution. *National Geographic*. 196: 98-107; Spotts, P. Dressed to kill: A feathered tyrannosaur is discovered in China. *Christian Science Monitor*. Posted on csmonitor.com April 4, 2012

3. Long, J., and P. Schouten. 2008. *The Feathered Dinosaurs: The Origin of Birds*. New York: Oxford University Press.

4. Thomas, B. Feathers Missing from 'Feathered Dinosaur' Display. *Creation Science Update*. Posted on icr.org August 25, 2011.

5. Xu, X. et al. 2012. A gigantic feathered dinosaur from the Lower Cretaceous of China. *Nature*. 484 (7392): 92-95.

6. Lingham-Soliar, T., A. Feduccia and X. Wang. 2007. A new Chinese specimen indicates that 'protofeathers' in the Early Cretaceous theropod dinosaur Sinosauropteryx are degraded collagen fibres. *Proceedings of the Royal Society B*. 274 (1620): 1823-1829.

7. Thomas, B. Mummified Dinosaur Skin Looks Young. *Creation Science Update*. Posted on icr.org July 30, 2009.

8. Melchor, R. N., S. de Valais, and J. F Genise. 2002. Bird-like fossil footprints from the Late Triassic. *Nature*. 417 (6892): 936.

9. Chatterjee, S. 2015. *The Rise of Birds: 225 Million Years of Evolution, 2nd ed*. Baltimore, MD: Johns Hopkins University Press.

10. Feduccia, A., T. Lingham-Soliar, and J. R. Hinchliffe. 2005. Do Feathered Dinosaurs Exist? Testing the Hypothesis on Neontological and Paleontological Evidence. *Journal of Morphology*. 266: 134.

11. Quick, D. E. and J. A. Ruben. 2009. Cardio-pulmonary anatomy in theropod dinosaurs: Implications from extant archosaurs. *Journal of Morphology*. 270 (10): 1232-1246.

12. Feduccia, A. 2018. Cretaceous Reverie: Review of Birds of Stone: Chinese Avian Fossils from the Age of Dinosaurs by Luis M. Chiappe and Meng Qingjin. *The Open Ornithology Journal*. 11 (1): 27-33.

13. Bergmann, U. et al. 2010. *Archaeopteryx* feathers and bone chemistry fully revealed via synchrotron imaging. *Proceedings of the National Academy of Sciences*. 107 (20): 9060-9065.

14. Zhang, F. et al. 2010. Fossilized melanosomes and the colour of Cretaceous dinosaurs and birds. *Nature*. 463 (7284): 1075-1078; Lingham-Soliar, T. 2011. The evolution of the feather: Sinosauropteryx, a colorful tail. *Journal of Ornithology*. 152 (3): 567-577.

15. Gao, T. et al. 2019. New insects feeding on dinosaur feathers in mid-Cretaceous amber. *Nature Communications*. 10: 5424.

16. Oard, M. 2012. Did Birds Evolve from Dinosaurs? In *Dinosaur Challenges and Mysteries*. Atlanta, GA: Creation Book Publishers, 144-155.

# 47

# DINOSAURS AND DRAGON LEGENDS

Brian Thomas, Ph.D.

**Summary:** How do dinosaurs fit with the biblical narrative? Dinosaurs caught in the global Flood drowned or were quickly buried in conditions that were just right for their remains to fossilize. Genesis indicates that two of each kind of dinosaur—along with the other land-dwelling, air-breathing creatures—were saved on the Ark. So, what happened to them afterward?

After the Flood, dinosaurs migrated far and wide. This migration happened only thousands of years ago. Ancient peoples recorded numerous encounters with dragon-like creatures in Europe, the Americas, Africa, and Asia. The various descriptions of these beasts match features found in dinosaur fossils. Dinosaur numbers dwindled as they lost their habitats through human interaction and natural climate change, eventually presumably dying out altogether.

Both dinosaur fossils and dragon encounters support the Bible's historical narrative.

Christians are often curious about how dinosaurs fit into the biblical narrative. Dinosaurs certainly existed. Their fossil remains are found on every continent, and ancient historical records, including the Bible, chronicle human encounters with large reptiles whose descriptions sometimes match dinosaurs. Dinosaurs that lived up to the time of the Flood were drowned in the Flood (except those on board the Ark), as were all land-dwelling creatures with nostrils, according to Genesis 7:22. Some of those outside the Ark were buried in fast-moving mud that quickly dried, turning their remains into fossils faster than their carcasses could decay. Most, if not all, dinosaur fossil layers also have fossil water creatures like fish and clams, and this is consistent with the Flood explanation.

Although there are hundreds of named dinosaur species, all of them belong to only about 60 different basic dinosaur kinds. That means that Noah and his family only had to manage perhaps 120 individual dinosaurs on the Ark. Could they have fit on board a vessel with the dimensions given in Genesis 6? No matter how large some dinosaurs grew, the largest dinosaur egg was not much bigger than a football. Even the *Argentinosaurus*, which could grow into a 120-foot-long monster, could have fit on the Ark if it was represented by much-smaller young ones. In addition, many dinosaurs were small even when fully grown. For example, the *Sinosauropteryx*, which is of the same kind as *Compsognathus* (except the former was found in China and the latter in Europe), was about the size of a turkey. The average size of a dinosaur was about that of an American bison. One hundred-twenty bison would require just a corner of one of the Ark's three decks.

We can infer from the reliable Genesis record that the descendants of the dinosaurs on the Ark traveled from the Middle East to places around the globe. This really only makes sense, however, when considering that the post-Flood climate was very different from today's. During the Ice Age, the Middle East was tropical and consistently watered. This would have set up suitable conditions for dinosaurs to multiply and fill many Earth environments. There are various clues, such as dinosaur fossils buried alongside tropical plant fossils, that indicate dinosaurs lived in wetlands. If they preferred wetlands before the Flood, then they probably preferred them after the Flood, too.

This dinosaur migration happened only thousands of years ago. Irish archbishop James Ussher in the 17th century calculated a date for the Flood at 2348 BC. Newer chronology research has refined that date estimate to between 2518 and 2532 BC.[1] How long did dinosaurs and other now-extinct land animals live after that, and why do they not still live?

After the Flood, creatures including dinosaurs dispersed across Earth's surface. The first few generations of post-Flood people, however, were determined to rebel against God's command to fill the earth. Instead, they built a tower in Babel and remained in its growing city. In response, God supernaturally compelled them to disperse across Earth by confounding their languages. When families eventually migrated to far-flung places, they may have encountered dinosaurs that had already been there for a few hundred years. Those encounters have been memorialized in writings, depictions, and legends from people groups across the globe.

As humans filled the post-Flood Earth, dinosaur numbers would have dwindled as they lost their preferred habitats. Today's wetland creatures find fewer places to call home. Loss of these habitats happens by human interactions and natural climate changes. The changing climate at the close of the Ice Age may have ultimately rendered the Middle East and other areas inhospitable to these creatures, eventually leading to their extinction. Even so, dinosaurs must have been living at least within the last hundreds of years, judging by the tales and artwork of humans who saw them.

The sheer number of names given to dragons, or dinosaurs, worldwide builds a strong argument that dragon legends hearken back to encounters with real creatures. Most languages, either in written or oral tradition, have their own unique words for dragon. By "dragon," we do not refer to popular images of a bulky, fire-breathing reptile that somehow flies with tiny wings. Rather, ancient Europeans used "dragon" to mean any large reptile. Other languages still use words like those shown in this table. The online encyclopedia Wikipedia lists many more dragon names.[2]

| Name | Description | Location or Language |
|------|-------------|---------------------|
| Aziwugum | Giant reptile | Innuit |
| Bax'an | Terrible water monster | Dakota Sioux |
| Behemoth | Giant swamp reptile | Hebrew (Job) |
| Drakon | Dragon | Greece |
| Grendel | Swamp monster | Denmark |
| Knucker | Swamp dragon | Wales |
| Long | Dragon | China |
| P'ih mw | Giant reptile | Egyptian hieroglyphs |
| Ro-qua-ho | Giant reptile | Iroquois |
| Smok | Dragon | Poland |
| Uk'tena | Horned water monster | Cherokee[2] |
| Worm (voorm) | Dragon | Germany |

Ancient historians described dragons as real, living creatures, right alongside their descriptions of other creatures more familiar to today's readers. For example, in his book *Natural History* written in approximately 78 AD, Pliny the Elder wrote that "it is India which produces the largest [elephants] as well as the dragon...and is itself of such enormous size as to envelop the elephants with its folds."[4]

During that same era, Flavius Philostratus wrote:

The whole of India is girt with dragons of enormous size; for not only the marshes are full of them, but the mountains as well, and there is not a single ridge without one. Now the marsh kind are sluggish in their habits and are thirty cubits long, and they have no crest standing up on their heads.[5]

History is littered with such accounts. Alexander the Great wrote of a dragon that his army encountered during his short time on Earth. The famous explorer Marco Polo described a dragon in his logbooks. Bill Cooper's book *After the Flood* describes many similar accounts from Europe. Cooper relayed a report written in 1484 by England's first printer, William Caxton, of a singular creature:

About the marches [marshes] of Italy, within a meadow, was sometime a serpent of wonderful and right marvelous greatness, right hideous and fearful. For first he had a head greater than the head of a calf. Secondly, he had a neck greater than the length of an ass, and his body made after the likeness of a dog. And his tail was wonderfully great, thick and long, without comparison to any other.[6]

The creature thus described matches Job's behemoth, which had a "tail like a cedar," lived in a marsh where it ate reeds, and as "the first of the ways of God" was obviously very large.[6]

People groups that did not maintain written records nevertheless retain oral traditions of dragon encounters. They describe the dragon's habitat and habits, and provide specific names for the dragons and the long-dead heroes who vanquished them. Towns, hillsides, and ponds across Europe still have their old dragon names—such as Drachenfels Castle and the town of Worms in Germany, Grindelwald in Switzerland, Dragon-hoard (near Garsington) in England, and many others.

But even more evidence shows that early peoples encountered dinosaurs. Dinosaur and other extinct reptile depictions occur in carvings, sculptures, bas reliefs, paintings, mosaics, tapestries, sculptures, pictographs, and petroglyphs from all over the world. Some of the telling features that help identify these images as dinosaurian are horns, spiky skin flaps along the spine called dermal frills, forked tongues, long tails, long necks, large teeth, and, perhaps most importantly, legs that went straight down from the body. Those walking reptiles with which we are most familiar today have legs that aim away from the sides of the body, then angle down to the ground at the elbows or knees. Dinosaur reptiles' legs were situated beneath their bodies (like a dog's are), just as shown in many ancient works of art.

For example, a medieval wood carving at Saint Davids Cathedral in Wales shows an overall body structure very similar to the sauropod known from fossils as *Nigersaurus taqueti*, found in Cretaceous system rock layers in Africa. The artwork even shows its wide mouth and relatively short neck. How did our distant ancestors know about these features so long before paleontologists uncovered them from beneath the earth?

Similarly, a cylinder seal long ago excavated from the ancient Mesopotamian civilization at Uruk shows a creature that secular archaeologists call a serpopard. The term refers to an imaginary mixture of serpent and leopard attributes. Possibly this depiction came purely from an ancient artist's imagination, but what historical evidence supports this contention? Arguments in favor of an overall anatomical resemblance to sauropods include legs positioned beneath the body, long necks and tails, and accurately carved bird to show a non-fantastical context. St. David's dragon and the Uruk cylinder seal supply just two examples of dinosaur look-alikes in ancient art. They suggest that our ancestors may have seen first or second-hand the animals they carved so long ago. The Dragon Encounters exhibit at the ICR Discovery Center for Science & Earth History in Dallas, Texas, displays even more.

Jasper cylinder seal and impression. Public domain.

Evolutionists object that dinosaur-looking artifacts are fakes. However, this objection does not stem from rigorous analysis of the data. Instead, it stems from an argument that goes like this: "This ancient man-made artifact looks like a dinosaur. But dinosaurs died millions of years before humanity evolved, making it impossible for ancient humans to know what dinosaurs looked like. Therefore, this artifact is a fraud." This kind of argument takes as true the very evolutionary history that the artifacts challenge. Ignoring evidence leads to wrong conclusions.

Medieval wood carving at Saint Davids Cathedral in Wales. Image credit: Brian Thomas

Dozens of dragon descriptions and the similarities between those descriptions across geographic space and historical time best fit genuine giant reptile encounters. The late popular cosmologist Carl Sagan considered the historical evidence for dragons such a serious threat to the evolutionary paradigm that he tackled the subject in his 1977 book *The Dragons of Eden*. In it, he speculated that unknown human ancestor primates may have encountered dinosaurs millions of years ago. The memories of those interactions were so traumatic that they were indelibly stamped onto the primate genes so that ancient humans inherited and drew their dinosaur pictures based on those memories. Because there is no scientific evidence that memories can be inherited, many scientists shunned Sagan's unscientific speculation. But to assert that myriad dragon legends are all fraudulent without even investigating their historical evidence is equally unscientific.

If the Bible is correct that representatives of all land-dwelling, air-breathing creatures were on the Ark, and if it is correct in describing an Ice Age dinosaur in the book of Job, then it makes sense to infer that people encountered (and rid themselves of) the threatening and fearsome reptiles during the centuries after the Flood. Perhaps every ancient culture wrote about, spoke of, painted, tiled, or carved us dragon legends.

*Notes*

1. Thomas, B. 2017. Two date range options for Noah's Flood. *Journal of Creation*. 31 (1): 120-127.

2. List of dragons in mythology and folklore. Wikipedia. Accessed June 2020.

3. Thomas, B. 2010. Oblivious to the obvious: dragons lived with American Indians. A review of *Fossil Legends of the First Americans* by Adrienne Mayor. *Journal of Creation*. 24 (1): 32-34.

4. Bostock, J. and H. T. Riley, trans. 1855. *Pliny's Natural History*. London: Bohn.

5. Flavius Philostratus (c170-c247 AD). 1912. *The Life of Apollonius of Tyana*, volume I, book III. F. C. Conybeare, trans. New York: Macmillan Co., 243-247.

6. Caxton, W. M. 1484. *Aesop*. Folio 138. Cited in Cooper, W. 1995. *After the Flood*. Chichester, UK: New Wine Press.

7. Job 40:15-24.

# ASTRONOMY

## CREATED COSMOS OR
## THE BIG BANG?

# 48

# BURSTING THE BIG BANG BUBBLE

Jake Hebert, Ph.D.

**Summary:** The Big Bang is the most popular model of the origin of the universe, but it has serious problems. The model claims the universe started out 14 billion years ago as a very hot, dense state that expanded. The universe could possibly be expanding today, but this isn't proof of a Big Bang.

Some point to "afterglow" radiation prevalent in the universe as evidence of the Big Bang, but it's too uniform to have been caused by chance. Cosmologists have speculated that there was a rapid expansion of the universe called inflation that explains the uniformity, but the evidence for inflation is wholly lacking. Multiple other problems plague this origins explanation.

Despite assorted and even weird attempts to prop it up, the Big Bang remains seriously flawed. Christians have no need to accept the Big Bang. The universe appears fine-tuned and designed because it was created that way.

The Big Bang is the most popular cosmological model. It holds that the universe was in a very hot, very dense state about 14 billion years ago but then began expanding for some reason.[1] Some Christians argue that the Big Bang was God's means of creating the universe. However, the model has serious theological and scientific problems.

## Big Bang Arguments

Three main arguments are given for the Big Bang. The first is the apparent expansion of the universe. Light from a distant galaxy forms a continuous, rainbow-like spectrum. However, within this continuous spectrum are discrete dark bands. These dark bands represent wavelengths of light that have been "subtracted" from the galaxy's light before that light reaches us.

However, astronomers can observe that these dark bands have been "shifted" toward the red part of the spectrum, relative to where they would be on the spectrum if they had been emitted from a stationary light source. For this reason, scientists usually interpret redshifted light from distant galaxies to mean that distant galaxies are receding away from us. In fact, the thinking is that the galaxies are not moving through space but that space *itself* is expanding, and that the galaxies are "carried along" with the expanding space.

The second main argument is that the Big Bang does a good job of accounting for the observed abundances of hydrogen and helium, the two most abundant chemical elements in the universe. The third is that the Big Bang model predicts that a faint but uniform "afterglow" of long-wavelength radiation will come to us from all directions in space. We do observe this so-called *cosmic microwave background radiation* (CMB). The afterglow is characterized by a very uniform temperature of 2.73 Kelvins.[2]

### Weaknesses in the Arguments

These arguments are not as strong as many believe. First, light can be redshifted for reasons other than an expanding universe, i.e., a gravitational redshift. Some scientists, both secular and creationist, are starting to question whether an expanding universe is even the correct interpretation of galaxy redshifts and have proposed possible alternate mechanism for the redshifts.[3,4]

Even if the universe is expanding, though, a Big Bang does not necessarily follow. One can imagine reasons God might perhaps impose an expansion on a created-but-full-size universe, perhaps to prevent gravity from collapsing the universe in on itself.

It is true that the Big Bang does a good job of accounting for the abundances of hydrogen and helium,[5] but this is because Big Bang theorists are allowed to choose a value for a number or parameter in order to ensure that the model gives the right answer![6-8] Even with this freedom, the Big Bang still cannot adequately account for the abundances of other light elements, such as lithium.[9]

The existence of the cosmic microwave background radiation is arguably the strongest argument for the Big Bang, since the existence of a CMB is predicted by the model. However, there are features in this CMB radiation, discussed a little later, that do *not* fit Big Bang expectations.

## Arbitrary Assumptions

The Big Bang model assumes, without proof, that the universe is roughly homogenous. In other words, it assumes that, on the "big picture" scale, matter and energy are more or less uniform throughout the universe. It also assumes that the universe will appear pretty much the same regardless of which direction in the sky we look. Together, these two assumptions make up what is called the *cosmological principle*.

These two assumptions are foundational to the Big Bang. Theorists made these assumptions very early on in the development of the theory. Yet, there is increasing evidence that these assumptions are wrong.[10-13] This is no small thing. If the cosmological principle turns out to be wrong, theorists would have to go back and start over from scratch!

## The CMB and Inflation

Remember that the Big Bang assumes that the universe should look pretty much the same whichever direction in space you look. This also applies to the CMB; it too should look the same in all directions in space. The temperature that describes the CMB spectrum should be nearly the same in every direction. Very small temperature differences over small parts of the sky (less than one degree in angle[14]) are allowed by the Big Bang, but not temperature differences that cover larger portions of the sky.

However, Big Bang theorists realized this presented a problem. It seemed unlikely that a very uniform CMB could happen by chance, so theorists argued that radiation from one part of the sky must have traveled to and "warmed up" another part of the sky, much in the same way that radiant energy from a hot stove can warm up a room on a cold day. However, this radiant energy travels at the very fast (but still finite) speed of light, and even 14 billion years is not enough time for this transfer of energy to make the CMB uniform. In other words, the Big Bang has its own version of a light-travel time problem![15]

In order to solve this and other problems, Big Bang theorists claimed that space itself expanded faster than light very early in the universe's history. This supposedly enabled the light to travel from one part of the sky to another in less than 14 billion years.[16] This alleged cosmic growth spurt is called *inflation*, and it is totally ad hoc. There is *zero* experimental evidence for inflation or for its alleged cause.[17,18] It was simply invented in order to "rescue" the Big Bang.

Moreover, features in the CMB do not agree with inflation. Remember, Big Bang theorists invoked inflation to explain how the CMB could be so uniform. Remember also that the Big Bang allows tiny temperature differences in the CMB, provided these temperature differences never occupy a part of the sky that is more than one degree across. However, sensitive satellite measurements have revealed tiny large-scale (*larger* than one degree across) temperature variations.[19] According to both the cosmological principle and inflation, these differences are not supposed to exist.[20,21]

So, even though the CMB is arguably the strongest argument for the Big Bang, even here there are things about the CMB that do not "fit" the Big Bang!

## Big Bang Weirdness

Modern cosmology is full of weird ideas like dark energy, exotic dark matter, inflation, and a so-called multiverse. Most of them are a direct consequence of the Big Bang. These weird ideas usually come about because Big Bang theorists encounter a problem, one that could be solved by assuming that the universe's properties were "fine-tuned." However, Big Bang theorists are adamantly opposed to fine-tuning because it suggests design, so they are compelled to tack on additional hypotheses to the Big Bang in order to solve these problems. These tacked-on hypotheses solved those problems but created new ones.[22]

Inflation is a good example. The early big Bang model was confronted with several serious problems, two of which could have been solved by invoking design.[23] In order to solve these problems without appealing to design, they invoked inflation, but inflation has since caused even more problems![24]

## Origin of Stars

An enormous problem with the Big Bang is that it cannot explain the origin of stars.[25] Big Bang advocates do have a model for star formation, but it requires other stars to already be in existence. Therefore, it is useless at explaining the ultimate origin of stars. Some Big Bang proponents claim that dark matter can solve the problem, but dark matter is controversial and is not yet even known to exist.

## The Biggest Problem of All?

The Big Bang is beset by multiple other miscellaneous problems.[26,27] One of the most serious of the problems is that these additional hypotheses have led theorists to conclude that 95% of all the "stuff" in the universe is of unknown composition. Supposedly, dark energy and exotic dark matter together comprise 95% of all the universe's energy content, but theorists don't know what these things are. The remaining 5% is thought to be the "normal" atomic matter that makes up our bodies and the things around us.

This means that Big Bang theorists claim to have a convincing, comprehensive, "natural" explanation for the existence and structure of our universe, even though, by their own admission, they know almost *nothing* about the universe's composition. This is akin to claiming to understand the recipe for a cake, even though you can't identify the cake's ingredients. In this light, the claims of Big Bang proponents are simply laughable.

## Conclusion

Contrary to popular perception, the Big Bang model is in serious disarray. Moreover, there are blatant contradictions between the model and the inspired creation account in Genesis that cannot be dismissed by Christians who take the Bible seriously.[28]

No one should be intimidated into accepting the Big Bang model, especially Christians.

### Notes

1. Big Bang theorists used to think that the universe started out as a tiny point, or singularity, with infinite density. Although they still think the primordial universe was in a very hot, very dense state, they no longer think the universe started out as a singularity.

2. In scientific jargon, the CMB's spectrum corresponds to that of an ideal black body with a temperature of 2.73 Kelvins.

3. Hartnett, J. 2011. Does observational evidence indicate the universe is expanding? – part 2: the case against expansion. *Journal of Creation*. 25 (3): 115-120.

4. Lerner, E. 2006. Evidence for a Non-Expanding Universe: Surface Brightness Data from HUDF. *AIP Conference Proceedings* 822.

5. This so-called baryon-to-photon ratio indicates the number of "heavy" subatomic particles (baryons) in the universe compared to the number of discrete units of light energy (photons). The Big Bang model produces the correct amounts of hydrogen and helium, provided that one assumes that there are roughly two billion photons for every baryon in the universe.

6. Bergstrom, L. and A. Goobar. 2008. *Cosmology and Particle Astrophysics*, 2nd ed. Chichester, UK: Springer Praxis Publishing, 167-176.

7. Krauss, L. M. 2012. *A Universe from Nothing: Why There is Something Rather Than Nothing*. New York: Free Press, 24-25.

8. Hoyle, F., G. Burbidge, and J. V. Narlikar. 2000. *A Different Approach to Cosmology: From a Static Universe through the Big Bang towards Reality*. Cambridge, UK: Cambridge University Press, 97.

9. Thomas, B. Big Bang Fizzles under Lithium Test. *Creation Science Update*. Posted on ICR.org September 22, 2014, accessed January 13, 2020.

10. Hebert, J. Giant Galaxy Ring Shouldn't Exist. *Creation Science Update*. Posted on ICR.org August 24, 2015, accessed January 13, 2020.

11. Hebert, J. A Cosmic 'Supervoid' vs. the Big Bang. *Creation Science Update*. Posted on ICR.org May 7, 2015, accessed January 13, 2020.

12. Wall, M. Largest Structure in Universe Discovered. *Space.com*. Posted on space.com January 11, 2013, accessed January 13, 2020.

13. Klotz, I. Universe's Largest Structure is a Cosmic Conundrum. *Discovery.com*. Posted on discovery.com November 19, 2013, accessed at InternetWayBackMachine January 13, 2020.

14. By comparison, the apparent size of the sun and moon are both about half a degree across.

15. Coppedge, D. 2007. The Light-Distance Problem. *Acts & Facts* 36 (6).

16. This does not necessarily violate Einstein's theory of relativity, which only holds that massive objects cannot reach or exceed the speed of light; space itself could theoretically expand faster than the speed of light.

17. Hebert, J. Big Bang Evidence Retracted. *Creation Science Update*. Posted on ICR.org February 12, 2015, accessed January 13, 2020.

18. Supposedly inflation was caused by an entity called a scalar field, but there is no evidence for this field's existence.

19. Wall, M. Observations of the Early Universe Reaffirm the Existence of Dark Matter and Dark Energy. *Space.com*. Posted July 18, 2018 on space.com, accessed January 28, 2020.

20. Discoveries from Planck may mean rethinking how the universe began. *Phys.org*. Posted on phys.org July 26, 2013, accessed January 13, 2020.

21. The Energy of Empty Space That Isn't Zero: A Talk with Lawrence Krauss. *Edge*. Posted on edge.org July 5, 2006, accessed January 13, 2020.

22. Hebert, J. 2012. Why Is Modern Cosmology So Weird? *Acts & Facts* 41 (8): 11-13.

23. These were the so-called magnetic monopole problem, the horizon problem, and the flatness problem. Theorists could have solved the horizon and flatness problems by assuming that the early universe was "fine-tuned." However, they are very much opposed to fine-tuning since it suggests design. Note, however, biblical creationists should *not* use these particular fine-tuning arguments since they implicitly assume the Big Bang.

24. Hebert, J. Big Bang Blowup at Scientific American. *Creation Science Update*. Posted on ICR.org May 29, 2017, accessed January 13, 2020.

25. Some might quibble that star formation is not part of the Big Bang model per se. This may be technically true, but it is nevertheless a cop-out. The Big Bang purports to be a comprehensive explanation for the origin and structure of our present-day universe, and as such it ought to be able to account for the origin of the trillions of stars that exist.

26. Hebert, J. Big Bang Hubble Contradiction Confirmed. *Creation Science Update*. Posted on ICR.org May 16, 2019, accessed January 13, 2020.

27. Thomas, B. Distant Galaxies Look Too Mature for Big Bang. *Creation Science Update*. Posted on ICR.org November 30, 2011, accessed January 13, 2020.

28. Morris, J. D. 1997. Is the Big Bang Biblical? *Acts & Facts*. 26 (5).

# 49

# THE UNIVERSE: BILLIONS OF YEARS OLD—OR JUST THOUSANDS?

Jake Hebert, Ph.D.

**Summary:** Secular science claims the universe is around 14 billion years old, but the Bible tells us God made everything about 6,000 years ago. Age can't be measured in a laboratory, so how do we determine who's right?

Many aspects of Earth and our solar system show signs of youth. Earth's magnetic field should have decayed down to nothing if billions of years were true. Jupiter, Saturn, Uranus, and Neptune radiate more energy than they receive from the sun, but they're still warm. Comets lose mass as they orbit the sun, so why haven't they all vaporized by now? Blue stars burn too hot to last this long, but they're still found throughout the universe.

There are many other arguments for a young age, but the strongest is that we have the eyewitness testimony of the One who was there in the beginning. He is the Creator Himself, and we should believe Him!

Secular scientists claim our universe is around 14 billion years old and that Earth and the solar system are 4.6 billion years old. These vast age estimates are in obvious conflict with the Bible's relatively short 6,000-year chronology.

However, science has not proven these vast ages. In fact, despite popular perception, science *can't* prove that the universe is old or young, for a very simple reason. Age isn't something that scientists can measure in a laboratory. When secular scientists claim that a rock is millions of years old, this is a calculated age estimate based on assumptions about the past. If the assumptions behind the calculation are wrong, the age estimate will be wrong too.

Lest you think this is an exaggeration, think how hard it would be to know even your own age if your parents had not told you the date of your birth.[1] Some people live hard lives and seem to age quickly, while others look much younger than their true ages.

## Testing Assumptions

Creation and secular scientists have very different starting assumptions. Secular scientists hold to a philosophy called *uniformitarian*, which assumes that "the present is the key to the past." A uniformitarian geologist would argue that because erosion today is slow and gradual, erosion has always been slow and gradual. A creation geologist, on the other hand, would argue that erosion rates were thousands of times faster during the Genesis Flood. Naturally, creationist and secular scientists will get radically different answers if they attempt to use erosion rates to date a geological feature.

So, is there a way that one can show that creation-based assumptions are better than secular assumptions? Yes, there is. If uniformitarianism is correct, then age estimates based on uniformitarian assumptions should not contradict other uniformitarian age estimates or assumptions.

Creationists often, for the sake of argument, assume uniformitarianism and then use those assumptions to obtain a range of possible ages for a physical system like the world's oceans or a planet or moon. The maximum possible ages might be in millions or billions of years, but they still contradict the evolutionary story. But because these are *maximum* possible ages, the true ages could be as young as the 6,000 years implied by Scripture, especially when an event like the Genesis Flood is taken into account.

## Evidence of Youth

Skeptics use two primary arguments for an old earth and universe: (1) the vast ages obtained from radioisotope dating methods, and (2) the presumed impossibility of distant starlight reaching Earth in just 6,000 years. Both of these issues are addressed in chapters 40 and 51.

However, there are dozens of indications of youth here on Earth, throughout our solar system, and in deep space. We will now examine some of these indicators.

## Earth's Magnetic Field

Magnetic fields are caused by currents of moving electrical charge. Both creation and secular scientists think Earth's magnetic field is produced by electrical currents within Earth's core. In the creation model, looping currents within the core were the almost-initial source of this magnetic field.

However, during the Flood, tectonic plates rapidly descended down into the mantle (see chapter 31). When these cooler plates touched the hot liquid outer core, convection began and up-and-down loops of fluid began circulating in the outer core. Furthermore, magnetic fields tend to be "frozen" within conducting fluids.[2] This means that if the fluid moves, the magnetic field lines embedded in the fluid will be "dragged" along. That produces new loops of electrical current going in the opposite direction to the original current loops.

These new current loops in the outer core cause a large, new, reversed magnetic field to be imposed on the original field. The upward parts of the fluid flows eventually push the original field entirely out of the core, and it rapidly dies away. That leaves only the reversed field. The up-and-down flows continue working on the reversed field, and a new reversal cycle begins.

As long as the up-and-down motions of fluid continue to be rapid (as during the Flood), they cause many cycles of rapid reversals of the overall magnetic field.[3,4] The fields decay over time so that Earth's total magnetic field would disappear in tens of thousands of years. Of course, since Earth is only 6,000 years old, this is not a problem for recent creation.[5]

Uniformitarian scientists, on the other hand, have devised a "dynamo" model in an attempt to explain how electrical currents could begin and maintain the Earth's magnetic field over billions of years. This model requires complicated current motions that can occur *only* in the liquid outer core. They have been working on this model for over a century, without success.[6] One secular geophysicist acknowledged in 2014 that he and his colleagues "do not understand" how the Earth could maintain a magnetic field for billions of years.[7]

Since uniformitarians don't have a workable dynamo model, simple, decaying loops of current in the core are the only viable explanation for Earth's magnetic field. Yet, these decaying currents can only maintain the earth's magnetic field for tens of thousands of years. Worse yet, the field's energy is decreasing by half roughly every 1,400 years. Extrapolating this observed decay rate into the past implies that Earth's magnetic field would have been outrageously strong tens of thousands of years ago, requiring electrical currents so large they would have melted the earth's crust and mantle![8] Earth's magnetic field *must* be young.

## Our Young Solar System

There is abundant evidence of youth within our solar system. These include the following.

**Warm Bodies.** If a planet or moon radiates energy to space faster than it is warmed by other sources (the sun, heat from radioactive decay, etc.), that object will cool. This is especially true of smaller objects like moons or small planets. Many objects in our solar system, although still quite cold by our everyday standards, are much warmer than expected if the solar system is billions of years old.

These include our moon, all the Jovian planets (Jupiter, Saturn, Uranus, and Neptune), and Pluto.[9-11] They also include Jupiter's moon Io and Saturn's moon Enceladus.[12] In some cases it might be possible for secular scientists to provide explanations for this unexpected heat, but in other cases, such as Jupiter, no plausible mechanisms have been proposed.[10,12]

**Magnetic Fields.** Cold space bodies should not have magnetic fields, according to the dynamo model. Yet many do! These include Mercury and Jupiter's moon Ganymede.[13,14] And our moon's past magnetic field is even harder for the dynamo model to explain than Earth's magnetic field.[15]

**Disappearing Acts.** Methane in the atmosphere of Saturn's moon Titan is broken down by solar ultraviolet radiation, forming ethane. Over billions of years, this process should have formed an ocean of ethane on Titan. Although lakes of ethane do exist on Titan, the predicted ethane ocean does not exist.[16-17]

Venus' surface looks relatively young, even by secular reckoning.[18] Likewise, comets lose material when ices vaporize as the comets come closer to the sun in their orbits. Gradually these comets disappear. Since comets are supposedly "leftover" remnants from the solar system's formation billions of years ago, comets should no longer be visible—yet they are. Secular scientists claim reservoirs of potential comets (such as the hypothetical Oort Cloud) can replace comets that have been destroyed, but there are many problems with this idea, not the least of which is that there is no observational evidence that the Oort Cloud even exists.[19]

## Our Young Universe

Evidence of youth is also found in deep space. Even by secular reckoning, the hottest and most massive blue stars should consume their nuclear fuel and explode in just a few million years.[20-21] Yet, blue stars still exist. Secular astronomers claim that new stars are born to replace these stars, but this idea has serious problems.[22]

Pinwheel-shaped spiral galaxies slowly rotate, but material closer to the galaxy center rotates faster than material that is farther out. This difference in rotation speeds causes a "winding up" of the galaxy's spirals that should become evident in just hundreds of millions of years and should completely destroy the spiral structure over billions of years. The fact that spiral structure is still evident in spiral galaxies is a strong argument that these galaxies cannot be billions of years old. Secular astronomers have invoked a "spiral density wave" model to get around this difficulty, but it has problems.[23-24]

Globular clusters are snow globe-like collections of stars that orbit ours and other galaxies. There are several aspects of globular clusters that surprised secular astronomers, because these features suggest that globular clusters are much younger than expected.[25-28]

## The Strongest Evidence of All

There are many other arguments for a young earth and universe.[29-31] But again, none of these arguments "prove" the universe is young since all these age estimates are based on assumptions about the past, and without a time machine we cannot prove whether these assumptions are correct or not.

So, what is the strongest argument for a young universe? We can answer that question by again considering your own age and birthday. We could attempt to calculate your age based on certain assumptions, but these would be just guesses that could be inaccurate. The best proof of your true age would be reliable eyewitness testimony, i.e., the testimony of your parents and the doctor(s) attending at your birth.

In the same way, the strongest argument for the true age of Earth comes from reliable eyewitness testimony. Fortunately, a reliable Eyewitness was present at the creation of the universe who *can* tell us how old it is.

This Eyewitness knows everything, never makes mistakes, and never lies. He is the Creator Himself. We should believe Him!

*Notes*

1. Williams, A. 2007. The universe's birth certificate. *Creation* 30 (1): 31.

2. This "freezing" of a magnetic field in a highly conducting medium was discovered by Swedish physicist Hannes Alfvén.

3. Humphreys, D. R. 1986. Reversal of the Earth's Magnetic Field During the Genesis Flood. In *Proceedings of the First International Conference on Creation*. R. E. Walsh, C. L. Brooks, and R. S. Crowell, eds. Pittsburgh, PA: Creation Science Fellowship, 113-123.

4. Humphreys, D. R. 1990. Physical Mechanism for Reversals of the Earth's Magnetic Field During the Flood. In *Proceedings of the Second International Conference on Creation*. R. E. Walsh and C. L. Brooks, eds. Pittsburgh, PA: Creation Science Fellowship, 129-140.

5. Humphreys, D. R. 1983. The Creation of the Earth's Magnetic Field. *Creation Research Society Quarterly.* 20 (2): 89-94.

6. Humphreys, D. R. 2013. Planetary Magnetic Dynamo Theories: A Century of Failure. In *Proceedings of the Seventh International Conference on Creationism*. M. Horstemeyer, ed. Pittsburgh: PA: Creation Science Fellowship.

7. Folger, T. Journeys to the Center of the Earth: Our planet's core powers a magnetic field that shields us from a hostile cosmos. But how does it really work? *Discover*, July/August 2014.

8. Humphreys, D. R. 2008. The Creation of Cosmic Magnetic Fields. In *Proceedings of the Sixth International Conference on Creationism*. A. A Snelling, ed. Pittsburgh: PA: Creation Science Fellowship, 213-230.

9. Hebert, J. Moon is Unexpectedly Still Cooling and Shrinking. *Creation Science Update*. Posted on ICR.org June 6, 2019, accessed January 14, 2020.

10. Samec, R. 2000. The age of the jovian planets. *Journal of Creation*. 14 (1): 3-4.

11. Redd, N. T. Part of Pluto's Heart Was 'Born Yesterday.' *Space.com*. Posted on space.com November 11, 2015, accessed January 14, 2020.

12. Hebert, J. Youthful Solar System Bodies Puzzle Evolutionary Scientists. *Creation Science Update*. Posted on ICR. org February 13, 2013, accessed January 14, 2020.

13. Choi, C. Q. The Enduring Mysteries of Mercury. *LiveScience*. Posted on livescience.com January 14, 2008, accessed January 14, 2020.

14. Williams, M. Jupiter's moon Ganymede. *Phys.org*. Posted on phys.org October 16, 2015, accessed January 14, 2020.

15. Humphreys, D. R. 2012. The moon's magnetic field – still a huge problem for evolutionists. *Journal of Creation*. 26 (1): 5-6.

16. Atreya, S. K. The Mystery of Methane on Mars and Titan. *Scientific American*. Posted on scientificamerican. com January 15, 2009, accessed July 5, 2018.

17. Steigerwald, B. NASA Research Estimates How Long Titan's Chemical Factory Has Been in Business. *NASA*. Posted on nasa.gov April 24, 2012, accessed July 5, 2018.

18. Thomas, B. Most of Venus' History is Missing? *Creation Science Update*. Posted on ICR.org January 31, 2014, accessed July 5, 2018.

19. Spencer, W. 2014. Critique of Modern Oort Comet Theory. *Creation Research Society Quarterly.* 50 (3): 146-153.

20. Chaisson, E. and S. McMillan. 2008. *Astronomy Today*, 6th ed. San Francisco: Pearson-Addison Wesley, 474.

21. Freedman, R. A. and W. J. Kaufmann III. 2002. *Universe: Stars and Galaxies*. New York: W. H. Freeman and Co., 481.

22. Tyson, N. deG. 2007. *Death by Black Hole and Other Cosmic Quandaries*. New York: W. W. Norton & Company, 187.

23. Chaisson and McMillan, *Astronomy Today*, 633-635.

24. Density Wave Model. COSMOS – The SAO Encyclopedia of Astronomy. Swineburne University of Technology. Posted on astronomy.swin.edu.au, accessed January 15, 2020.

25. Nethercott, P. 2016. Neutron Stars in Globular Clusters: Evidence of Young Age? *Creation Research Society Quarterly.* 53 (1): 14-18.

26. Surprising black-hole discovery changes picture of globular star clusters. *Phys.org.* Posted on phys.org October 3, 2012, accessed January 15, 2020.

27. Davis, J. Physicists find black holes in globular star clusters, upsetting 40 years of theory. *Phys.org.* Posted on phys.org November 4, 2013, accessed January 15, 2020.

28. Globular clusters rotate at heart. University of Texas McDonald Observatory press release. Posted on phys.org May 9, 2014, accessed January 15, 2020.

29. Hebert, J. 2019. Five Global Evidences for a Young Earth. *Acts & Facts* 48 (7): 10-13.

30. Hebert, J. 2018. Our Young Solar System. *Acts & Facts* 47 (9): 10-13.

31. Hebert, J. 2019. Deep-Space Objects are Young. *Acts & Facts* 48 (9): 10-13.

# 50

# COULD THE LAWS OF PHYSICS HAVE CREATED THE UNIVERSE?

Jake Hebert, Ph.D.

**Summary:** Some scientists think the laws of physics could have created the universe from nothing. To do so, however, they need to argue around some of the fundamental rules of physics.

One suggestion is that the universe resulted from a quantum fluctuation, but the energy for the fluctuation would have had to already be present. And even if energy could "pop" into existence, there are still serious problems with the quantum fluctuation scenario.

Physicists offer various ways to rescue the scenario, one of which requires the energy of the universe to be exactly zero. But it's beyond the capability of any human being to verify that. Other arguments suffer from serious logical difficulties that their proponents haven't yet solved.

The argument that laws of physics could have created the universe is unreasonable, and we don't have to buy it.

Explaining the origin of the universe is an enormous challenge for those seeking to explain our existence apart from a Creator. How could a universe come from nothing?

The challenge is so great that some have argued that the universe simply did not have a beginning but has somehow existed eternally. However, because most professing atheists have accepted the Big Bang model, they have accepted the premise that our universe did indeed have a beginning.[1] Therefore, they need to explain that beginning. Physicist Lawrence Krauss claimed, along with others, that the laws of physics could have created the universe from nothing.[2]

Before discussing this claim in detail, it is important to note that the law of conservation of energy (COE) is one of the most fundamental rules in physics. This law states that energy is neither created nor destroyed, although it can be transformed from one kind to another. Thus, evolutionists would prefer that their theories for the origin of the universe not violate this basic rule.

Another rule in physics is the Heisenberg uncertainty principle (HUP), one version of which says that a rapidly changing quantum mechanical system cannot have a well-defined energy.[3] Theoretical physicists often interpret this version of the HUP to mean that COE is not truly absolute but may be violated over very short timespans.

Evolutionary physicists claim that our universe could have resulted from a quantum fluctuation, the spontaneous appearance and disappearance of "virtual particles" from a vacuum. Such particles are thought to be responsible for a number of phenomena, including a very subtle effect on the spectrum of the hydrogen atom called the *Lamb shift*. Virtual particles have extremely short lifespans, too short to be directly observed, and—in accordance with the HUP—the greater the energy of the particles, the shorter their lifespans must be.

Although it is frequently said that the HUP allows short-term violations of COE, this claim is not universally accepted. One respected quantum mechanics textbook says that such an understanding of the HUP is simply wrong.[4] Even evolutionary theorists have acknowledged that the energy for quantum fluctuations could be coming from the vacuum itself, in which case COE is not violated since the energy for the fluctuation was already present in the vacuum.[5] A respected creation physicist has made a similar argument.[6]

If the energy for the quantum fluctuation that supposedly created our universe came from the vacuum itself, then it is obvious that this evolutionary scenario does not really involve creation out of nothing since the energy for the fluctuation was already present within the vacuum—their "nothing" was actually a "something." At best, this would involve a transformation of pre-existing energy into other forms. As such, it is essentially a disguised version of the claim that the cosmos is eternal.

However, even granting the claim that energy can genuinely "pop" into existence, there are serious difficulties with the idea that the universe resulted from a quantum fluctuation. This idea is not new; it was suggested by Edward Tryon in 1973.[7] One would expect the energy content of the entire universe to be enormous. Even if one were to argue that the universe did pop into existence via a quantum fluctuation, the energy content of the universe would be so large that the HUP would require the corresponding time to be incredibly small, and the newly born universe would then immediately vanish.[8] How, then, could our universe have resulted from such a fluctuation?

Tryon argued that if the total energy of the universe were zero, it could have resulted from such a fluctuation and yet persist indefinitely without violating the HUP. Others have more recently argued that a quantum fluctuation did not need to persist indefinitely but only long enough to initiate a process that rapidly "blew up" a volume of space that ultimately became our universe.

A component of the Big Bang model called *inflation theory* claims that our universe could have resulted from this process without the need for any additional creation of energy. In such a scenario, the total energy of the universe would be exactly zero. As noted earlier, this is important, since the creation of a universe with zero total energy would not involve a large-scale violation of COE. Evolutionists admit that the initial quantum fluctuation in their models could involve a tiny violation of COE, but they do not see this as a problem since they believe such a violation would be too small to be measured.[9]

Although secular cosmologists now seem to favor the second scenario, either scenario would require the energy of the universe to be exactly zero. This could be the case if the universe's negative gravitational potential energy were exactly balanced by the positive energy of particles within the universe. But is the total energy of the entire universe exactly zero?

Evolutionary theorists assert that it is, but in order to confirm this claim, one would have to account for all the forms of energy in the universe (gravitational potential energy, the energies of all particles, etc.), add them together, and then verify that the sum truly is exactly zero.[10] This is absolutely beyond the capability of any human being.

The claim of a "zero energy" universe is based not on direct measurements but upon an interpretation of the data through the filter of the Big Bang model and inflation theory. But inflation was from the beginning an ad hoc idea that was attached to the original Big Bang model in order to solve a number of serious—and even fatal—difficulties.[11] Proponents are making the claim of a zero-energy universe simply because it is expected in inflation theory.[12,13]

For someone without a prior commitment to inflation theory, it would seem extremely unlikely that the universe's total energy would be exactly zero.

Likewise, when virtual particles momentarily appear within a vacuum, they are appearing in a space that already exists. Because space is part of our universe, the spontaneous creation of a universe requires space itself to somehow pop into existence.

Proponents have acknowledged this difficulty but speculate that quantum gravity (a theory that merges quantum mechanics and general relativity) could allow for this.[14] An obvious problem with this argument is that a workable theory of quantum gravity does not yet exist!

Moreover, their argument suffers from serious logical difficulties. Our understanding of the laws of physics is based on observations from thousands of experiments. No one has ever observed a universe "popping" into existence. This means that any such laws of physics that would allow, even in principle, a universe to pop into existence are completely outside our experience. The laws of physics, as we know them, simply are not applicable here. Rather, the spontaneous creation of a universe would require higher "meta" or "hyper" laws of physics that might or might not be anything like the laws of physics that we know.

But this raises another problem. Since such hypothetical meta or hyper laws of physics are completely outside our experience, why do atheistic physicists naively assume that rules like the HUP and COE would even conventionally apply when describing the universe's creation? They freely speculate about other unobservable universes in an alleged "multiverse" that can have physical constants and even laws of physics that are different from our own. Since these laws are known to be valid only within our existing universe, it is not at all clear why they would necessarily apply at the universe's creation. Perhaps COE and the HUP are indeed part of these hyper laws of physics, but perhaps they are not. One can engage in all kinds of speculation here, but speculation is clearly not science.

This is why it is illogical for an evolutionist to argue that COE forbids a supernatural creation. Yes, such a supernatural creation of the universe would involve the creation of energy out of nothing. But again, the laws of physics (including COE) are known to apply only within our physical universe. The atheist can argue that COE forbids supernatural creation only if he knows that the laws of physics were operating before and at the universe's creation.

Of course, he has no way of knowing this, since he wasn't present at the creation (Job 38:4). Of course, God is not bound by such laws, since He Himself established them![15]

This reasoning leads to still another difficulty for evolutionists' claim: In order for the laws of physics to create the universe, they must exist apart from the universe. But this presents a dilemma for the atheist who says that the cosmos is all that exists. Before his death, Carl Sagan acknowledged in correspondence with ICR scientist Larry Vardiman that he recognized this problem for his worldview: His view of origins required the laws of physics to create the cosmos, but because he did not acknowledge his Creator, he could not explain the origin of the laws themselves.[16] The existence of physical laws external to the universe itself was an obvious violation of his well-known axiom "the Cosmos is all that is or ever was or ever will be."[17]

Despite the impressive academic credentials of those promoting the claim that the laws of physics could have created the universe from nothing, it is utterly unreasonable, and no Bible-believing Christian should be intimidated by it.

### Notes

1.  Some evolutionists now claim our universe is only one of infinitely many universes in a great multiverse, and that it is only *our* universe that began 13.8 billion years ago. See chapter 52 for details.

2.  Krauss, L. 2012. *A Universe from Nothing.* New York: Free Press.

3.  Griffiths, D. J. 2005. *Introduction to Quantum Mechanics,* 2nd ed. Upper Saddle River, NJ: Pearson Educational, Inc., 114-116.

4.  Ibid, 118.

5.  Pasachoff, J. M. and A. Filippenko. 2007. *The Cosmos: Astronomy in the New Millenium,* 3rd ed. Belmont, CA: Thomson Brooks/Cole, 474-475.

6.  Humphreys, D. R., personal communication, May 23, 2012.

7.  Tryon, E. P. 1973. Is the Universe a Vacuum Fluctuation? *Nature.* 246 (5422): 396-397.

8.  Ross, H. 2001. *The Creator and the Cosmos.* Colorado Springs, CO: NavPress, 170. Cited in reference 11, 120. But beware Dr. Ross' promotion of the unbiblical Big Bang theory.

9.  Pasachoff and Filippenko, *The Cosmos: Astronomy in the New Millenium,* 474.

10. Hawking, S. 1996. *A Brief History of Time.* New York: Bantam Books, 133.

11. Williams, A. and J. Hartnett. 2005. *Dismantling the Big Bang.* Green Forest, AR: Master Books, 121-125.

12. Krauss, *A Universe From Nothing,* 98-104.

13. Lemley, B. Guth's Grand Guess. *Discover Magazine.* Posted on discovermagazine.com April 1, 2002.

14. Krauss, *A Universe from Nothing,* 163-164.

15. This does not rule out the possibility that God may have used natural physical processes during the course of the six-day creation week, but He was certainly free to modify or suspend those rules as He pleased. And

He is free to do so today if He pleases, as in the case of miracles.

16. Vardiman, L. 2012. Did the "God Particle" Create Matter? *Acts & Facts.* 41 (3): 12-14.

17. Sagan, C. 1985. *Cosmos.* New York: Ballantine books, 1.

# 51

# HOW CAN WE SEE DISTANT STARLIGHT IN A YOUNG UNIVERSE?

Jake Hebert, Ph.D.

**Summary:** If the universe is only 6,000 years old, how can we see starlight coming from billions of light-years away? Some people use this question to challenge the creation account, but the Big Bang has its own starlight-travel problems.

Creation physicists have offered various solutions. Light acts in strange ways, and Einstein's theory of relativity provides possible answers. Time dilation means that time can pass at different rates in different places. Clocks in deep space could "tick" billions of times faster than clocks on Earth, allowing starlight to travel here in a short amount of time. Some people suggest God created starlight "in transit," while others tie the solution to the impossibility of measuring the one-way speed of light.

There are still cosmology issues to explore, but Christians need not be intimidated by the distant starlight question.

Bible believers are frequently asked "How can we see distant starlight in a young universe?" To understand the reason for the question, it might help to review some basics about the speed of light.

To calculate the speed of light, very precise clocks measure the time it takes for light from a light source to bounce off a mirror and return to its starting location. If the distance between the mirror and the light source is, say three meters, then the speed of light is twice this distance (six meters) divided by the round-trip travel time. When scientists make these measurements, the speed of light is about 186,000 miles per second. This is an incredibly fast but still finite speed. Physicist use the symbol $c$ to represent the speed of light.

Because distances between galaxies are incredibly large, it is inconvenient for scientists to use miles or kilometers as units of distance. So, they define a light-year as the distance travelled by light in one year. A light-year is about six trillion miles.

Scientists have good reason to think that many stars and galaxies are millions and even billions of light-years away from us.[1] So, shouldn't light from distant stars take millions or billions of years to reach us? How then can we see light from these stars in a universe that is just 6,000 years old?

## Light Is Weird

Many skeptics see this as an unanswerable argument against biblical creation. However, the issue is more complex than they realize. Light in some ways doesn't behave the way we often think it should. These strange attributes mitigate the skeptic's argument.

A simple example illustrates this weird behavior. Suppose you are standing on the side of the road and a convertible is travelling toward you at 50 miles per hour. Suppose also that a professional baseball pitcher is sitting in the passenger seat, and he throws a baseball at you at 50 miles per hour. How fast is the ball coming toward you? That's easy, right? It's just 50 + 50 = 100 miles per hour.

But let's replace the car with a hypothetical spacecraft that can travel at almost the speed of light. Suppose that spacecraft is coming toward you at 99.99% the speed of light, or $0.9999c$, and then the spacecraft fires a laser at you. The laser, of course, travels at the speed of light $c$. So how fast is the laser coming toward you? The laser is coming toward you at almost twice the speed of light, $1.9999c$—right?

Wrong! As counterintuitive as it seems, the measured speed of the laser is $c$, regardless of how fast the spaceship is moving. It doesn't matter if the spaceship is stationary or moving toward or away from you, the speed of the laser will *always* be 186,000 miles per second.

This weirdness of light is one of the factors that led Albert Einstein to formulate his special theory of relativity. When one accepts this seemingly bizarre result and then "turns the crank," the strange effects that we associate with relativity such as length contraction and time dilation logically follow.

This ought to be a clue that the issue of distant starlight isn't quite as simple as the skeptics make it out to be. Indeed, it is ironic that episode 4 in the 2014 reboot of the *Cosmos* TV show spent considerable time explaining how relativity theory invalidated the audience's "commonsense" understandings of distance and time. That same episode, however, used "commonsense" understandings of distance and time to argue that distant starlight makes biblical creation unreasonable![2]

## Big Bang's Starlight Problems

Big Bang proponents who accuse the Bible of having a starlight travel dilemma should first show that their model does not suffer from one either. But the Big Bang suffers from at least *two* such problems.

The first is called the *horizon problem*, and it's a big one. Background microwave radiation from space is very uniform. Big Bang proponents argue that this cosmic microwave background radiation (CMB) is an "afterglow" from about 400,000 years after the supposed Big Bang.

Such uniformity is unexpected from a cosmic accident like the Big Bang. However, this uniformity could be achieved if radiant energy from one part of the sky "warmed up" another part of the sky, much in the same way that heat from a stove can warm a room. The problem with this view is that radiant energy travels at the speed of light, and even billions of years is insufficient time for radiant energy to ensure a very uniform CMB. In order to solve this problem, theorists tacked on a process called *inflation* to the Big Bang. However, there is zero experimental evidence for inflation, and inflation theory has become so weird that even Big Bang theorists now harshly criticize it.[3-5]

A second problem for Big Bang speculations comes from distant galaxies that often seem more mature than expected by Big Bang reckoning. If distant light really does take billions of years to reach us, we should be seeing distant galaxies not as they are now, but as they were billions of years ago. This means that these very distant galaxies should consistently look "unevolved" and "immature"—for example, having relatively few stars. Yet, Big Bang scientists repeatedly express surprise at the apparent maturity of extremely distant galaxies.[6-8]

Both Big Bang problems come from the assumption that distant light needs billions of years to reach us.

## Distant Starlight: Natural or Supernatural?

Many creation physicists think the correct answer to this question is natural, not supernatural. Since distant starlight is presumably still reaching us today, the answer for how it reaches us can't involve a creation miracle since those miracles presumably ceased on Day 6, per Genesis 2:1-2.

And if God is using normal physics to get the distant light to us, it seems reasonable that He *also* used normal physics to get that first starlight to Earth on Day 4. So, although creationists have no problem in principle with God using a bona fide miracle to get distant starlight to us, many think the correct answer involves natural rather than supernatural explanations.

## Light Created in Transit?

Many Christians have asked "Couldn't God have just supernaturally created the light in transit?" Couldn't God, on Day 4, have created streams of photons (units of light energy) that were billions of light-years long, radiating outward in all directions from every single star? In that case, the outermost photons in the streams might have been created just a few *light-seconds* from Earth. The first of these photons would have then reached Earth just a few seconds after they were created, eliminating the light-travel time problem.

Although suggested by respected creation scientists, there is a biblical problem with this idea. Genesis explicitly states that God created the stars and other heavenly bodies to provide light on the Earth. The text says, "God set them in the vault of the sky to give light on the earth, to govern the day and the night, and to separate light from darkness. And God saw that it was good" (Genesis 1:17-18).

If God simply created distant starlight in transit, then these heavenly luminaries aren't really necessary. God could have simply created the light trails without making any heavenly bodies at all. The fact that the Bible says God made the luminaries for the purpose of giving light on the Earth plainly means that this light really *did* originate from the luminaries themselves.[9]

## Can We Even Talk About a Light-Travel Problem?

Remember that physicists measure the speed of light by bouncing light off a mirror and dividing the round-trip distance by the total travel time. You might wonder "Why not just measure the one-way speed of light? Why even bother using a mirror in the first place?"

There is a reason for this. In order to accurately measure the one-way speed of light, you need two clocks—one to record the time the light begins its journey and a second one to record the time at which the light ends its journey. However, the speed of light is so fast that those two clocks must be precisely synchronized since the tiniest error will cause the results to be way off.

Here is the problem—according to relativity theory, even if the two clocks start out synchronized, the very act of moving one clock causes them to become unsynchronized. This means that one cannot measure the speed of light this way. In fact, despite many clever ideas, no one has ever figured out a way to measure the one-way speed of light. Apparently, it is *impossible* to do so![10]

But this raises a question. If we can never measure the one-way speed of light, this means that it is impossible to calculate the time it takes for distant starlight to reach Earth during its one-way trip from the stars to us. And if you can't calculate a light-travel time, does a light-travel time problem even exist? Can we even talk about a light-travel time problem if calculating such a time is physically impossible?

## Relativity to the Rescue?

As the above subheading suggests, many creation physicists are convinced that Einstein's theory of relativity, in one form or another, is the key to solving this apparent problem. Generally, creation-based solutions to this problem take two different approaches.

The first approach makes use of our inability to measure the one-way speed of light. One proponent of this approach is Jason Lisle.[10] More recently, Tichomir Tenev, John Baumgardner, and Mark Horsteymer have proposed a similar but modified solution.[11] Physicist Phillip W. Dennis has extended this "simple" solution to include gravity.[12]

The second approach involves something called *time dilation*. According to both theory and experiment, clocks can "tick" at different rates depending on differences in speed or gravity. This approach has clocks in deep space ticking billions of times faster than on Earth. This would allow distant starlight billions of years (as measured by clocks in distant galaxies) to reach us, even though only six 24-hour days elapsed on Earth.[13] Physicist Russell Humphreys first proposed this idea in 1994.[14]

Both approaches have pros and cons. The first approach does indeed solve the problem, but some may see the solution as theologically and philosophically unsatisfying. Some deep-space observations (such as apparently colliding galaxies) seem to suggest process, which may favor the time dilation idea. However, Russell Humphreys has significantly changed his original model,[15-18] and other creationist experts in relativity question whether gravitational effects can provide the needed amount of time dilation.[19]

## Conclusion

Creation researchers still adjust their cosmology models but have already bettered the Big Bang. So, Christians should not feel at all intimidated by distant starlight. First, the Big Bang model has at least two problems of its own involving distant light. Second, the issue is not nearly as simple as some make it out to be due to the "weird" behavior of light. Third, creationists have presented scientifically responsible ways for distant starlight to have reached earth, and may have already solved the problem in principle.

*Notes*

1. Simple geometry can be used to show that some stars are thousands of light-years away, and these directly measured distances can then be used to calibrate greater distance measurements. There is no good reason to doubt that the most distant galaxies are indeed billions of light-years away.

2. A Sky Full of Ghosts. *Cosmos* TV show, season 1, episode 4.

3. Coppedge, D. 2007. The Light-Distance Problem. *Acts & Facts.* 36 (6).

4. Hebert, J. Big Bang Blowup at Scientific American. *Creation Science Update.* Posted on ICR.org May 29, 2017, accessed January 13, 2020.

5. A claim of observational evidence for inflation was made in 2014 but was quickly retracted.

6. Thomas, B. 'Old' galaxy found in 'young' part of universe. *Creation Science Update.* Posted on ICR.org May 24, 2011, accessed April 27, 2020.

7. Most distant galaxy: Hubble breaks cosmic distance record. *Astronomy.com.* Posted on astronomy.com March 3, 2016, accessed April 27, 2020.

8. Distant Galaxies Show a Young Universe. European Space Agency. Posted on sci.esa.int March 2, 2005, accessed April 27, 2020.

9. There is another problem with this idea. In 1987, about 6,000 years after the creation week, astronomers saw a burst of light from an exploding star, a supernova. The star that exploded lies 168,000 light-years from Earth. The created-starlight-in-transit idea implies that God created a burst of light 6,000 light-years away from Earth along our line-of-sight to this star. When that burst of light reached us in 1987, it made it appear that the star had exploded. But in that case, the burst of light did not actually come *from* the star but was created 6,000 light-years away from us, causing us to see an "explosion" that never happened! This would mean that our observations of the heavens might not have any connection to what is really happening out in deep space. Everything we are seeing would be a giant "movie" created by God's strategic placement of photons at different distances from Earth. Needless to say, this is theologically unsatisfying and does not easily fit with the truthful nature of God's character.

10. Lisle, J. 2010. Anisotropic Synchrony Convention – A Solution to the Distant Starlight Problem. *Answers Research Journal.* 3: 191-207.

11. Tenev, T. G., J. Baumgardner, and M. Horstemeyer. 2018. A solution for the distant starlight problem using creation time coordinates. In *Proceedings of the Eighth International Conference on Creationism*. J. H. Whitmore, ed. Pittsburgh, PA: Creation Science Fellowship, 82-94.

12. Dennis, P. W., Consistent young earth relativistic cosmology, *Proceedings of the Eighth International Conference on Creationism*, 14-35.

13. Note that this does not violate the doctrine of a literal six-day creation. The creation of the universe took place in six literal days, as measured by six full day/night cycles ("evening and morning") on Earth. Experiments have shown that clocks can tick at different rates, so it is possible, at least in principle, for clocks in deep space to tick much faster than clocks here on Earth.

14. Humphreys, D. R. 1994. *Starlight and Time: Solving the Puzzle of Distant Starlight in a Young Universe.* Green Forest, AR: Master Books.

15. Humphreys, D. R. 2008. New time dilation helps creation cosmology. *Journal of Creation.* 22 (3): 84-92.

16. Vardiman, L. and D. R. Humphreys. 2010. A New Creationist Cosmology: In No Time at All Part 1. *Acts & Facts.* 39 (11): 12-15.

17. Vardiman, L. and D. R. Humphreys. 2011. A New Creationist Cosmology: In No Time at All Part 2. *Acts & Fact.s* 40 (1): 12-14.

18. Vardiman, L. and D. R. Humphreys. 2011. A New Creationist Cosmology: In No Time at All Part 3. *Acts & Facts.* 40 (2): 12-14.

19. Comment by P. W. Dennis during panel discussion of biblical cosmology, August 1, 2018, Eighth International Conference on Creationism. The panel consisted of Danny Faulkner, Jason Lisle, Russell Humphreys, and Phillip Dennis, and was moderated by Robert Hill. Jason Lisle has also expressed a similar concern. Of course, it should also be noted that Russell Humphreys has questions about Lisle's solution to the problem.

# 52

# DO OTHER UNIVERSES EXIST?

Jake Hebert, Ph.D.

**Summary:** Some evolutionary physicists speculate our universe might be just one of an infinite number. The idea stems from modern inflation theory, an ad hoc explanation tacked on to the Big Bang in an effort to solve its problems.

Theorists claim that once started, inflation never completely stopped. Instead, different regions stopped inflating at different times, leaving "islands" that were essentially their own universes in which conditions could be different from those in ours.

However, a multiverse is impossible to scientifically test. And even if laws of physics and chemistry were different in other universes, that still wouldn't solve the problem in our universe of the impossibility of life generating from non-life—among other issues.

Despite its science fiction appeal, a multiverse can't explain an existence without a Creator. The God of Genesis is still the best explanation for life and everything we see around us.

Some evolutionary physicists argue that our universe is only one of infinitely many universes in a *multiverse*. Why do they say this, and is there any evidence to support their claim?

The idea of a multiverse has gained popularity in recent years primarily because it appears to be a logical consequence of modern inflation theory. Earlier versions of the Big Bang model suffered from a number of serious difficulties, including the horizon problem, the flatness problem, and the magnetic monopole problem. In an attempt to solve these problems, Big Bang advocates invoked inflation, an extremely large but short-lived increase in the expansion rate of the universe.

Although inflation seemed to solve these problems for the Big Bang, it is important to realize that it is an ad hoc explanation. Inflation is not a successful prediction of the Big Bang, but rather something that has been tacked onto the original Big Bang model in order to prop it up. The main arguments for inflation are essentially circular—the fact that the Big Bang doesn't work without inflation is taken as evidence that inflation must have happened! Although Big Bang theorists are hoping to someday find "smoking gun" evidence for inflation, such evidence does not currently exist.[1-3]

Inflationary theorists believe a hypothetical field called the *inflaton* drove inflation in the early universe.[4] Although early inflation theories viewed inflation as occurring shortly after the Big Bang, modern inflation theories (discussed below) see inflation as being the cause of the Big Bang.[5] An editorial by popular author and theoretical physicist Michio Kaku was published the day after the announcement of the discovery of the Higgs boson on July 4, 2012.[6] Because the editorial was titled "The Spark That Caused the Big Bang," it likely gave many the mistaken impression that the field associated with the Higgs boson (the Higgs field) was actually the *cause* of the Big Bang. This is inaccurate, as Big Bang theorists generally believe that the inflaton cannot be the Higgs field and that the cause of the alleged Big Bang is still unknown.[7-9]

As noted earlier, inflation was originally proposed to be a brief accelerated expansion of the universe. However, theorists are now claiming that inflation, once started, would never completely stop. It is thought that quantum mechanical effects would cause different regions of space to stop inflating at different times. This would produce "islands" of non-inflating space that are surrounded by enormous regions of space that are still inflating. Each island of non-inflating space would contain matter and radiation, and would, in effect, be a universe unto itself. This process would continue without end, with inflation always occurring in some regions of space.[10]

Because this inflation process would never end, it would result in a multiverse filled with infinitely many universes. This would mean that, according to the Big Bang model, it was only our universe that had a beginning 13.8 billion years ago, *not* the multiverse itself.

So, is there any evidence for a multiverse, and what are the implications for Christianity and the creation-evolution controversy?

First, despite what you may see in science fiction television shows and movies, there is no evidence whatsoever for the existence of universes other than our own. Second, inflation theory, which is the basis for the claim of a multiverse, has become increasingly bizarre and is being criticized by a growing number of secular scientists.[11] Massachusetts Institute of Technology cosmologist Max Tegmark said, "Inflation has destroyed itself. It logically self-destructed."[12] Even Paul Steinhardt of Princeton University, one of the world's leading inflationary theorists, has become critical of inflation theory.[13]

Third, one can make a case that the idea of a multiverse is genuinely unscientific. Because of the enormous gulfs separating these supposed "island" universes, it is difficult to see how the existence of universes other than our own could ever be confirmed or denied, even in principle. Therefore, because the idea of a multiverse cannot be falsified, it fails the test of a scientific hypothesis. Inflation theorists would likely counter that although the idea of a multiverse per se falls outside the domain of science, it should not be classified as unscientific since it is a consequence of inflation theory, which may potentially be falsified.

However, even if one grants this point, a critical issue must not be overlooked—the idea of a multiverse gives no help whatsoever to the person who is trying to explain our existence without God. Secularists claim that the multiverse somehow explains our seemingly improbable existence, arguing that these different universes could each have their own physical constants, or perhaps even their own laws of physics. They argue that it does seem wildly improbable for life to have spontaneously evolved but that we just happen to live in one universe (out of infinitely many) having conditions that permit the existence of life. Therefore, we do not need a Creator to explain our existence.[14]

However, there are flaws in this argument, one of which is the following: In order for the idea of a multiverse to truly remove the need for a Creator, it is not sufficient for conditions in our universe to merely *permit* life to exist. Obviously, they do permit life to exist or none of us would be here! Rather, these conditions (the laws of physics and chemistry, as well as the values of the physical constants) must also permit *evolution*. Specifically, they must allow for abiogenesis—they must allow life to come from non-life.

This, then, raises an obvious question: Do the laws of physics and chemistry in our universe permit abiogenesis? Apparently not. For decades, creationists have been pointing out the immense difficulties with "chemical evolution" scenarios.[15,16] Even some evolutionists are occasionally candid enough to acknowledge the seriousness of these problems.[17]

These difficulties don't simply vanish because someone claims that other (unobservable) universes might exist. In *this* universe, the one in which we actually live, spontaneous generation has never been observed.[18] Furthermore, everything we know about chemistry and physics is telling us that life simply cannot come from non-life.

Even if one were to argue that the chemistry and physics of every single one of these other supposed but unobservable universes did allow for life to spontaneously appear, this would not help one bit—how can the laws of physics and chemistry in *another* universe explain the existence of life in *this* universe? This is such an obvious point that one would think it should have occurred to those making the argument.

So, although the idea of a multiverse may superficially seem to make the evolutionary "goo to you" scenario more believable, a little careful reasoning shows that it gains the professing atheist nothing in his attempt to explain existence without the Creator.

### Notes

1. Faulkner, D. Have cosmologists discovered evidence of inflation? Creation Ministries International. Posted on creation.com March 29, 2006.

2. Appell, D. Planck Satellite Mission Set to Explore Cosmic Secrets. *Scientific American.* Posted on scientificamerican.com November 18, 2008.

3. As creation astronomer Danny Faulkner has noted (see reference 1), there is a great deal of circular reasoning in the interpretation of cosmological data, so even a claim that inflation has been "proven" should not be uncritically accepted. In fact, secular scientists claimed to have found "smoking gun" evidence for inflation in 2014, but they then had to retract that claim soon after.

4. A field assigns a value to each point in space. For instance, a field that describes how temperature varies from point to point within a room would be an example of a scalar field, while the familiar example of an electrical field surrounding a charged object would be an example of a vector field. The hypothetical inflaton field would be an example of a scalar field.

5. Guth, A. The Inflationary Universe: Alan Guth. *Edge: Conversations.* Posted on edge.org November 19, 2002.

6. Kaku, M. The Spark That Caused the Big Bang. *The Wall Street Journal.* Posted on wsj.com July 5, 2012.

7. Steinhardt, P. J. The Inflation Debate. *Scientific American.* April 2011: 36-43.

8. Krauss, L. What is the Higgs boson and why does it matter? *New Scientist.* Posted on newscientist.com December 13, 2011.

9. Falk, D. Canadian physicist Robert Orr on the Big Bang breakthrough. *The Globe and Mail.* Posted on theglobeandmail.com July 6, 2011.

10. Steinhardt, The Inflation Debate, 41-42.

11. A number of physicists now claim that an argument for a multiverse can also be made from string theory, a highly speculative research program. However, one of the main criticisms of string theory is that it currently is not capable of being tested.

12. Gefter, A. What kind of bang was the big bang? *New Scientist.* Posted on newscientist.com July 2, 2012.

13. Ibid.

14. Guth, A. Eternal inflation and its implications. Text of talk presented at the Second International Conference on Quantum Theories and Renormalization Group in Gravity and Cosmology, Barcelona, Spain. Text posted on arxiv.org June 11-15, 2012.

15. McCombs, C. 2004. Evolution Hopes You Don't Know Chemistry: The Problem of Control. *Acts & Facts.* 33 (8).

16. McCombs, C. 2009. Chemistry by Chance: A Formula for Non-Life. *Acts & Facts.* 38 (2): 30.

17. Williams, A. 2007. Great minds on the origin of life. *Journal of Creation.* 21 (1): 38-42.

18. According to the Bible, some people did witness supernatural transformations of non-life into life (Exodus 7:8-13; 8:16-19), not to mention the raising of the dead in Luke 24. But skeptics reject this eyewitness testimony since acknowledging these events would require them to acknowledge the supernatural in general, and God's existence in particular.

# CONCLUSION

The Institute for Creation Research's core mission is to uncover and present the empirical facts of science as evidence for the accuracy, authority, and sufficiency of Scripture. The contributors to the information in this book are highly qualified in their respective fields. All of them are open and strong Christians, solid in their faith, and joyfully committed to the absolute integrity and inerrancy of the written Word of God.

The record of a six-day recent creation is not merely a Genesis story. God spoke and frequently demonstrated creation power throughout the Old Testament. After all the miracles demonstrated to Israel, God's anger was stirred at their unbelief. "The LORD said to Moses: 'How long will these people reject Me? And how long will they not believe Me, with all the signs which I have performed among them?'" (Numbers 14:11).

The Bible is full of the evidence of God's omnipotence and omniscience, first demonstrated during the creation week. The same supernatural creation power is evidenced in the 10 plagues of Egypt and the great miracles of the manna and the provisions for the nation of Israel. Joshua saw it demonstrated when the sun stood still for a whole day and night during the battle with the Amorites.

Elijah watched as creation fire consumed the altar in front of the priests of Baal. Hananiah, Mishael, and Azariah walked with the Creator in the fiery furnace of Nebuchadnezzar. Daniel felt it when the lions refused to kill him in the den.

Jesus Himself used His creation power when He turned the water into wine, gave a new arm and new eyes to deformed men, and raised four-days-dead Lazarus from the grave. Jesus insisted: "Believe Me that I am in the Father and the Father in Me, or else believe Me for the sake of the works themselves" (John 14:11). And God continues to create every time a spiritually dead sinner is "created" in "true righteousness and holiness" when they are twice-born (Ephesians 4:24).

The sacrifice that Christ made for humanity must be sufficient to pay for and forgive all sin for every human being from Adam and Eve through the last moment of time. If Jesus is merely a good teacher and not the Creator Himself, then His death on the cross is not sufficient. If Jesus was not fully human, there could be no legal substitution. But as the infinite, omnipotent, and omniscient Son of God, He did "purchase" those who believe for eternity (Titus 2:13-14).

The book of Genesis is the foundation for all of our faith. If God lied to us in the words of Genesis, then how can we trust Him to keep any other promise? Consider this:

- The fiat creation recorded in Genesis is the best description of the power of God to save you.

- The sentence of God passed on Adam and Eve is the best description of the effect of sin on you.

- The provision of clothing by God for Adam and Eve is the best description of the authority of God to forgive you.

- The global Flood recorded in Genesis is the best description of the power of God to judge you.

- The covenant of God to Noah is the best description of the sustaining power of God to keep you as His child.

It is our hope that the evidence within these pages will add to your knowledge and build your confidence in the trustworthiness of the Bible for "all things that pertain to life and godliness" (2 Peter 1:3).

Henry M. Morris III, D. Min.
ICR Chief Executive Officer

# APPENDIX

# THE SCIENTIFIC CASE AGAINST EVOLUTION

Henry M. Morris, Ph.D.

Belief in evolution is a remarkable phenomenon. It is a belief passionately defended by the scientific establishment, despite the lack of any observable scientific evidence for macroevolution (evolution from one distinct kind of organism into another). This odd situation is briefly documented here by citing statements from leading evolutionists admitting their lack of proof. These statements inadvertently show that evolution on any significant scale does not occur at present, and never happened in the past, and could never happen at all.

## Evolution Is Not Happening Now

First of all, the lack of a case for evolution is clear from the fact that no one has ever seen it happen. If it were a real process, evolution should still be occurring, and there should be many transitional forms that we could observe. What we see instead, of course, is an array of distinct kinds of plants and animals with many varieties *within* each kind, but with very clear and unbridgeable gaps between the kinds. For example, there are many varieties of dogs and many varieties of cats, but no "dats" or "cogs." Such variation is often called microevolution, and these minor horizontal (or downward) changes occur fairly often, but such changes are not true vertical evolution.

Evolutionary geneticists have often experimented on fruit flies and other rapidly reproducing species to induce mutational changes hoping they would lead to new and better species, but these have all failed to accomplish their goal. No truly new species has ever been produced, let alone a new basic kind.

Evolutionist Jeffrey Schwartz, professor of anthropology at the University of Pittsburgh, acknowledged:

It was and still is the case that, with the exception of Dobzhansky's claim about a new species of fruit fly, the formation of a new species, by any mechanism, has never been observed.[1]

The scientific method traditionally has required experimental observation and replication. The fact that macroevolution (as distinct from microevolution) has never been observed would seem to exclude it from the domain of true science. Even evolutionist Ernst Mayr, longtime professor of biology at Harvard, who alleged that evolution was a "simple fact," nevertheless agreed that it was a "historical science" for which "laws and experiments are inappropriate techniques"[2] by which to explain it. One can never actually *see* evolution in action.

## Evolution Never Happened in the Past

Evolutionists commonly answer the above criticism by claiming that evolution goes too slowly for us to see it happening today. They used to claim that the real evidence for evolution was in the fossil record of the past, but the fact is that the billions of known fossils do not include a single unequivocal transitional form with transitional structures in the process of evolving.

> Given that evolution, according to Darwin, was in a continual state of motion…it followed logically that the fossil record should be rife with examples of transitional forms leading from the less to the more evolved.[1]

Even those who believe in rapid evolution recognize that a considerable number of generations would be required for one distinct kind to evolve into another more complex kind. There ought, therefore, to be a considerable number of true transitional structures preserved in the fossils—after all, there are billions of *non-transitional* structures there! But (with the exception of a few very doubtful creatures such as the controversial feathered dinosaurs and the alleged walking whales), they are *not* there.

> Instead of filling in the gaps in the fossil record with so-called missing links, most paleontologists found themselves facing a situation in which there were only gaps in the fossil record, with no evidence of transformational intermediates between documented fossil species.[1]

The entire history of evolution from the evolution of life from non-life to the evolution of vertebrates from invertebrates to the evolution of man from the ape is strikingly devoid of intermediates—the links are all missing in the fossil record, just as they are in the present world.

With respect to the origin of life, researcher Leslie Orgel, after noting that neither proteins nor nucleic acids could have arisen without the other, concluded:

> And so, at first glance, one might have to conclude that life could never, in fact, have originated by chemical means.[3]

Being committed to total evolution as he was, Orgel could not accept any such conclusion as that. Therefore, he speculated that RNA may have come first, but then he still had to admit that:

> The precise events giving rise to the RNA world remain unclear.... investigators have proposed many hypotheses, but evidence in favor of each of them is fragmentary at best.[3]

Translation: "There is no known way by which life could have arisen naturalistically." Unfortunately, two generations of students have been taught that Stanley Miller's famous experiment on a gaseous mixture practically proved the naturalistic origin of life. But not so!

Neither is there any clue as to how the one-cell organisms of the primordial world could have evolved into the vast array of complex multi-cell invertebrates of the Cambrian period. Even dogmatic evolutionist Stephen Gould admitted:

> The Cambrian explosion was the most remarkable and puzzling event in the history of life.[4]

Equally puzzling, however, is how some invertebrate creature in the ancient ocean, with all its hard parts on the outside, managed to evolve into the first vertebrate—that is, the first fish—with its hard parts all on the inside.

> Yet the transition from spineless invertebrates to the first backboned fishes is still shrouded in mystery, and many theories abound.[5]

Other gaps are abundant, with no real transitional series anywhere. A very bitter opponent of creation science, paleontologist Niles Eldredge, acknowledged that there is little, if any, evidence of evolutionary transitions in the fossil record. Instead, things remain the same!

It is a simple ineluctable truth that virtually all members of a biota remain basically stable, with minor fluctuations, throughout their durations....[6]

So how do evolutionists arrive at their evolutionary trees from fossils of organisms that didn't change during their durations?

Fossil discoveries can muddle over attempts to construct simple evolutionary trees—fossils from key periods are often not intermediates, but rather hodge podges of defining features of many different groups....Generally, it seems that major groups are not assembled in a simple linear or progressive manner—new features are often "cut and pasted" on different groups at different times.[7]

As far as ape/human intermediates are concerned, the same is true, although anthropologists have been eagerly searching for them for many years. Many have been proposed, but each has been rejected in turn.

All that paleoanthropologists have to show for more than 100 years of digging are remains from fewer than 2000 of our ancestors. They have used this assortment of jawbones, teeth and fossilized scraps, together with molecular evidence from living species, to piece together a line of human descent going back 5 to 8 million years to the time when humans and chimpanzees diverged from a common ancestor.[8]

Anthropologists supplemented their extremely fragmentary fossil evidence with DNA and other types of molecular genetic evidence from living animals to try to work out an evolutionary scenario that will fit. But this genetic evidence really doesn't help much either because it contradicts fossil evidence. Anthropologist Roger Lewin notes:

The overall effect is that molecular phylogenetics is by no means as straightforward as its pioneers believed....The Byzantine dynamics of genome change has many other consequences for molecular phylogenetics, including the fact that different genes tell different stories.[9]

Summarizing the genetic data from humans, another author concludes, rather pessimistically:

Even with DNA sequence data, we have no direct access to the processes of evolution, so objective reconstruction of the vanished past can be achieved only by creative imagination.[10]

Since there is no real scientific evidence that evolution is occurring at present or ever occurred in the past, it is reasonable to conclude that evolution is not a fact of science, as many claim. In fact, it is not even science at all, but an arbitrary system built upon faith in universal naturalism.

These negative evidences against evolution are, at the same time, strong positive evidences for special creation. They are, in fact, specific predictions based on the creation model of origins.

Creationists would obviously predict ubiquitous gaps between created kinds, though with many varieties capable of arising within each kind, in order to enable each basic kind to cope with changing environments without becoming extinct. Creationists also would anticipate that any vertical changes in organized complexity would be downward, since the Creator (by definition) would create things correctly to begin with. Thus, arguments and evidences against evolution are, at the same time, positive evidences for creation.

### Notes

1. Schwartz, J. 1999. *Sudden Origins.* New York: John Wiley and Sons, Inc., 300.

2. Mayr, E. 2000. Darwin's Influence on Modern Thought. *Scientific American.* 283 (1): 83.

3. Orgel, L. 1994. The Origin of Life on the Earth. *Scientific American.* 271 (4): 78.

4. Gould, S. 1999. The Evolution of Life. *Evolution: Facts and Fallacies,* ed., J. Schopf. San Diego, CA: Academic Press, 9.

5. Long, J. 1995. *The Rise of Fishes.* Baltimore, MD: John Hopkins University Press, 30.

6. Eldredge, N. 1998. *The Pattern of Evolution.* New York: W. H. Freeman and Co., 157.

7. Shubin, N. 1998. Evolutionary Cut and Paste. *Nature.* 349: 12.

8. Tudge, C. 1995. Human Origins Revisited. *New Scientist.* 146: 24.

9. Lewin, R. 1998. Family Feud. *New Scientist.* 157: 39.

10. Takahata, N. 1995. Genetic Perspective on the Origin and History of Humans. *Annual Review of Ecology and Systematics.* 26: 343.

*Dr. Henry M. Morris (1918-2006) was Founder of the Institute for Creation Research.*

# CONTRIBUTORS

### HENRY M. MORRIS III, D.MIN.
CHIEF EXECUTIVE OFFICER

Dr. Henry Morris III holds four earned degrees, including a D.Min. from Luther Rice Seminary and the Presidents and Key Executives MBA from Pepperdine University. A former college professor, administrator, business executive, and senior pastor, he is the eldest son of the Institute for Creation Research's founder. Dr. Morris has served for many years in conference and writing ministry.

### JOHN D. MORRIS, PH.D.
PRESIDENT EMERITUS

Dr. John Morris, perhaps best known for leading expeditions to Mt. Ararat in search of Noah's Ark, received his doctorate in geological engineering at the University of Oklahoma in 1980. He served on the University of Oklahoma faculty before joining the Institute for Creation Research in 1984. Dr. Morris held the position of professor of geology before being appointed president in 1996. He currently serves as President Emeritus.

### RANDY J. GULIUZZA, P.E., M.D.
PRESIDENT AND CHIEF OPERATING OFFICER

Dr. Randy Guliuzza has a B.S. in engineering from the South Dakota School of Mines and Technology, a B.A. in theology from Moody Bible Institute, an M.D. from the University of Minnesota, and a Master's in Public Health from Harvard University. Dr. Guliuzza served nine years in the Navy Civil Engineer Corps and is a registered professional engineer. In 2008, he retired as Lt. Col. from the U.S. Air Force, where he served as Flight Surgeon and Chief of Aerospace Medicine.

### JEFFREY P. TOMKINS, PH.D.
DIRECTOR OF RESEARCH

Dr. Jeffrey Tomkins earned a master's degree in plant science in 1990 from the University of Idaho. He received his Ph.D. in genetics from Clemson University in 1996. While at Clemson, he worked as a research technician in a plant breeding/genetics program. He joined ICR in 2009 as Research Associate and was appointed Director of Life Sciences in 2016 and Director of Research in 2020.

## Vernon R. Cupps. Ph.D.
### Research Associate

Dr. Vernon Cupps received his B.S. and M.S. in Physics at the University of Missouri-Columbia, and his Ph.D. in Nuclear Physics at Indiana University-Bloomington, where he worked at the Indiana University Cyclotron Facility. He worked at the Los Alamos National Laboratory, and from 1988 to 2011 directed and supervised a radiochemical analysis laboratory at Fermi National Accelerator Laboratory. He is a published researcher with 73 publications, 18 of which are in refereed journals.

## Brian Thomas, Ph.D.
### Research Associate

Dr. Brian Thomas received a master's in biotechnology in 1999 from Stephen F. Austin State University, and a Ph.D. in paleo-biochemistry in 2019 from the University of Liverpool. He was a junior high and high school teacher at Christian schools in Texas, as well as an adjunct and assistant professor at Dallas-area universities. In 2008 Dr. Thomas joined ICR as a science writer and editor. He was appointed as Research Associate in 2019.

## Timothy Clarey, Ph.D.
### Research Associate

Dr. Timothy Clarey received a Master of Science in Geology in 1984 from the University of Wyoming, and a Master of Science in Hydrogeology in 1993 and Ph.D. in Geology in 1996 from Western Michigan University. From 1984 to 1992, Dr. Clarey worked as an exploration geologist at Chevron USA, Inc. He was Full Professor and Geosciences Chair at Delta College for 17 years before leaving in 2013 to join ICR as Research Associate.

## Leo (Jake) Hebert III, Ph.D.
### Research Associate

Dr. Jake Hebert earned a master's degree in physics in 1999 from Texas A&M University, where he studied optics and was a Dean's Graduate Fellow 1995-1996. He received his Ph.D. in 2011 from the University of Texas at Dallas, where his research involved a study of the possible connection between fair-weather atmospheric electricity and climate.

## FRANK SHERWIN, M.A.
### RESEARCH ASSOCIATE, SENIOR LECTURER, AND SCIENCE WRITER

Frank Sherwin received his bachelor's degree in biology from Western State College, Gunnison, Colorado, in 1978. He attended graduate school at the University of Northern Colorado, where he studied under the late Gerald D. Schmidt, one of the foremost parasitologists in America. During his time in graduate school, Mr. Sherwin discovered a new species of parasite, the study of which was published in a peer-reviewed secular journal. In 1985, Mr. Sherwin obtained a masters degree in zoology.

## JAMES J. S. JOHNSON, J.D., TH.D.
### CHIEF ACADEMIC OFFICER

Dr. James Johnson received his J.D. in 1984 from the University of North Carolina, which included studies at Duke University Law School, and in 1996 obtained his Th.D. His educational background includes earned degrees in religion and the natural sciences. For his scholarship in biblical languages and their cognates, Dr. Johnson was awarded the American Bible Society Award in 1982.

# RESOURCES FROM ICR

Creation or evolution? This debate is one of the most vital issues of our time. ICR's original DVD series present the evidence that confirms the biblical account of creation and provide defensible answers to questions of faith and science. Ideal for group study, these compelling and engaging presentations demonstrate that not only does the scientific evidence *not* support evolution, it strongly affirms the accuracy and authority of God's Word.

Find out more about these DVD series and other resources at **ICR.org/store**.

INSTITUTE FOR
CREATION
RESEARCH

ICR.org

How well do you know the fundamentals of creation? Get the facts with ICR's hardcover, full-color *Guide to Creation Basics*. This comprehensive 120-page guide, authored by ICR scientists and scholars, is loaded with hundreds of illustrations!

Find out about other creation resources at **ICR.org/store**.

ICR.org

# FOR MORE INFORMATION

## Sign up for ICR's FREE publications!

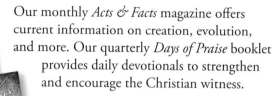

Our monthly *Acts & Facts* magazine offers current information on creation, evolution, and more. Our quarterly *Days of Praise* booklet provides daily devotionals to strengthen and encourage the Christian witness.

To subscribe, call 800.337.0375, mail your address information to the address below, or visit ICR.org/subscriptions.

## Visit ICR online

ICR.org offers a wealth of resources and information on scientific creationism and biblical worldview issues.

- ✓ Read our news postings on today's hottest science topics
- ✓ Explore the evidence for creation
- ✓ Investigate our professional education programs
- ✓ Dive into our archive of 40+ years of scientific articles
- ✓ Listen to our radio programs and podcasts
- ✓ Follow us on social media
- ✓ Order creation science resources at ICR.org/store
- ✓ And more!

## ICR Discovery Center for Science & Earth History

Located in Dallas, Texas, the ICR Discovery Center demonstrates how science confirms the Bible through high-tech exhibits, stunning planetarium shows, and live science presentations. Go to ICRdiscoverycenter.org to plan your visit to this world-class facility.

INSTITUTE FOR CREATION RESEARCH

P. O. Box 59029
Dallas, TX 75229
800.337.0375